*Chemistry
and
Beyond*

Chemistry
and
Beyond

A selection from the writings of the late
Professor F. A. PANETH

Edited by

HERBERT DINGLE
*Emeritus Professor of History and Philosophy of Science,
University of London*

G. R. MARTIN
Professor of Chemistry, University of Kent at Canterbury

with the assistance of

EVA PANETH

INTERSCIENCE PUBLISHERS
a division of John Wiley & Sons Inc.
New York – London – Sydney

First published 1964 by John Wiley & Sons Ltd.

All Rights Reserved

Library of Congress Catalog Card Number 64–25217

Made in Great Britain at the Pitman Press

Contents

The number in square brackets is the number of the article in the bibliography on page 273

APPENDICES

Introduction

When Friedrich Adolf Paneth died on September 17th 1958, the world lost an outstanding and all too rare type of scientist. As a result of the intense specialization of the present age it has become almost essential for a worker in the physical sciences to choose between contributing to the advancement of his subject on the one hand and understanding its relation to wider fields of human interest on the other. For Paneth the choice was not necessary; he excelled in both endeavours. Indeed, so closely were they associated that his most original researches, as presented by him, were readily intelligible to the lay mind, while his popular articles and lectures were as likely as not to contain material of immediate technical importance. In a field in which the language of mathematics is rapidly becoming almost the only possible means of communication for the research worker, he was able to avoid it almost entirely and yet to express novel and relevant ideas with no loss of precision.

It has seemed to some of his friends that a selection of his writings could profitably be made available in a more easily accessible form than has so far been possible, and we have accordingly undertaken the editorship of the present volume. From the wealth of material at our disposal it has not been easy to make a selection. Our aim has been primarily to exhibit the scope and character of Paneth's extra-chemical interests, but in such a way as to show how intimate was the connection in his mind between chemistry, to which professionally he owed his chief allegiance, and the more general curiosity aroused in thinking minds by the mysteries of the world in which they find themselves.

Little need be said of Paneth's life, for full obituary notices will be found elsewhere;* we give only the briefest account to set the background against which his work was done.

Friedrich Adolf Paneth was born on August 31st 1887 at Vienna, the second of three sons of Dr. Joseph Paneth, a physiologist of note, who discovered certain histological cells which now bear his name. Fritz was trained as a chemist, and began in the organic field, but soon changed to the new science of radiochemistry, becoming

* See, for example, those by Dr. J. Mattauch (*Physikalische Verhandlungen, Verbandausgabe*, 165–169, 1958) and by Professor H. J. Emeléus (*Biographical Memoirs of the Royal Society*, Vol. 6, November 1960).

assistant to Professor Stefan Meyer in the Institut für Radiumforschung in Vienna. In 1913 he came to work in Glasgow, with
Soddy, and also visited Manchester where Rutherford was then
pursuing his revolutionary researches. After a short period in
Prague he moved to Hamburg and then to Berlin, and in 1929 he
was appointed to the Chair of Chemistry at Königsberg. A career of
great promise there was brought to an abrupt end by the Nazi
conquest of Germany, whereupon, in 1933, Paneth, who was of
Jewish blood, moved with his family to London. For six years he
worked at the Imperial College of Science and Technology at South
Kensington, and in 1939 was appointed to the Chair of Chemistry at
Durham, where he remained until reaching the retiring age in 1953.
He was then invited to become Director at the Max-Planck-Institut
at Mainz, and returned to Germany, though without relinquishing
the British nationality which he had acquired in 1939. He remained
in this post until his death. In 1913 he had married Else Hartmann,
daughter of the historian Ludo Hartmann. His wife and his two
children—Eva and Heinz Rudolf—survive him.

Paneth has an assured place in the annals of experimental
science. With Hevesy he was responsible for the discovery and
development of the radioactive tracer technique which now finds
application in so many branches of pure and applied science. A
natural chain of developments then led him first to the isolation of
the volatile hydrides of several of the heavier metals, and later to the
demonstration of the independent existence of the organic radicals
which are the short-lived intermediaries in many chemical reactions
—a discovery which has opened up a vast field of study in chemical
kinetics. An interest in the problems of the measurement of gases on
the micro-scale led to important contributions to geochemistry—
especially in the study of the upper atmosphere—to "cosmochemistry" and to nuclear physics. Some idea of the extent and
variety of his contributions in these and other fields will be gathered
from the bibliography on p. 273.

Rather characteristically, Paneth was inclined to attribute this
record of achievement to "serendipity"—the faculty of making
happy and unexpected discoveries by accident. If this was so, he
seems also to have possessed in full measure the flair for divining
which "accidental" observations were worth following up, with the
result that his laboratory was always an exciting place in which to be.

We have dealt thus briefly with Paneth's contributions to experimental science as our main object here is to make some attempt at
depicting the kind of man he was. In those who had the privilege of

his friendship we hope the following pages will reawaken cherished memories; for those who did not know him we hope to supplement to some degree the image which emerges from the writings themselves.

If one had to choose a single word to indicate Paneth's personality, that word would be "vitality". He was alive in every aspect of his multifarious activities. One felt it the moment he entered the room; the atmosphere became transformed, and whatever caught his attention, no matter how commonplace it might have appeared, at once became animated. He irresistibly brought to mind Thomas Traherne's picture of the child: "All appeared new, and strange at first, inexpressibly rare and delightful and beautiful. . . . All Time was Eternity . . . Eternity was manifest in the Light of the Day, and something infinite behind everything appeared".

Yet his was no child's mind, nor was his response to the world an uncontrolled enthusiasm. The word *poise*, which conveys Dr. Götte's view of him as expressed in a passage to be cited presently, gives a true idea; he was perfectly balanced between a natural optimism and a rational appraisal of the situation in which he found himself. One of us remembers an occasion on which he brought to Paneth's notice a comment on Kant which seemed to run counter to Paneth's estimate of the philosopher. "O, but that's old work," he exclaimed immediately; "much has been found out since then." And then, after a moment's pause, in more sober tones: "Still, it is no worse for being old". There was the spontaneous reaction, at once tempered by the dictates of reason.

These qualities, most manifest in personal encounters, were also evident in his lectures. He had a happy faculty for combining clarity with felicitous phrasing, and, no matter whether he was speaking in German or in English, he could hold his audience to the last word. One of his first engagements on coming to England in 1933 was the delivery of a short course of lectures at Imperial College under the auspices of the University of London, which indeed had been arranged before the necessity of leaving Königsberg for good had become evident. After the first lecture a distinguished member of the College remarked: "When he began I thought, 'I wish I could lecture like that in German'; when he had finished I thought, 'I wish I could lecture like that in English'!" Many were to share that experience.

His sense of humour is reflected in many of the articles in this book, but he had a way of interjecting comments which did not always appear in the published version of his remarks. Once, when recounting the story of Henry VI's alchemical gold which was not recognized in Scotland (see pp. 4–5), he added, as an aside: "In those days the Scots were very cautious in money matters"—leaving his non-historically-minded Scottish Chairman without effective retort. On another occasion he conveyed his evident disbelief in an alleged experiment by the remark: "This experiment seems to have been successful only once". He amassed a considerable collection of examples of what he described as "pathological chemistry", consisting of those incredibly foolish theories with which every scientist is familiar, which are too intangible to offer possibility of refutation, superfluous in any case, and which can only be laughed out of court.

His knowledge of German literature was profound. Naturally he was less at home with English writers, yet there must have been few of those not born and bred in England, and probably none among non-English scientists, whose knowledge and appreciation of English literature could rival his. Happening once to read in a scientific paper a line of a minor English poet which appealed to him, he inquired as to its authorship, obtained the collected works of the poet, and read them with care. This was typical.

His interest in poetry was not merely passive; he liked to play with parodies and imitations. The lines pencilled in his copy of Sidgwick's Life of William Herschel may be quoted:

In Polyhymnia's Dienste verbracht' er die Hälfte des Lebens,
doch der Unsterblichen Kranz reichte Urania ihm;
Töne sind's nicht allein, die zum Parnassus uns führen,
Kunst und Wissenschaft sind *beide* den Musen geweiht.

(In Polyhymnia's service he spent half his life,
But Urania presented to him the immortal wreath;
Music is not the only guide to Parnassus,
Art and Science are *both* votaries of the Muses.)

Indeed, one must bear in mind his inherent faculty for turning circumstances to the best account, in order properly to understand the course of his life. Superficially, events seemed to favour his particular predilections remarkably well. He was interested in Kant, and found himself in Königsberg. His interest in Kant created an interest in Thomas Wright, and fate sent him to Durham. It happened that while he was in Durham, studying meteorites, one fell in Wales. He went to Mainz, and one fell at Breitscheid. He concerned himself with the history of chemistry, and in his own family was a codex in which he discovered a previously unknown copy of a lost treatise by Albertus Magnus on alchemy. He was fascinated by amber, and happened to live in East Prussia where the best specimens are to be found. Was it all luck, or was he a philosopher's stone, turning to gold everything with which he came into contact?

Two of his friends have kindly provided us with reminiscences which show the kind of impression he made on those with whom he lived and worked at different stages in his career. We give them *in extenso* since they not only throw light on his character but also recall certain incidents in his life which are of special interest from that point of view.

Dr. P. L. Günther, Professor of Chemistry at Munich,* was first associated with Paneth in Berlin in the 1920's. He accompanied him to Cornell University, Ithaca, New York, in 1926–7, and later to Königsberg, and is thus particularly well qualified to speak of Paneth's earlier years. He writes:

It was in Berlin in 1926 that the first experiments for the age determination of meteorites were undertaken. Paneth had just returned from a journey to his home town of Vienna. There he had inspected a large collection of meteorites in the institute of Professor Czermak. The idea of determining the age of meteorites by the helium method presumably first occurred to him on this occasion. He had been given a few small pieces of the iron meteorite "Mount Joy", altogether about 30 grams. Full of enthusiasm, he showed them to his co-workers in Berlin. This enthusiasm was not wholly shared by the writer of a Doctor's thesis, who had to enlarge its theme, "On the helium content of sylvines and beryls", by the addition of "and on the age of meteorites".

The meteorite "Mount Joy" became at the same time the origin of a collection which increased year by year and which he liked to show with all the pride of a collector to his numerous visitors from home and abroad, as well as relating the interesting anecdotes of the ways in which the various pieces had been acquired.

In 1926 among these visitors was L. M. Dennis, Director of the Chemical Institute of Cornell University, who was making his annual tour of Europe in order to recruit a non-resident lecturer. He was very happy to reach an agreement with Paneth, and

* Professor Günther unfortunately died on April 24th 1961.

deeply satisfied that, according to his own words, he had succeeded in bringing to the United States "the most outstanding inorganic chemist of the younger generation". Because of the special circumstances, it was possible to take one of Paneth's Ph.D. candidates as an assistant to Cornell, so that experimental work could be done in Ithaca with special apparatus brought over from Germany.

Conditions of work at the Institute in Cornell were ideal. Paneth had for his sole use a very modern, well-equipped laboratory in which his eight Berlin co-workers could easily have worked. For a chemist coming from Germany there seemed to be in this building, which was only a few years old, an atmosphere of abundance and wealth—an impression intensified by Dennis's account of the finances involved. Paneth's introductory lecture on "Ancient and Modern Alchemy",* delivered in the large, overcrowded auditorium of the Institute, was a masterpiece in content and style, and gained for him at once the respect of workers in his new sphere of activity. His command of the English language was such that he could deliver the lecture faultlessly in the language of the country. This was but one example of his unusual linguistic gifts, which were not confined to modern languages: he found no difficulty in translating such texts as the Latin of an alchemist fluently and without the help of reference books. This gift was very conscientiously developed at Cornell. Fowler's *The King's English* and *The Concise Oxford Dictionary* were his constant companions, and in his library at home were numerous works concerned with languages. He took special pleasure in discussing philological questions, and astonished—and indeed occasionally embarrassed—many an expert philologist. A pungent discussion was for him a pleasure; any weaknesses revealed by his partner he would point out, not inconsiderately but graciously.

His stay in the United States ended in an extensive lecture tour, which he found most stimulating and which he took pleasure in talking about afterwards to friends as well as to larger audiences. He gave particular attention to a comparative study of the American and German methods of university instruction, and liked to summarize his judgement in a short statement: The vigorously scheduled university system in the U.S.A. brings up a good average—there are no students who have wasted their time; in Germany the gifted ones have a better chance to develop

* See p. 3.

peak achievements, but there are too many who have wasted their time. Great Britain seems to be most successful in avoiding the faults of both systems.

The appointment of Paneth as an Ordinary Professor and Director of the Chemical Laboratory of the University of Königsberg in East Prussia was a deviation from the usual practice. It was the first time in Prussia (and possibly in Germany) that an inorganic chemist had been appointed to such a post. This caused some astonishment, for the opinion prevailed, especially among the organic chemists, that only they, having a better general view of the whole field of chemistry, should be appointed directors of institutes. For Paneth, this appointment was not only a personal compliment but also a very notable recognition of the branch of chemistry which he so successfully represented, and which in the eyes of the general public had been somewhat overshadowed by the great successes of organic chemistry.

In the spring of 1929 work started in Königsberg, whither all his Berlin co-workers had accompanied Paneth. None of them regretted his decision to join Paneth in going East. They were pleasantly surprised by the town and the life there, and soon got accustomed to the new, but not modern, scene of activities. The laboratory buildings in the Drummstrasse—a brick structure, which had been finished about the turn of the century—left much to be desired, and, since up to that time only organic chemistry had been practised in it, all special equipment for the inorganic chemist was lacking and the general equipment available was old and worn out.

Through persistent negotiations with the Ministry, Paneth succeeded in having some improvements made in the Institute and in acquiring some new equipment. About ten years after a lost war, the installation of a telephone with some ten extensions, the fitting of dark rooms in the laboratories, and the acquisition of usable epidiascopes were not regarded as matters of course. To give just two examples—the necessity of giving out mixtures for analysis in a wooden enclosure under the sloping array of benches of a large auditorium, and the quite inadequate ventilation, were handicaps which had to be accepted. With exemplary modesty, the Director of the Institute confined himself to an office with one window and about twelve square metres of floor space, in which the simultaneous presence of more than three people was hardly possible. It contained a venerable safe, but one would have looked in vain for treasures in it. The budget of the Institute was so small that only the general bills for gas, water, electricity, and chemicals could be paid from it; there was thus more than Prussian austerity and simplicity. Scientific work in these circumstances would not have been possible if the *Notgemeinschaft* of German science had not again and again put materials and finances at the laboratory's disposal in answer to Paneth's recurrent requests. He did indeed succeed, by skilful use of all available organizations, in obtaining the essential equipment for his researches—without abundance, it is true, but sufficient for his needs; this is proved beyond doubt by the great number of publications on the three main topics which were being pursued intensively in Königsberg: free radicals, helium determination, and meteorites.

There is, however, one feature which must not be forgotten. Even if the house in the Drummstrasse did not look too pretentious, all who visited it were inspired by Paneth's "infectious high spirits".* These were expressed in the many studies which he followed up outside the special framework of his own subject, e.g., historical and philosophical investigations relating to chemistry, amongst which his article "On the Epistemological Status of the Concept 'Chemical Element' "† unfortunately did not reach a sufficiently wide public because it was published in the writings of the Königsberger Gelehrte Gesellschaft.

Paneth went so far as to give a one-hour lecture each week on "selected chapters from the history of chemistry". The numbers attending were considerable. There are still rather few students of any branch of science who are so interested in the history of their subject as to sacrifice time for it, so if students attended these lectures they were attracted by the speaker, to whom it was such a pleasure to listen. Did Paneth perhaps erroneously interpret this as an interest in the history of chemistry? This question is justified as, obviously for the first time in Königsberg, he did on

---

* In the original a reference to Goethe's

> Übermütig sieht's nicht aus,
> Grosses Dach und kleines Haus—
> Allen, die darin verkehrt,
> Ward ein guter Mut beschert.

> No pretension to this home
> Tiny house and outsize dome:
> Everyone who was its guest
> With its cheerfulness was blest.   [Ed.]

† See p. 58.

one occasion put to an examination candidate a question on this subject. He must have seen the candidate at his lectures. Not only did the question remain unanswered, but the effect was devastating; since most candidates in examinations incline to attribute bad marks received to the absurdity of the questions set by the examiner, much worry was caused in the ranks of the students. One of his assistants was asked to "intercede" with Paneth in order to prevent the occurrence of questions of this type in future. Paneth was appalled, for his intention had been to ease the tension of the examination by such questions, and to relieve the frequently paralysing atmosphere of the examination room.

After this event he never again put questions on the history of chemistry, though the lectures continued, for Paneth was not, and did not wish to be, an examiner who perplexed his candidates; on the contrary, he was always anxious in the examination to find out where the strength and the weakness of the candidates lay, in order to give preferential treatment to the stronger points and to avoid the weaker ones.

As Director of the Institute, Paneth avoided anything that might have given the impression of standing on his dignity as a superior. Violent scenes or reprimands, even when they would have been justified, were distasteful to him. Paneth's criticism and rejection, which often found expression in the simple words, "Oh, what a nuisance!", were easily ignored by coarser natures. With all his readiness to understand others, he kept his distance and did not like it when his readiness to help was met by an unwarranted familiarity.

Paneth stayed only four years in Königsberg. When Hitler came to power he was on a lecture tour in England, from which he did not return. On the high road to further successes, he, who was fundamentally not a political man, gave up his still secure existence for political reasons; he made this difficult decision because he clearly recognized what had really happened in Germany, and that in future absolute dictatorship would prevail.

Paneth was destined to occupy the Chemistry Chair at Durham longer than any of his other posts, although for the first six years of his stay there little was accomplished on account of the war; indeed, for part of this time he was seconded to serve as Head of the Chemistry Division of the Joint British–Canadian Atomic Energy Laboratory in Montreal. Immediately on his return to Durham, however, he set about the task of establishing his "Institute", and few could equal the skill and resource he displayed, at that most difficult period, in persuading the authorities to provide accommodation, equipment, and collaborators for his work.

The Paneths had settled in an old house of some character just outside the city, and "The Corner House" soon became a centre of the local intellectual life. In Durham, where Science had only rather recently been added to the long-established Faculties of Arts and of Divinity, the University was delighted to find a scientist who could "speak the same language" as his colleagues in the humanities, and Paneth had the opportunity to develop to the full his interest in philosophy and history, along with a wide range of fields of scientific endeavour. Many visitors came to the laboratory, and were entertained most hospitably at the Paneths' house; the evening coffee parties there were lively affairs and emphatically "interdisciplinary", with Paneth gently encouraging discussion with provocative contributions, sometimes serious, sometimes less so, but always stimulating.

All too soon the statutory retiring age was reached, with Paneth still full of life and most unwilling to abandon an active participation in affairs. This situation was providentially resolved by the offer of the appointment at the Max-Planck-Institut für Chemie in Mainz. Dr. H. Götte, now at Farbwerke, Hoechst, who worked with Paneth after his return to Germany, is able, from experience of the third period of Paneth's life, to confirm the impressions made on those who knew him in the first German period and during his residence in England. He writes:*

A particularly impressive characteristic of Professor Paneth was a most unusual type of distinction. Its roots were to be found not so much in his innate vitality or in the patriarchal character of his personality, but rather in a central poise, the origin of which was mainly intellectual. This poise was obviously not acquired but was *sui generis*, and thus did not need confirmation of any kind, which made it particularly fascinating. His superiority was never obtrusive, but it could always be sensed in his relations with men of every type, whatever their rank, position or reputation. From it derived a rare independence of thought and judgement, enabling him to examine situations, events and persons uninfluenced by the general attitude or the opinions of others, and to arrive at an opinion essentially his own. As his comprehensive interest in all

* The contributions of both Professor Günther and Dr. Götte have been translated from the original German.

mental activities, with the exception of music (he himself acknowledged that he was unmusical), made him pursue many trains of thought, he had well-considered judgements of his own about most historical and contemporary events, which all too frequently differed from those generally accepted.

An active interest in his fellow men was not the least of his concerns. He looked for their positive qualities with, at the same time, a deep and understanding insight into their weaknesses, which he recognized as integral parts of their personalities. His humorous and, indeed, frequently ironic criticism, therefore, was always tinged with benevolence or indulgence. He could be delightfully amused by human imperfections, but his humour always showed some likeness to that of the German humorist Wilhelm Busch, who laid bare the weaknesses of his contemporaries without hurting. With an apt sentence—indeed, by means of a single question—he was able to illuminate a situation or the qualities of a man in such a way that he could leave it to the intelligence and powers of association of his audience to form a picture of its own, whose main features, however, were determined by his prompting.

Anyone who met him was at once captivated by his charm and impressed by his natural dignity. As he was well informed in so many branches of knowledge, had an excellent memory and was always ready to follow the lead of any partner in conversation, he readily made contact with persons of widely different types. His genuine interest in the activities and attitudes of mind of others came out so clearly in such conversations, and his readiness to profit from any discussion was so obvious, that for those who had the opportunity to speak with him it was a joy not only to listen but also to contribute to the conversation.

His tact made it easy for him to establish relations of confidence with others. While remaining at a distance, determined by his distinction and personality, he yet established across this distance —in, as it were, another dimension of human relationships—an equality in conversation which gave a feeling not so much of immediate personal nearness as of a very friendly and close contact based on mutual esteem.

His readiness to help was shown in the same way; he was always anxious to remove emotional prejudice and to substitute objective argument. As head of department he used to give his instructions in the form of suggestions or proposals. Usually he tried to let his ideas and wishes develop in the collaborator so that he should be under the impression that he was conceiving ideas of his own. It was always Professor Paneth's concern to persuade, and to arrive at decisions by mutual understanding and agreement. In cases where his tactful and subtle way of conveying wishes failed, he was at a loss and almost helpless, and usually found a way of transferring the necessary commissions to someone else.

Anyone who knew Professor Paneth thus personally was able to understand, on the basis of the qualities described, the admirable attitude which he adopted after his return to Germany, where there was so much that he appreciated. There was no trace of any resentment or bitterness. He did indeed shun contact with co-workers and colleagues who, as active National Socialists, had turned against him, but there was never any feeling of general dislike of Germans. His liberal-mindedness, and especially his objectivity, would have forbidden any other attitude.

All who made the acquaintance of Professor Paneth in the last years know that we have lost not only one of the last really universal scholars but also an unusual personality, whose example as a scientist and a man will be a model for many of us for many years to come.

A few details remain to be added.

Some of the articles which follow were originally written in English and some in German: the former are reproduced exactly as Paneth wrote them, with only typographical or trivial amendments; the latter have been translated. The translations of all the articles originally published in German were made by Eva Paneth, whose help has been freely given at all stages of the work in ways too numerous to mention; we owe her our grateful thanks. Until his untimely death on January 28th 1963, the encouragement and assistance of Dr. P. Rosbaud, who first suggested the preparation of this volume, were freely available, and we are glad to record our debt to him. We are indebted also to the Editors of various journals, mentioned elsewhere, for permission to reproduce, either in their original form or in English translation, articles and illustrations for which they hold the copyright, and to the British Museum (Natural History) for prints of the photographs (Figs. 19–26) of the Beddgelert meteorite reproduced in Chapter 15. Unless otherwise stated, footnotes belong to the original articles; those inserted by way of annotation are distinguished by the comment [Ed.] at the end. The sequence of the articles within each main group is only partly chronological; it has been thought best to arrange them with chief regard to the subject matter and in the order in which they can most profitably be read by the general reader. The list of contents on p. v gives the dates of the original publications. It would not have been possible entirely to avoid repetition without mutilation of the text, which would have been a much greater evil. Its occurrence, however, is rare, and will not, we think, be found objectionable. The work on Thomas Wright of Durham, however, has needed special treatment, which is described in the Foreword to the section dealing with that subject.

H.D.
G.R.M.

History of Chemistry

FOREWORD

This section contains a selection of Paneth's papers on chemical subjects, in which his essentially historical and personal approach is clearly manifested. The classification is rather difficult, but, so far as possible, papers on related subjects are kept together, and their chronological order pertains to the subject written about rather than to the writing. Thus, Chapters 4, 5 and 6 are concerned with the discovery of the periodic system of the elements, and Chapters 7 to 11 with the development of radioactivity.

The discussion in Chapter 6 of the meaning to be attached to the word "element" had a special significance at the time of its first appearance, arising from a controversy which had its origin in the discovery of isotopes. Before that discovery an "element" could be characterized unambiguously by either its atomic weight or its chemical properties, but the existence of isotopes implied that substances with the same chemical properties could have different atomic weights. The question therefore arose whether an "element" should be characterized by its chemical properties (in which case the same element could have several different atomic weights) or by its atomic weight (in which case many elements would be chemically indistinguishable and, unless a very drastic amplification of nomenclature were introduced, would bear the same name). Fajans and others favoured the second alternative, but Paneth was prominent among those who preferred the first, and most of the earlier papers in Section VIII of the Bibliography (p. 280) are concerned with this question. His view involved a distinction between physical and chemical means of separation, and he advocated the ascription of the term "element" to a substance which could not be analysed into distinguishable parts by chemical means. By the time the Address printed in Chapter 6 was delivered, the question had been decided in favour of Paneth's view, but the controversy was much in his mind, since the other designation would have made it impossible to speak of the "periodic system of elements" which Mendeleeff did so much to establish.

The only other point that seems to call for elucidation is the fact that Chapter 7, on Auer von Welsbach, consists largely of an Address presented to that scientist by the German Chemical Society. The justification for including it here is that this Address was in fact composed by Paneth himself at the request of the Society.

I | Ancient and Modern Alchemy

First of all let me express my high appreciation of the honour of the invitation to come to Cornell as non-resident lecturer for the present term. When I received the friendly letter of Professor Dennis, my first thought was that it would give me the opportunity of staying for some time in the finest chemistry laboratory now existing in the world, with which I was already acquainted from the description of the building that had been sent to me. It was with great pleasure that I accepted the invitation to join the well-known staff of the department and to avail myself of the privilege of presenting throughout the term some of my researches to a Cornell audience, and to continue my investigations in this building which offers such excellent facilities for experimental work.

It may be a matter of surprise to you that as the subject of my introductory lecture I have chosen alchemy, since that is not generally believed to belong to exact chemistry at all. Only a few decades ago Hermann Kopp, one of the best historians of chemistry, called the history of alchemy "the history of an error". If, however, it was an error, it was one of the most persistent of the false doctrines in the development of any science, and my reason for selecting alchemy as the topic of my address is to be found in the fact that the trend of modern chemistry is toward rather than away from the theories which were condemned by the official science of the last century, of which Kopp may be regarded as the representative.

Alchemy was in disrepute during really only a comparatively short space of time. For many centuries it was highly esteemed as the "sacred science" and no independent science of chemistry existed. It retained its dignity even when chemistry, as distinguished from alchemy, was being developed. It was never entirely abandoned, although after chemistry had won a much higher position, the disfavour of scientists forced it for a time to hide in the obscurity of private laboratories and secret societies. In recent years it has again emerged into the full daylight of modern scientific theory and

3

research. There is no doubt that much of the alchemists' creed was
"an error", but their idea that it must be possible to change one
chemical element into another, as lead to silver or silver to gold, has
been strongly supported by the researches of our time.

But if the difficulty of observing an artificial transmutation of an
element is so great that all the careful experiments of the chemists of
a few years ago seemed definitely to disapprove such change, how is
it to be explained that in former centuries the confidence in its
correctness was so deeply rooted and that alchemy and the alchemists
played such an important part in the life of that period? For the
influence of the alchemists can hardly be overestimated. For example, official State papers of the sixteenth and seventeenth centuries make it clear that one of the important problems confronting
a monarch or Elector in Central Europe was to procure for his
country an able alchemist who was expected to improve the financial
status of the realm by transmuting base metals into valuable gold.
It naturally followed that the alchemist was highly favoured at
court—so long as belief in his ability lasted. He was honoured by the
friendship of his sovereign and sometimes by elevation to nobility,
and more than one of the crowned protectors of alchemy assisted
personally in the experiments, so that he might convince himself of
the correctness of the achievements of his alchemistic employee. The
Emperor Rudolph II is reported to have himself worked with his
alchemists, and a visitor to the Hradshin, the beautiful castle of
Prague, the residence of the emperor, may even today see the
five or six little houses, with disproportionately large fireplaces,
which were built by Rudolph's command close to his own palace
and which were used by his "gold-cooks". Rudolph appointed to a
high position in his court Tycho de Brahe, who, although usually
referred to in the history of science as an astronomer, was perhaps
chosen by Rudolph because he was also of high repute as an alchemist. This is evidenced by the fact that the emperor provided
him not only with an observatory but also with a laboratory for his
chemical experiments.

In a more practical way Henry VI of England supported alchemistical experiments. To aid in the payment of the debts of the state
he recommended to all noblemen, scholars and theologians the study
of alchemy, and he conferred upon a company the privilege of
making gold from base metals. This firm produced a metal (probably an alloy of copper and mercury) which had the appearance of
gold, and from this coins were stamped. History does not record
whether King Henry believed that transmutation had actually been

accomplished, but the careful Scots were evidently sceptical, for the Scottish Parliament issued an order that this English "gold" should not be allowed to enter any of their ports or to cross their frontier.

The example given by the mightiest rulers of the time was imitated on a more modest scale by several of the smaller princes of Europe. Historical records tell us of one who tried to obtain a first-class alchemist from his neighbour, first by kindness and then by force; of another prince who loaned his alchemist to another court for a definite period, and of treaties between two States in which alchemists were regarded as mere chattels. Many of the rulers of that time were such firm believers in alchemistical doctrines that a lawyer of the period advocated making disbelief in these theories a *crimen laesae majestatis*. But although the lords of the realms generously supported the experiments of their alchemists, the financial returns never seemed to equal the disbursements. One repeatedly finds in the records that at the end of the research the sovereign lost his temper and that the alchemist, when hard pressed to show his product of manufactured gold, was usually well satisfied if he succeeded in escaping from the clutches of his former benefactor. If he failed to do so, he was severely punished and generally put to death. As showing the cruel humour of the times, it was a frequent joke to gild with tinsel the gibbet on which the alchemist was to meet his end.

We read of a great number of such executions and of innumerable failures of experiments. The successful transmutation of some cheap material into gold was very seldom reported, and in every case the transmutation, for some reason or other, could not be repeated; either the alchemist had disappeared or the stock of the "philosopher's stone", the miraculous powder which alone enabled him to accomplish "the great work", had been exhausted. The value of the gold that he claimed to have produced always amounted to a very small fraction of the money that had been spent upon him and his experiments.

How is it to be explained that in view of such constant and utter failures the belief in the possibility of the production of gold was not destroyed? Several reasons may be offered.

In the first place, there were some observations which even from a critical standpoint seemed to prove the possibility of transmutation. The best chemical experts of that time were not greatly impressed by the results of the alchemists, for success invariably disappeared as soon as the experimenter was forced to permit a sharp control of his materials and apparatus. It was clearly recognized that in all such cases the element that the alchemist claimed to have manufactured was present in the material from the beginning, but was so well hidden, or so finely distributed, or in such chemical combination that the layman was unable to detect its presence. In the reputed art of gold-making they had no further proofs of success than vague historical statements that on a certain occasion a powder, provided nearly always by an "unknown stranger", had exhibited the properties of the "philosopher's stone" and as evidence of the miraculous transmutation into gold accomplished by experiment a gold nugget of metal was shown. One may see at the present time in some of the European museums such gold products of the alchemists with detailed explanations of the manner of their production. But in no case is the invaluable powder itself that had brought this about to be found in any museum.

The early chemists were, however, firmly convinced that transmutation was possible, and their conviction rested largely upon an experiment which clearly seemed to create copper and which could successfully be repeated at any time. This experiment consisted in immersing an iron vessel in the water of certain natural springs and allowing it to remain there for some hours. When it was removed its shape was unaltered but the vessel had apparently been changed to copper. I have seen such copper utensils with poetic inscriptions upon them to remind one of the mysterious origin of the metal. One reads thus:

> Hart Eisen ich einst war.
> Ein Wasser rein und klar
> Macht mich in wenig Stund'
> Zu Kupfer in Herrngrund.*

Apparently a "water pure and clear" produced the transmutation. This water, however, was not as pure as it appeared to be, but contained traces of a copper salt, and when the iron vessel was immersed in the liquid the metallic copper, the "nobler" metal, was deposited upon the less noble metal, iron. The vessel was not, of course, changed as a whole into copper but simply received a thin coating of that metal. But the coating was real copper and showed all the details of the former iron surface.

It is not surprising that in those times, when the small content of copper in the water could not be detected by chemical analysis, the phenomenon which I have just described was thought to be the transmutation of iron into copper; but on reading alchemistical treatises, one is nevertheless astonished to meet again and again this

* Herrngrund is a small town in Hungary.

one example as the chief uncontested experimental argument for the whole doctrine of transmutation. This fact shows how scanty was the experimental evidence, in spite of the innumerable attempts which were not only made in the laboratories of emperors, kings and noblemen, but were also carried on by many commoners, and which never yielded gold in any appreciable quantity. From all this we may safely conclude that the reason for the firmness of the belief in the doctrine of alchemy was not the strength of the experimental evidence, but that it had quite a different basis, namely, psychological motives.

It is an old-known fact that men readily believe what they wish to believe. Modern psychology has deepened and extended the scientific knowledge of this fact by the discovery that such a wish is not less effective if it remains in our subconscious mind. Its presence may then be even more dangerous, since we are generally not aware to what degree it influences our thoughts and acts. Any strong wish may by "repression" obscure or extrude from our memory all that does not conform to it. Those of you who are acquainted with the work of the Vienna scientist, Sigmund Freud, will realize the importance of this field. I do not think that any psychologist will wonder that the judgement of those who lived in the days of the alchemists was misled by the wishes of such overpowering strength as played a role in connection with the idea of transmutation. It is not easy for us today to estimate correctly the power of this wish. It was not merely the hunger for gold. The habit of mind in those times found it quite natural to believe that a thing capable of changing all the metals into gold would also possess the faculty of curing every kind of illness. The all-embracing astrological conception of the world, to which the alchemical doctrine belonged, brought certain ideas into close relation by what we now consider to be only a weak analogy. In the case which we are discussing the analogy might be formulated—*the cure of metals and the cure of men*; for, using the terms of Albertus Magnus, gold was "the only metal free from any illness". The philosopher's stone, that mysterious powder for which every alchemist was searching, was believed to be able to change any other metal into gold by mere contact (they termed it "projection"), the stone being capable of transmuting many thousand times its own weight. It was further supposed to guarantee to its owner extremely long life, free from any shadow of illness. *Wealth* and *health*, these were the gifts of the philosopher's stone, and when you consider further that in the Dark Ages the ghosts of poverty and illness threatened the people in even more dreadful

forms than in the present day, you will probably not think absurd
the quotation which I recently saw in an alchemical treatise:

> Everybody must try to get two things, eternal bliss and earthly
> happiness: the former is granted by the Kingdom of God, which
> is taught by the theologian, while the latter is granted by the
> philosopher's stone of the alchemist.

Thus we can easily understand that, under the influence of this
vital struggle, people who were not trained by profession in critical
scepticism over-estimated all which looked like a successful transmutation. But what about the scientists of that day? Surely they
must have realized the weakness of the chemical proof of transmutation. But the most prominent men of science did not doubt its
essential correctness, and this is to be explained by the third pillar
of the alchemical creed, namely, that the doctrine of transmutation
was in accordance with the universally accepted philosophical
conceptions of the day.

We know that in the Middle Ages, and even in modern times, the
system of Aristotle ruled the minds of men, and that in science his
theories were almost as firmly believed as were in religion the dogmas
of the Church. Now, according to Aristotle, all bodies are formed
from a fundamental substance—the "primordial matter". This is
pure matter without any form, and therefore not yet truly existent.
If united with the properties *cold* and *wet*, it becomes the element of
water. If it has the two properties *warm* and *wet*, it becomes the
element air. To the element earth were ascribed the properties
cold and *dry*, and to the element fire the properties *warm* and *dry*.
The "four elements" in the Aristotelian sense are therefore nothing
ultimate but only modifications of the primordial matter. By
changing the properties, one can transmute one element into another.
If in such a manner even these foundation stones of the whole sub-
lunar world, bodies as different from each other as are fire and water,
could be transmuted, no scholar trained in the philosophy of
Aristotle could doubt that bodies so closely allied as are the metals
could interchange their differentiating qualities. In manuscripts
of the thirteenth century we read, as something almost self-evident,
that silver, which in many respects is related to gold, can be changed
into real gold more easily than can any other metal. It was quite the
same conception which centuries later made the alchemists believe
that by making copper white, which can be done by alloying it with
other metals, they were on the way towards its conversion into silver,
and that by giving to the copper a yellow colour—think of the colour

of brass—they had achieved the first steps of the production of gold. Although, in other regards, such as the specific gravity of the product, the transmutation did not seem to have fully succeeded, it was nevertheless clear that the copper had been transmuted into something better. For, according to his theory of perception, Aristotle did not believe that, in a mixture of two metals, the components remained. This would have led him to the standpoint of his opponents, the atomistic philosophers, who discriminated between appearance and reality. Just as a drop of wine in a barrel of water disappears, according to Aristotle, not only for our senses but even in reality, so the element copper was supposed to be no longer present in brass.

From these brief references to the Aristotelian philosophy, it is easy to see that nothing could be more natural to a scholar educated in these ideas than the transmutation of metals. If the alchemists were not successful, it was surely the fault of those "sooty empirics", for the experimental workers were quite as highly disdained by the scientists of that time as by the philosophers of ancient Greece.

The authority of Aristotle in chemical theories was broken only when experimental research had won its independent position in science. The conviction then became general that metals could not be changed one into another in spite of the doctrine of the "primordial matter" and the transmutability of all bodies; and there gradually developed the belief that elements were not the four hypothetical bodies of Aristotle, nor the three "principles", salt, sulphur and mercury, which some alchemists preferred, but were all such substances as could not experimentally be divided into simpler ones. It was urged that instead of fixing the number of elements *a priori* one should try to ascertain this number *a posteriori*, that is, by systematic experimental study. This new programme was first developed by Joachim Jungius, a many-sided and ingenious scientist who lived at Hamburg in the first half of the seventeenth century. It is especially remarkable that Jungius further made a very clear attempt to substitute for the doctrine of Aristotle the atomic theory which later played such an important part in the development of modern chemistry. He, the author of a textbook on logic, was such a well-trained thinker that he did not fail to recognize that on the ground of the atomic theory the existence of isomerism and even stereoisomerism could be foreseen. Most of the papers of Jungius were distributed in the form of manuscripts and reached only a small number of sympathetic readers, but shortly after his death there appeared a book of similar tendency in which the problems were presented in such attractive literary style that they appealed to the widest circles: that was *The Sceptical Chymist*, by Robert Boyle. But even the immense influence of Boyle did not succeed in immediately subduing the elements of Aristotle. Only when Lavoisier, holding to the same definition that "a chemical element is a body which cannot be resolved into simpler ones", found in the chemical balance a definite instrument for critically testing this belief, did the modern conception of a chemical element find general acceptance. Dalton completed the foundation of modern chemistry by the assumption that every chemical element consisted of a special kind of indestructible atoms, and you know that this theory of the composition of matter dominated the tremendous development of chemistry during the nineteenth century.*

This assumption of Dalton's—that there existed as many kinds of atoms with different qualities as there were chemical elements— so completely satisfied the theoretical needs of the chemist that the idea of a primordial matter fell into disrepute, but it was never completely forgotten. There were always some who felt that the existence of a great number of independent elements was unnatural. This feeling was strengthened by the discovery of the periodic system. The harmony which appeared in the ordering of the approximately seventy elements that were then known clearly showed that they did not consist of that number of perfectly independent chemical atoms; one had to return to the conception of something common to all these atoms or abandon all hope of explaining the interrelationships between the elements. Mendeleeff himself, it is true, was so convinced of the stability of the chemical elements that he violently criticized any hint that his periodic table supported the view that there existed a primordial substance. But it is a characteristic of important ideas that they very soon begin to live their own life in the mind of mankind, independent of the brain which first produced them. Just as the deeper understanding of Dalton's theory had to be developed against Dalton's opposition by Guy Lussac, Berzelius and others, in similar manner, quite contrary to the ideas of Mendeleeff, the periodic system has come to be regarded as strong evidence that the atoms of the elements are built up of smaller particles.

This view, derived by observation of the chemical behaviour of the elements, was independently confirmed by physical researches. To explain the optical spectra of the elements, physicists were compelled to picture the atom not as a solid sphere but as a very complicated structure consisting of much smaller particles which moved inside the space formerly ascribed to the spherical atom. As to the nature

* But see Chapter 3. [Ed.]

of these particles the investigations of the physicists during recent years seem inevitably to lead to the conclusion that they are nothing else than the positive and negative building-stones of electricity.

One difficulty, however, seems immediately to arise. If the atomic structure of all the elements is so closely akin, how is the constancy of the elements to be explained? Why is it that they cannot easily be transformed one into another? Why did not the alchemists succeed in transmutation? The answer is that while *theoretically* we must concede the possibility of such transmutation as soon as we accept the view that the atoms are aggregations of smaller particles, yet *practically* the forces inside the atoms which hold these particles together may be so strong as to defeat attempts to effect a change.

Let me at this point call your attention to a historical fact which does not appear to be so widely known as it deserves. What I refer to is the theory of the structure of matter which was proposed by Robert Boyle. As experimental chemist, Boyle saw earlier than his contemporaries the necessity of assuming that there were many different chemical elements, but he considered this conception to be merely a necessary aid for the understanding of chemical reactions. As theorist and philosopher he adhered firmly to the old idea of a primary matter and he sought to explain in wholly modern fashion the qualitative differences of the elemental atoms by assuming different numbers and arrangements of the minute particles of the primary substance. That the elements remain unchanged in chemical reactions he considers to be due to the *relative* stability of these atoms. The "corpuscles of gold and mercury" are composed of minute particles of the primordial matter, but are nevertheless (I quote his words) "able to concur plentifully to the composition of several very different bodies without losing their own nature or texture, or having their cohesion violated by the divorce of their associated parts or ingredients". With an insight even more remarkable than that of his successors, Lavoisier, Dalton and Mendeleeff, he thus brought forward more than two hundred years ago a theory for bringing into accord the multiplicity of the chemical elements with the existence of a simple fundamental substance, a theory which modern science now bases upon an immeasurably richer assembly of facts. He lacked every possibility of experimentally demonstrating the composite nature of those substances which the strongest reagents of chemical analysis cannot even today decompose. The theory of the complicated structure of the atoms of all elements was therefore with him only a philosophical postulate.

3

Yet since he stated "that it will be scarce denied that corpuscles of compounded nature may in all the wonted examples of chymists pass for elementary", it is self-evident that he always had in mind the possibility that a specially active agent might be discovered which would be able to pull the parts of the corpuscles asunder. He says: "There may be some agent found out so subtile and so powerful, at least in respect of those particular compounded corpuscles, as to be able to resolve them into those more simple ones, whereof they consist".

I have quoted Boyle's exact words because they seem to be almost prophetic of Rutherford's experiments on the breakdown of the atom. Rutherford actually found this "agent so subtile and powerful". Yet previous to his success in experimentally disrupting an element, nature had given a much more definite indication than was furnished by the periodic system, spectra, etc., that the endeavours of the alchemists could perhaps be realized. This indication was found in the newly discovered radioactive bodies which furnished examples of chemical elements which *spontaneously* changed into other elements.

After Rutherford and Soddy had conceived the idea that the radiation from such substances resulted from the disruption of these radioactive bodies and the expulsion of fragments of the atoms with enormous velocity, it seemed to them probable, for reasons which I will not take time to present, that these fragments were nothing else than atoms of helium. If their supposition was correct, it appeared to follow that one should be able to detect the formation of the element helium from radioactive bodies, and Ramsay and Soddy actually succeeded in experimentally proving that when radium breaks down helium is formed. This was the first instance in which one element, helium, was evolved from another element, radium. Both of them are real elements, for they cannot be resolved by chemical means, and both show different chemical qualities and characteristic spectra. The experiment, therefore, established beyond a doubt the possibility of the transmutation of elements. But in a transmutation of this character it has been found that man has no power to influence it. The production of helium from radium takes place with absolute constancy, and no means at man's disposal, neither extremely high nor extremely low temperature, nor very high nor very low pressure, nor electric nor chemical energy, can quicken or retard the rate of the transmutation. The radioactive substances therefore appeared to support fairly well the view that many held in the Middle Ages and even later. They thought that elements were formed in nature, that for example in the depths of the mountains bismuth changed in the progress of time into silver, and silver into gold, but that man could do nothing except to interrupt this ripening process at the proper moment and withdraw from the influence of the "mountain fire" the noble metal that had been produced. This withdrawal at the proper stage was deemed necessary, for they believed that with the further lapse of time the silver and the gold deteriorated and again reverted to base metal. (It may be pointed out in this connection that the alchemists claimed also to possess a substance which, as a negative philosopher's stone, could destroy gold. This negative body was naturally much less highly prized than the real philosopher's stone.)

Several years after the experiments of Ramsay and Soddy, it developed that radioactive substances not merely show the elemental change which takes place of itself, but also have put in our hands the agent which can cause such a change at the will of the experimenter. It was again Rutherford who established this fact. His experiments, which are to be regarded as the first successful ones of an alchemistical nature, are of such extraordinary significance that I will endeavour to give you an approximate idea of his technique so far as that is possible without the use of the special phraseology of radioactivity. A metal tube some decimetres in length is placed in a carefully darkened room and a radioactive preparation is put into one end of this tube. The substance sends through this tube rays which are themselves invisible to the naked eye. The preparation can be pushed into the tube to any desired distance. A glass plate in the further end of the tube is coated with zinc sulphide, a substance that possesses the property of glowing under the action of radium rays, just as the well-known Röntgen screen renders the X-rays visible. When the radium preparation stands at a distance of more than seven centimetres from the screen the latter does not glow, because this particular kind of radioactive ray travels only that distance. If a thin sheet of aluminium is placed between the radium preparation and the zinc sulphide screen it is to be expected that this barrier to the rays will extinguish the glowing of the screen at a shorter distance than seven centimetres. Experiments show that although the screen now becomes almost entirely dark, there is still perceptible a very weak luminosity caused undoubtedly by the action of a small residue of the rays. But these residual rays behave in a very surprising manner. They reach the screen even when it is removed to a distance of ninety centimetres, although at this greater distance the glow is extremely faint. One can scarcely imagine a less striking experiment. The glow of the screen is indeed so feeble that only the trained eye can perceive it under the most favourable conditions. We must therefore marvel at the boldness of Rutherford, who ventured to draw revolutionary conclusions from this apparently negligible phenomenon. He argued that if, behind the sheet of aluminium, rays appear which reach further than those which fall upon the aluminium, these new rays must come from the aluminium itself; in other words, the aluminium atoms must be disrupted and send out particles from their inner structure, and the glow of the screen at a distance of ninety centimetres must be due to the impact of these fragments of the atoms. These particles can easily be caused to deviate from their paths by electrical or magnetic forces, and from the amount of this deviation Rutherford concluded that they are particles of the size of the hydrogen atom. This means that the aluminium atom has been broken down and that hydrogen has been generated, although in so small an amount that it would take about a million years to obtain in this manner one cubic centimetre of the gas.

This experiment demonstrated actual atomic disintegration, and it has been found by Rutherford and by investigators in the Radium Institute of Vienna that not only aluminium, but also quite a number of other elements, such as sodium, potassium, phosphorus and chlorine, break down in this manner. This evidence seems clearly to indicate that hydrogen is the long-suspected primordial element. In spite of the unimpressive character of this experiment, the conclusions which one may draw from it are of far-reaching significance, and we have here a striking example of the fact that the importance of an investigation is to be judged not by its external brilliancy, but rather by the deductions that can logically be based upon it.

Thus we see that in a certain sense radium possesses the first and principal property ascribed to the philosopher's stone: it has the power of transmuting elements, although not of producing gold. And, oddly enough, even in respect to the second property which was ascribed to the philosopher's stone, radium seems to have got something from its fabulous predecessor: it is a very valuable aid in the treatment of some severe diseases, although not a perfect remedy for every illness. So that to a certain degree the radium rays really produce the two very different effects of the philosopher's stone, transmutation and healing.

But in another direction this modern substitute of the philosopher's stone brought a severe disappointment. You remember the expectation of the alchemists that "by projection" the stone would transmute many thousand times it own weight. Unfortunately quite the contrary happens in such a case as the breakdown of aluminium by radium rays, for many hundred thousand atoms of the new stone must disintegrate before only one atom of hydrogen is formed.

The spontaneous disintegration of the radio-elements, and particularly Rutherford's success in artificially disrupting the atoms of some other elements, inspired investigations upon the artificial transmutation by other means. For the disruption of elements in the way shown by Rutherford is, strictly speaking, nothing but "induced radioactivity", if we may employ a term originally coined for another phenomenon, but which today is no longer used. With very large quantities of radioactive material, we can "induce" a hardly detectable activity in elements which are usually inactive. Of course it would be much more valuable to find a method of transmutation not limited to this very expensive and very slightly effective form of energy, and this thought revived the alchemistical experiments with renewed force. Scientific opinion had now reverted to the view of some critical scientists in the alchemical period, which is perhaps stated in the most concise form in a book by the polyhistoric Jesuit Athanasius Kircher: "Alchymia scibilis est, non tamen adhuc scitur". ("Alchemy is a science not yet known, but which may become known.")

Our return to this view explains why today not only the daily papers but also scientific journals are ready to accept contributions to this theme. Even if we were to limit the present review to the articles appearing in scientific journals, the number of papers would be too large to allow of full discussion. But this need not cause us sorrow, because the publications of some of these modern authors remind us of the chemical ignorance and credulity of their ancient forerunners. Let me call to your attention, however, one or two publications of a higher type which caused wide discussion. You may have heard that just before the [1914–18] war, from Ramsay's laboratory, Collie and Patterson announced that helium and neon were formed when an electric discharge was sent through hydrogen that was in a closed vessel. But shortly afterwards, Strutt, the present Lord Rayleigh, showed that this experiment could not be repeated if air, which always contains both helium and neon, was perfectly excluded. Nevertheless the assertion that they are thus formed was repeated a few months ago in the *Proceedings of the Royal Society of London*, but this experiment fails to convince one that Strutt's criticism is incorrect. In experiments, as yet unpublished, which were carried out by Dr. Peters and myself at the University of Berlin, the entire apparatus was submerged in water, which served so to cool the glass walls as to render them impermeable to atmospheric helium. After hours of continuous electric discharge, we found no trace of helium.

Many of you are doubtless familiar with the fact that last year a German chemist, Miethe, and a Japanese physicist, Nagaoka, independently asserted that by electric discharge gold may be formed from mercury. It is a special irony of fate that in this case alchemy reappeared in the old-known vestment of the artificial production of gold. Gold is particularly apt to cause this error because it may be present in various materials but so finely distributed as to escape detection by ordinary methods of analysis. But in various ways the gold may be concentrated to such an extent that it can now be detected without difficulty. Concentration was, therefore, in all the ages very often misunderstood as production. In the experiments of Miethe and of Nagaoka quite the same happened. Today extremely small quantities of gold can be recognized, and the scarcely visible beads of gold which Miethe could identify under the microscope would have entirely escaped the observation of the alchemists of the seventeenth century. But if in the final product we are satisfied with such small quantities of gold, this necessitates the employment of much more delicate methods of ascertaining that the original material is perfectly free from gold. Hence the difficulties and the danger of error have been about the same in all centuries. That this modern "transmutation", like that of old, amounted only to a concentration of gold and not to its genesis, has been proved by Tiede, Riesenfeld, Haber and their co-workers in Germany and by Sheldon, Estey and Harkins in this country (the U.S.A.).

If at the end of this lecture we try to compare ancient and modern alchemy, we cannot fail to realize that modern alchemy, at least in so far as serious workers are concerned, is a matter of theoretical knowledge, not of practical utility. This distinguishes it from the attempts of the many thousands who carried on alchemistical work in the earlier centuries with the purpose of getting rich as quickly as possible. But let us not be unjust towards those in earlier times who were interested in alchemical experiments in the same manner as in the other theoretical problems of natural history. As early as in the thirteenth century the Franciscan monk, Roger Bacon, distinguished between *alchimia practica* and *alchimia speculativa*. Later we note that Newton, Leibniz, Tycho de Brahe and Goethe, to mention the names of only a few of the greatest, showed in some periods or during their whole life a distinct interest for this much-disputed science, and their interests are surely to be classified under *alchimia speculativa*. But such men were exceptions in the olden time, as great exceptions as are today, we hope, the men who expect pecuniary profit from such experiments. Of course, we will not deny the possibility that sometime in the future practical profit may result. We should not forget that, for example, wireless telegraphy, with its enormous importance for most of the branches of modern civilization, has its origin in the purely scientific and practically useless experiments of Heinrich Hertz. It is quite impossible to prophesy that alchemy will never have practical importance, but any one who today would enter this field with the idea of deriving pecuniary advantage from it will surely be disappointed.

These considerations remind us of the three pillars on which old alchemy rested. We see that two of them rotted away. The pretended transmutation of visible quantities was recognized as a mistake, and the longing for riches and health, which by no means has disappeared in our times, can be more quickly and safely realized in other ways than by experiments in transmutation. But the third, the pillar of natural philosophy, as we may concisely call it, still stands. The tendency which induced the old Greek philosophers to search for a uniform primordial matter behind the complexity of phenomena is still at work in the considerations of modern natural philosophers and, curiously enough, this struggle at last shows success. The ancient hypothesis that a uniform primordial matter might exist has been substantiated by modern knowledge, at first theoretically and later experimentally.

Here we arrive at the gate of a new problem. Its discussion belongs to the field of philosophy rather than of chemistry, and consequently I will only briefly touch upon it in this lecture. How is it possible that philosophers, so often despised by naturalists, could predict a scientific result centuries in advance? Different answers are possible. One could regard it as a mere casual coincidence of some old doctrines with the present state of our experimental knowledge. In this connection it is worth while to remind oneself that only one and a half centuries ago the well-known French chemist, Macquer, pointed out the important coincidence that the four elements of Aristotle were substantiated by the results of the most modern chemical analyses. But I am not willing to concede that the conclusions of today are based on such an unsteady foundation as that so-called "experimental proof for the Aristotelian elements". Secondly, following the school of the Neo-Kantian philosophers, one could regard our problem as an example that the laws of nature are in the deepest sense created by the human mind and do not exist in an objective world. It is quite impossible on this occasion to discuss this philosophical tenet which has so large a number of followers, but I think you will agree with me that careful scrutiny of the very history of alchemy shows that it does not support this doctrine. Astrology, to which alchemy belonged, attempted to prescribe to nature the laws which it should follow—laws which, developed in detail, were expected to govern the mutual relationships between metals and planets, between microcosmos and macrocosmos, etc. But nature did not consent to be governed by these laws, and generations of thinkers could not impress them upon her. But when the chemist, following the example of Boyle, abandoned the idea of establishing laws *a priori* and entered upon the experimental study of natural phenomena, the way was opened for the successful development of chemistry. And thus we see that, in contrast with the philosophical standpoint mentioned above, the history of chemistry can only strengthen our belief that the laws of nature are independent of the human mind in their existence, not in their conception, a belief shared since antiquity by some schools of philosophy.

We must therefore regard the return of modern science to the old ideas of the Greek philosophers as a sign that they have correctly realized a principle which was formulated in different ways during the development of science and which Kepler worded as follows: "Nature likes simplicity". This term "simplicity" does not mean that nature always acts in the simplest manner that can be imagined. Kepler's own example serves to demonstrate this. The astronomical system which he developed and in which it was assumed that the planets revolved in elliptical orbits is infinitely more simple than the old one which it replaced, but elliptic orbits are not the most simple that we can imagine: circles would be still simpler, but the planets do not rotate in circles. The same considerations hold as regards the idea of primordial matter. Strictly speaking, we do not now think that there is one primordial substance but rather that there are two. The atom of hydrogen consists of both positively and negatively charged particles, protons and electrons, and it does not now seem probable that we will reach a simpler view of this structure. But the general tendency of the Greek philosophers, especially of those belonging to the Atomistic School, to remove complexity as far as possible and to assume quantitative differences instead of the qualitative ones, we must regard as a sound principle of natural philosophy throughout the ages. Therefore, if modern and ancient alchemy are very closely in agreement as to the existence of a primordial matter, this should be regarded not as a mere accident nor as an impress of human ideas upon nature, but as a distinct evidence that from earliest times eminent thinkers have rightly conceived the unity in the multiplicity of things. The greatest significance of modern alchemy is that it has enormously strengthened this early conception and has furnished convincing proof of the unity of the material universe.

2 | St. Joachimstal and the History of the Chemical Elements

The famous Russian chemist, Mendeleeff, once delivered a lecture in London on the chemical elements. In order to impress on his large audience the importance of this problem he quoted a famous saying of Kant: "Two things fill the mind with ever new and ever increasing admiration and reverence the more frequently and the more persistently one's thoughts dwell upon them: the starry sky above me and the moral law within me". According to Mendeleeff "the chemical elements before me" should be added as an equal third, for their study too fills the mind with ever new and ever increasing awe and admiration.

It may well be that for every scholar in the arts or the sciences, that problem on which he is most actively and most successfully engaged seems the most mysterious and the most inexplicable. Mendeleeff might well base the special claim of the chemical elements to this high rank on the fact that the question of the substances of which the "World" consists was amongst the very first to engage the attention of man as poet, philosopher or investigator. Innumerable answers have been given in the course of the centuries, and it is impossible in a short lecture to survey the main attempts at solving this problem unless one confines oneself to a mere enumeration (water, air, infinity, fire, number, etc.) which, apart from its contribution to a *Weltanschauung*, would hold no interest. I shall therefore on this occasion, in addressing a German Bohemian audience, limit myself to those aspects of the history of the chemical elements in relation to which one small place in German-speaking Bohemia played, either directly or indirectly, an important part. It happens, however, to be a place specially favoured by circumstances in that in the course of four hundred years it twice became world-famous and, owing to the special character of its mineral treasures, provided new and significant knowledge for contemporary science. The place is St. Joachimstal in the Erzgebirge mountains.*

* The German word, *Erz*, indicates their wealth in ores.

Many of you will be familiar with the main facts of the history of St. Joachimstal; you will know that the silver mines there first flourished at the beginning of the sixteenth century and that in that "Tal", as it was called for short, originated the first "Taler". This designation of silver coins soon became generally accepted in Germany, and is preserved even today in the American "dollar". It is, however, not the significance of Joachimstal for the history of minting and mining that concerns us now, nor its importance as a modern spa, but the much less well-known part which it has played in the history of chemistry. The beginning of the sixteenth century saw, as you know, the revival of inductive science, when, in all realms of thought, men began to burst the fetters of scholasticism and to look for knowledge no longer to Aristotle and his commentators but directly to nature herself. The question thus arises whether our debt to the Joachimstal mines might not be intellectual as well as commercial. This indeed has proved to be the case to an extraordinary degree.

The first name that calls for mention is that of the renowned Dr. Georgius Agricola, who was the *Stadtarzt* (medical officer of health) of St. Joachimstal. Versed in many branches of knowledge and deeply imbued with the spirit of the new age, he wrote, on the basis of intensive studies in the mines and conversations with experienced miners, a book which inaugurated a new epoch in mineralogy and proved of great significance for chemistry as well. It is entitled *Bermannus sive de re metallica dialogus* (published in 1530). In this dialogue two doctors discuss with Lorenz Bermann, a citizen of Joachimstal, who appears in other treatises as well, the question of the identity of the minerals which the Greeks and Romans designated by the names handed down to us. They gradually come to realize that the abundance and variety of minerals actually occurring so far surpass the knowledge of the ancient philosophers that progress is not possible through reading their writings but only on the basis of independent observations of one's own. The book, however, contains not only the recognition of this fundamental principle on which the new school of science was to be based, but also a wealth of accurate observations relating to the occurrence of silver, lead, arsenic and bismuth—which little-known element was first recognized with certainty as a new metal in St. Joachimstal—and to cinnabar, gypsum, graphite, fluor-spar, pyrites (Kies) and gangue minerals. "Thus were laid the foundations of scientific mineralogy. A German doctor was destined to be its father, Joachimstal its cradle." (G. C. Laube.) After which a plea for a leading place in the

history of the systematic study of the chemical elements, and especially of the metals, for Agricola and his *Bermannus* would be redundant.

The Sceptical Chymist by Robert Boyle (published in 1661)—a
book that can be regarded as a landmark in the history of chemistry
—furnishes an interesting proof that experience gained in Joachimstal played an important part even in later days in discussions of the
nature of the chemical elements, and that the mines were famous
even in distant lands. It is well known that from the appearance of
Boyle's book dates the beginning of scientific chemistry, just as
Bermannus inaugurated scientific mineralogy. Boyle's work contains
a declaration of complete independence from all reliance on authority: it repudiates the assertion of the Aristotelians that the four
elements of the world are fire, water, air and earth as being just as
arbitrary and unfounded as the attempts of the medieval alchemists
to assign that status to the "Principles", salt, sulphur and mercury.
Boyle recognized as elements only substances which can actually be
isolated by chemical analysis and are not further divisible; his
definition has proved so serviceable that chemists still use it without
alteration. He did not, however, provide a simple criterion for
determining what substances satisfied these conditions; such a
criterion was not found until a hundred years later by Lavoisier
through the use of the balance. It is owing to this circumstance,
and to the very limited amount of factual material available in his
time, that Boyle did not arrive at any definite decision as to what
substances could be regarded as elements within the new meaning
of the word, and that he regarded, for instance, the formation of
metals in historical times as a fact for which the evidence was
reasonably good. One of the most important proofs which he adduced is connected with Joachimstal; it comes from the Latin work
of a professor of medicine called Gerhard, and says: "That in
Joachimstal silver grows in the manner of a herb from stones, as if
from a root, up to the height of one finger is vouched for by Dr.
Schrötter, who often in his house showed such veins of a charming
and weird aspect to others or gave them away as presents".

It might be of some interest to enquire what kinds of observation
could have induced in writers whom a man as cautious as Boyle
explicitly called reliable the opinion that in Joachimstal silver grew
like grass from minerals. The answer is that this phenomenon can be
observed there even today! If you visit the mineralogical museum in
the mining office of St. Joachimstal, you will find there ores from
which silver wire projects, and Oberbergrat J. Štěp, the worthy
Chairman of the Administration of the Mines and Works in St.

Joachimstal, can tell you that he himself has seen the growing of such silver moss; samples of argentite, which, to his knowledge, had not previously been exposed to air, developed these strange growths, well known to mineralogists, within the short span of a decade. So it was not Dr. Schrötter's and Professor Gerhard's observation, but only their interpretation, that was erroneous: in reproducing the report, Boyle, who, without more detailed data, was of course not able to discover the mistake, did not display any lack of judgement but was adhering to his firmly held principle—neither to reject nor to accept reports without proof.

If we wish to learn the general ideas concerning metals which were current amongst the miners of Joachimstal when the silver mines flourished, we are not dependent on mineralogical and chemical technical journals only, but can find a particularly lively picture in the unique journal, *Bergpostille*, of Johannes Mathesius, Pastor of the village, who is well known as a pupil, friend, and biographer of Luther. From a Bible passage he took the title "Sarepta" for his collection of sermons, which he preached, according to report, in the garb of a miner, in the years 1552 to 1562 on Shrove Tuesdays for the edification and entertainment of his congregation, consisting mainly of miners. In each sermon he preached on a topic directly connected with mining, introducing the few Bible passages directly bearing on it which he had industriously gathered, as well as numerous others which, by exercising some freedom of interpretation, he succeeded in regarding as symbolic. While for him the lessons and admonitions which he thus made palatable to his parishioners were the main concern, we of course are much more interested in the mining practice itself than in its symbolic interpretation. For, owing to his long stay in the "Tal", Mathesius was a brilliant expert in the whole of the working of the mines, and although he speaks with great respect of the simple miners to whom he owed his knowledge and whose reports "he was as ready to believe as Aristotle those of his fishers and huntsmen", yet undoubtedly few had had opportunities of acquiring such comprehensive knowledge of the work in the mines and in the smelting works as this vicar who, like his friend Melanchthon, had pronounced scientific as well as theological interests. Since it is necessary for his purpose to give not his own peculiar views but only those generally accepted by the miners, his sermons mirror particularly faithfully the doctrines current at that time. We hear for instance that changes in the nature of the ore, the formation and, in its turn, disappearance of precious metals, are everyday occurrences.

From many passages in Mathesius we gather how firmly rooted this idea must have been with the miners of his time; one such passage will also prove that nevertheless Mathesius did not believe in the success of alchemistic endeavours: "A caterpillar becomes a cockchafer and a beetle a butterfly, wood turns into stone (*sic*). Thence miners get their idea that veins and ores in the earth alter too and become better and more valuable from year to year, improving their quality until they reach sterling worth or arrive at a state of rest and perfection. Nature, since she is not hindered by the curse of God and continues in her natural workings, never rests but always works according to the destiny for which she was created, until she reaches the end and the target of perfection towards which she is directed; this is the foundation of the alchemists' presumption that they can transmute the metals by their own art, and turn copper into silver and gold. But though their art may dare to try to imitate nature, yet it cannot achieve everything, the reason being that God's order and the natural workings of God's workshop under the earth are beyond the art of the alchemists, wherefore they fall behind and may well further their own amusement to no purpose until they are thereby impoverished and weary of it." And in another passage he writes: "This is the place to mention the common testimony of our miners, when they hew a beautiful bismuth they are wont to say 'we have come too early', thus confessing that if this type of ore had remained longer in the fire of the mountain, it would have turned into good silver". That there was nothing absurd in crediting nature with a transmutation of elements, impossible in the laboratory, we realize nowadays through our knowledge of the naturally pre-ordained transmutations of the radioactive elements; in this case too, all human endeavours to copy the processes have so far resulted in failure.*

Many further items connected with the chemical elements could be quoted from the mining sermons; I shall, however, confine myself, as an example of the way in which he established connections, to the spiritual interpretation which Mathesius gives to lead. He starts with the beautiful simile from Isaiah, which must have been especially impressive for his audience, in which "the pure doctrine is compared to refined silver", while "the lead in the melt from which the silver is refined is called heresy".† This he regards as

* Artificial radioactivity had, of course, not been achieved when this was written. [Ed.]

† The reference is to Isaiah I. 25, which in the English Authorized Version runs thus: "And I will turn my hand upon thee, and purely purge away thy dross, and take away all thy tin". In Luther's German text, however, the word here translated as "tin" appears as "Blei" (lead). It appears to be impossible now to determine which is the more correct,

sufficient ground for assuming that, in the Bible, lead "always signifies the false doctrine". "You miners might well let your thoughts dwell on the simile when you see the lead in the furnace go up in smoke or become glet,* then you might say that this is a picture of heresy and idolatry." That is also the reason why "the Roman Catholic church generally must seal its letters and pardons with lead", so that we should be "all the more anxiously on our guard against her". But "Jesus as the true smelter has caused the doctrine which had been adulterated by Roman lead and various paternoster stones, to pass through the furnace and be purified again". At this point, one might well be tempted to follow Mathesius' example in establishing elaborate artificial connections, and assert that the lead of Joachimstal is particularly liable to be associated with heresy; indeed it was the first element to revolt against the dogma of the constant atomic weight! It is this lead which is responsible for the fact that the "Concilia" of the International Atomic Weights Commission have now to deal with the problem of how to amend the fundamental chemical concepts. Keeping to chronological sequence, however, we must first mention another important step forward which the history of the chemical elements owes to Joachimstal.

The times of prosperity for the silver mines had been followed within a few decades by an inevitable regression. Unsystematic workings by immigrant adventurers and consequent ruining of many mines; a decrease in the timber resources of the district; the garrisoning of armies; contributions and despoliations during the Schmalkaldian and especially during the Thirty Years' war; the expulsion of the Protestant population, which formed the majority of the inhabitants, by the counter-reformation; and finally (and, according to the results of recent investigations, this seems to be the main factor) the peculiar geological configuration of the mines which carried easily accessible silver only in the upper strata—all these things made State subsidies necessary in order to keep the work going at all. In the seventeenth century mining was at times stopped completely. In the eighteenth century the silver production

---

or indeed if the substance denoted by the original Hebrew word was clearly identified in the mind of the writer. "There was a good deal of confusion between tin and lead in ancient times, nor was any means known of separating one from the other." (F. Sherwood Taylor, *A History of Industrial Chemistry*, Heinemann, London, p.43. 1957.) The miners of St. Joachimstal, however, would have been familiar with lead as a base impurity in silver, and would have had no difficulty in following Mathesius' application of Luther's text. [Ed.]

* Litharge. [Ed.]

was small, but arsenic, lead, bismuth and cobalt were produced. About the middle of the nineteenth century the extraction of uranium ore and the manufacture of uranium pigments began, but all these enterprises could at best only cover their cost. The new economic prosperity, as well as the new scientific fame of St. Joachimstal, dates only from the discovery of radium (1898); the material from which Madame Curie succeeded in preparing this most precious of elements in quantities that could be weighed were two waggon-loads of pitchblende residues which the Austrian Ministry of Agriculture had most readily sent from Joachimstal to Paris in answer to her request. Most of the radium extracted since has been isolated under the direction of Dr. Ulrich in Joachimstal itself. The radium found in Joachimstal was used not only by Professor Stefan Meyer and other scientists in the Institute for Radium Research in Vienna, but also in Manchester, by Professor Rutherford and his pupils who carried out the most important of their investigations on a sample from the same source put at their disposal by the Vienna Academy of Sciences. The surprising vistas into previously unexplored regions of physics and chemistry which were opened up by tiny quantities of this substance have already been described in numerous popular treatises about the astonishing properties of radium, so that I need not go into details here. I shall only mention those aspects which are significant for our concept of the chemical element.

After the foundations of modern chemistry were laid by Lavoisier, the conviction, based on the failures of the alchemists and on numerous more recent experiments, gained ground that the chemical elements were absolutely unalterable, and that never since the present natural laws applied had transmutation of one element into another taken place. The possibility of an "evolution of matter" was granted for stellar bodies in process of formation, but scientists despaired completely of being able to observe a similar process on our earth. Radium, polonium, actinium and other substances produced from the Joachimstal material are, however, involved in constant transmutation, in spite of the fact that they have to be granted the status of chemical elements because of their indivisibility in all chemical attempts at separation; from radium, for instance, with its clearly defined spectrum, two other elements, helium and radium emanation, develop, which are in their turn chemically indivisible and thus true elements, showing spectra of their own, quite different from that of radium. *The important new conclusion that follows, concerning the concept of the chemical element, is thus that the transmutation of one element into another is by no means an impossible process.* Admittedly we cannot, as the alchemists tried to do, induce this process at will in elements of our choosing; we can only observe it in particular cases as spectators.

While this discovery was such as to cause great surprise amongst chemists, their surprise was perhaps even further enhanced when a few years later the news appeared in the scientific journals that the atomic weights of the elements lead and thorium, when extracted from Joachimstal pitchblende, were considerably lower than the normal values. The peculiar behaviour of the radio-elements did not shake the foundations of our concept of the element so profoundly, since the phenomenon of transmutation could be detected only by specially developed methods and was never observed in the ordinary operations of chemistry. The atomic weights, however, and all calculations connected with them, are part and parcel of the fundamentals of chemistry, and the most precise determinations of atomic weight had previously always resulted in showing this figure to be a constant; i.e. no matter where it was found, copper, for instance, always had the atomic weight 63·57, lead 207·20, thorium 232·1. But lead from Joachimstal pitchblende (and from a few other uranium minerals investigated at the same time) provided the first exception to this rule; it had an atomic weight of only 206·4. The only element in which up to then the same anomalous behaviour had been observed was thorium, which, when isolated from the pitchblende of Joachimstal, shows an atomic weight of 231·5.

These investigations, the accuracy of which is guaranteed by the names of the scientists who have carried them out (Hönigschmid, Richards *et al.*), forced chemists to acknowledge the fact, previously held to be impossible, *that one and the same chemical element can occur in different forms.* These forms can differ considerably in atomic weight (in the case of lead, weights as low as 206·0 and as high as 207·9 have now been found), and yet behave so absolutely identically in all chemical reactions that there is no analytical chemical means of separating them once they have been mixed by nature or in the laboratory. For this reason we have to regard them as different modifications of the same element, not as different elements similar to one another. Spectrographic examination too, which is one of the most sensitive methods for ascertaining the identity or otherwise of two elements, provides us with pictures which it is absolutely impossible to distinguish from one another, thus confirming the conclusion drawn from the chemical inseparability. The narrow limits of this lecture forbid me to discuss in more detail the connection of

4

the varieties of lead and thorium with the substances known in radio-activity—the "isotopes", radium D, radium G, thorium D with lead, and ionium with thorium, respectively.

We thus owe to the mines of St. Joachimstal the recognition in the sixteenth century of bismuth as a new metal and the closer investigation of numerous other metals and ores that had been insufficiently studied until then. Scientific mineralogy originated there. Documents from the "Tal" still provide an interesting source for the historical study of the concept of the element.

About the turn of the nineteenth century there came from the mines the first radium and polonium and several other radio-elements discovered at that time; most of the investigations into the properties of such elements in process of transmutation were carried out with material from Joachimstal. Finally, the beginning of the twentieth century brought the discovery that the well-known elements lead and thorium show abnormally low atomic weights when extracted from pitchblende; this experimental proof of the fact that a chemical element can occur in different modifications is perhaps the most important scientific discovery to which the mineral resources of St. Joachimstal have contributed.

Surveying thus the whole history of the mines, we may say, without fear of exaggeration, that no other place on earth has contributed as much to the clarification of our ideas about the chemical elements as the small valley of St. Joachimstal.

3 | The Trend of Inorganic and Physical Chemistry since 1850

Chemistry is a very young science, considerably younger than, for instance, physics. It was only near the end of the eighteenth century that Lavoisier laid the foundation of modern chemistry, and at the beginning progress was comparatively slow; most of the developments took place during the last hundred years, and it is obvious that in the time at my disposal I can only touch on a few of the most important features. I think I shall be justified in confining myself principally to the developments of two of the fundamental conceptions of chemistry, those of "element" and "atom".

How much did a university student of chemistry hear about elements and atoms in 1850, if he had the privilege of listening to a really competent teacher? We can answer this question very accurately, as luckily the notes taken by a very gifted student during such lectures have been preserved. Perhaps the most famous chemist of those days was Justus von Liebig and his lecture course on "Experimental Chemistry", delivered at Giessen until 1852, was taken down nearly verbatim by a pupil destined to obtain almost equal fame—August Kekulé. From his lecture notes we can see that Liebig dealt with a greater number of elements than were known in Lavoisier's days—61 instead of some 40—but he did not go any deeper into the question of their mutual relationship, and hardly mentioned the atomic theory, although about forty years had elapsed since John Dalton's ideas had been promulgated by Thomas Thomson, and sixty years since William Higgins had for the first time coupled atomistic conceptions with Lavoisier's chemistry. All Liebig had to say was:

"For this doctrine of equivalents some explanation can be given by the atomic theory which, although being only something conceived, a hypothesis, is so far the only explanation. One assumes: each body consists of indivisible particles of equal size which, infinitely small, rest at infinitely small distance. If one assumes further that 1 atom of a body unites with 1 atom, or with 2 or 3 of another, the ratios of combination explain themselves. The equivalents are then the ratios of the weights of the atoms. For instance

$$\begin{array}{ccccccc} H & & O & & Cl & & S \\ 1 & : & 8 & : & 35 \cdot 4 & : & 16 \end{array}$$

With one metal atom 1 or 2 or 3 atoms of oxygen combine; this explains at the same time the law of multiples.''

These few lines were apparently all a student of chemistry was supposed to know about this "hypothesis" one hundred years ago.

Liebig's indifference to the atomic theory was not a peculiarity of his own. It did not greatly interest any of the leading chemists, because it had made so little progress during the half century of its existence. Neither Higgins nor Dalton nor the chemists of the following generation had succeeded in establishing the relative values of the atomic weights with any degree of certainty, although Avogadro's hypothesis, published in 1811, could have provided the solution; but physics and chemistry were still quite separate sciences, and even a chemist of the order of Liebig did not feel the necessity of choosing the atomic weights in conformity with the physicists' ideas; after performing in his lecture the combination of two volumes of hydrogen with one of oxygen he wrote the formula of water HO. Even a decade after Kekulé had studied under Liebig, in the question of atomic weights there was still complete "anarchy", to use Wurtz's expression. In 1860, on Kekulé's suggestion, a meeting of the best-known chemists from many countries took place in Karlsruhe, in which an attempt was made to come to an agreement, but without immediate success. However, the Italian chemist, Cannizzaro, gave to some visitors of the congress, amongst them the German Lothar Meyer and the Russian Mendeleeff, a little printed pamphlet, from which they learned the superiority of Avogadro's method of calculating atomic weights. Within a few years these corrected atomic weights enabled them to discover the relationships between the chemical elements embodied in the so-called periodic law. Its importance and its most impressive service, the prediction of undiscovered elements, is too well known to need repetition. This prophesying is usually credited to Mendeleeff, but actually the English chemist Newlands who, also using Cannizzaro's atomic weights, was the first to draft a table with the main features of the periodic system, had already foreseen an element between silicon and tin, as is clearly indicated on one of his tables. In Mendeleeff's table there were gaps not only for this eka-silicon (germanium) but also for eka-boron (scandium) and eka-aluminium (gallium). On the other hand, it indicated that 19 elements should find their place between barium and tantalum and foreshadowed even a few trans-uranium elements, as homologues of the lower ones in the same groups. As we know now, these predictions came only very partially true.

Newlands's publications on the periodic system date from 1863 to 1866, Mendeleeff's and Lothar Meyer's from 1869 and 1870. In 1887 the British Association for the Advancement of Science held a very remarkable meeting at Manchester, coinciding with the Golden Jubilee of Queen Victoria. It was especially memorable for chemists as the President of the Association was one of their ranks, the pro-fessor of chemistry at Manchester University, Sir Henry Roscoe. When in his presidential address he gave a survey of the develop-ment of chemistry during the past fifty years, he spoke to an audience which, among other famous foreign chemists, included Mendeleeff and Lothar Meyer. He referred to their share in the discovery of the periodic system in the following words:

"Germany, in the person of Lothar Meyer, keeps, as it is wont to do, strictly within the limits of known facts. Russia, in the person of Mendeleeff, being of a somewhat more imaginative nature, not only seizes the facts, which are proved, but ventures upon prophecy."

This Manchester session of the British Association was the only time when Mendeleeff and Lothar Meyer met. This happy occa-sion was celebrated by a group picture, including also Roscoe, which does not seem to be much known in this country. A copy of it was given to me by Lothar Meyer's son, when in 1930 a meeting was held to commemorate the centenary of his father's birth, and we may perhaps take a quick glance at this interesting group (Fig. 1). Newlands apparently did not attend the Manchester gathering but in the same year was honoured by the Royal Society by the award of the Davy medal—somewhat belatedly, as the same honour had been bestowed five years earlier on Lothar Meyer and Mendeleeff.

Roscoe's characterization of the relative merits of Mendeleeff and Lothar Meyer is, I think, somewhat oversimplified. It is true that Meyer, as he himself said later, had been lacking in courage to predict the properties of undiscovered elements, but in another respect he was even more daring than Mendeleeff and certainly had the deeper insight. While Mendeleeff emphatically denied that the periodic system indicated any genetic relationship of the chemical elements, Meyer saw clearly that it was a strong argument in favour of the assumption of some kind of primordial matter.

However, in those days no more could be said about the deeper meaning of the periodic system, although many chemists tried to go beyond Lothar Meyer and, by rearranging the tables or curves in all

Fig. 1.
From left to right
Sitting: Mendeleeff, Mrs. L. Meyer, Roscoe.
Standing: Wislicenus, L. Meyer, Atkinson, Quincke.

imaginable ways, hoped to discover more about the secret of the relationship of the elements. All these frantic attempts proved to be scientifically completely sterile. Whoever is interested in them may find a comprehensive survey in a historically very valuable little book published by the Russian Academy of Sciences in 1934 on the occasion of the centenary celebration of Mendeleeff's birth. One of the figures, showing the elements arranged in a three-dimensional spiral, has perhaps some topical interest, as, unfortunately, it has been resuscitated from well-deserved oblivion for this year's (1951) Festival of Britain in the South Bank Science Exhibition in London, embellished, it is true, with coloured electric lamps which go on and off. It is undeniably a pretty sight, but would be more appropriately housed in the neighbouring Fun Fair of Battersea Park than under the Dome of Discovery.

In studying these various representations one is frequently afraid that the authors did not quite realize that a curve connecting the elements must never give the impression of any continuity in the periodic system. The chemical elements are distinct individualities which can occupy only separate points. A continuous line drawn from point to point, as for instance Lothar Meyer's famous atomic volume curve, is useful in bringing out very clearly the periodicity in the position of the points, but has no other meaning. Such a simple and straightforward arrangement of the elements on the abscissa, and of the chosen property on the ordinate, later enabled Moseley to show in a convincing way the strict dependence of the characteristic X-rays of the chemical elements on their ordinal numbers, and to clear up definitely the question as to the number and position of undiscovered elements. Table I (page 36) shows you the periodic system as it was drawn after Moseley's fundamental work, leaving only six gaps for undiscovered elements between hydrogen and uranium.

This reference to Moseley brings us to the period when, from entirely different quarters, chemistry received decisive help in the understanding of the nature of the chemical elements and of the foundation of the periodic system. In 1896 Becquerel discovered the phenomenon of radioactivity; in 1898 Pierre and Marie Curie extracted radium from pitchblende; and in 1902 Rutherford and Soddy developed the theory of radioactive disintegration.

These fundamental steps were followed by a wealth of other new and revolutionary observations. Of special importance for chemistry was the recognition of the following three facts:

1. Chemical elements are not immutable.
2. Atoms are complicated structures containing a tremendous store of energy.
3. Atomic weights are not fundamental constants. Atoms of different weight may belong to the same chemical element, and atoms of the same weight to different elements. They are called "isotopes" and "isobars" respectively.

This very important discovery of the limited significance of the atomic weights has in a sense been implicit in any table of the periodic system, because here—in contradistinction to its representation by curves—the elements were always arranged at equal distances from each other and not according to the actual values of the atomic weights. The first scientist who drew the consequences from this fact was the Swedish physicist Rydberg who, in a paper of 1897, stated with admirable clarity: "In investigations on the periodic system not the atomic weights, but the ordinal numbers of the elements, have to be used as independent variables".

Decisive progress in the understanding of the periodic system could only be made when chemists had freed themselves from their overestimation of the theoretical consequence of atomic weights. Today it is perhaps a little difficult for the younger generation of chemists to imagine how reluctant forty years ago were the vast majority of chemists to admit the possibility that different elements could have the same atomic weight.

Since the discovery of the periodic system the fundamental importance of the atomic weights had been emphasized, indeed over-emphasized. This is probably one of the reasons why Dalton has been so exalted as the founder of the atomic theory and Higgins's obvious priority completely neglected. Higgins's book of 1789 is rare, and it was frequently believed that he had assumed that all atoms have the same weight, while Dalton was supposed to have been the first who had found the truth that each element has a characteristic atomic weight. Such an account of Higgins's views was given by an English historian of chemistry in 1939, and repeated by him in 1948, and again this year; but it is incorrect. Higgins nowhere states as a principle that atoms of different elements have the same weight but only in one or two cases deduces from experimental facts that there was no difference in their weights. When he wrote the formula of water HO, he was perfectly aware that there is a vast difference in the atomic weights of hydrogen and oxygen. (The very competent and careful German historian of chemistry, Hermann Kopp, gave him credit for that.) But when he assumed the formula of sulphur dioxide to be SO, he necessarily came to the conclusion that sulphur and oxygen had the same atomic weight. He suggested equality of atomic weights too in the case of nitrogen and oxygen; that was not at all bad as a first approximation, in order to derive the atomistic constitution of N_2O, NO, NO_2, etc. However, in the second half of the nineteenth century and later it seemed to chemists that anyone who ascribed the same weight to the atoms of oxygen and nitrogen violated the very foundation of the atomic theory. Today we know of the existence of isobars, and are aware that in the case of the elements oxygen and nitrogen there are actually no less than four pairs of them; the four nitrogen isotopes ^{14}N, ^{15}N, ^{16}N and ^{17}N are isobaric with the four oxygen isotopes ^{14}O, ^{15}O, ^{16}O and ^{17}O; so, in the light of our modern knowledge, there is nothing contradictory in Higgins's atomic conceptions, and as his book was published years before Dalton developed his atomic theory the challenge uttered recently by Professor Frederick Soddy to give more credit to the Irish chemist seems only too justified. If we want to denote the chemical atomic theory by a special name, the least we should do would be to call it the Higgins–Dalton Theory, and not the Dalton Theory.

The experimental results briefly sketched above, and other researches I have not time to mention here, enabled Rutherford and Bohr in the second decade of this century to crown the atomic theory by a theory of the atom and to explain the periodic system on the lines dimly foreseen by Meyer. I can only mention this great achievement which, I am sure, is so well known that this brief reference will suffice.

The theory of the atom was also able to shed light on the question of the "chemical forces". In classical chemistry they were considered as something quite different from the forces dealt with in physics and hardly capable of further explanation. As atoms are now known to be structures built up of electrically charged particles, the combination of atoms to form molecules is to be understood as a consequence of electric forces. All valency bonds are essentially electrostatic in nature, although the mechanism of interaction is different in the two cases of electrovalency and covalency. The exact mathematical treatment is difficult except in the simplest cases, but the possibility of explaining in principle all the so-called chemical forces by the laws known to physicists can no longer be doubted. There is still a great amount of hard work to be done by the theoretical physicists if they want to understand in detail the vast accumulated data of classical chemical statics, e.g. the valency of the elements, and we must admire the energy and persistence of those who are working in this field; for it is unusual in theoretical science to see so much labour devoted to studies which can hardly be expected to do more than explain known facts; it seems that this field is almost completely devoid of the most glittering prize of theoretical work, the possibility of predictive discoveries.

The advances made in the understanding of the nature of chemical atoms and of their mutual relationship are by no means only of theoretical interest. The study of naturally occurring radioactive substances was followed by the artificial disruption of stable atoms, by the production of many radioactive isotopes of inactive elements —today nearly 1,000 different nuclides are known—and, most

Table I

Period	Group I a	Group I b	Group II a	Group II b	Group III a	Group III b	Group IV a	Group IV b	Group V a	Group V b	Group VI a	Group VI b	Group VII a	Group VII b	Group VIII	O
I	1 H 1·008															2 He 4·00
II	3 Li 6·94		4 Be 9·1		5 B 10·8		6 C 12·00			7 N 14·008		8 O 16·000		9 F 19·00			10 Ne 20·2
III	11 Na 23·00		12 Mg 24·32		13 Al 27·1		14 Si 28·3			15 P 31·04		16 S 32·07		17 Cl 35·46			18 A 39·9
IV	19 K 39·10	29 Cu 63·57	20 Ca 40·07	30 Zn 65·37	21 Sc 45·10	31 Ga 69·9	22 Ti 48·1	32 Ge 72·5	23 V 51·0	33 As 74·96	24 Cr 52·0	34 Se 79·2	25 Mn 54·93	35 Br 79·92	26 Fe 55·85 27 Co 58·97 28 Ni 58·68	36 Kr 82·92
V	37 Rb 85·5	47 Ag 107·88	38 Sr 87·6	48 Cd 112·4	39 Y 88·7	49 In 114·8	40 Zr 90·6	50 Sn 118·7	41 Nb 93·5	51 Sb 120·2	42 Mo 96·0	52 Te 127·5	43—	53 I 126·92	44 Ru 101·7 45 Rh 102·9 46 Pd 106·7	54 X 130·2
VI	55 Cs 132·8	79 Au 197·2	56 Ba 137·4	80 Hg 200·6	57-71 Rare Earths*	81 Ti 204·4	72—	82 Pb 207·2	73 Ta 181·5	83 Bi 209·0	74 W 184·0	84 Po 210	75—	85—	76 Os 190·9 77 Ir 193·1 78 Pt 195·2	86 Em 222
VII	87—		88 Ra 226·0		89 Ac		90 Th 232·1		91 Pa		92 U 238·2					

* Rare Earths

Period															
VI 57-71	57 La 139·0	58 Ce 140·25	59 Pr 140·9	60 Nd 144·3	61—	62 Sm 150·4	63 Eu 152·0	64 Gd 157·3	65 Tb 159·2	66 Dy 162·5	67 Ho 163·5	68 Er 167·7	69 Tu 169·4	70 Yb 173·5	71 Lu 175·0

spectacular of all, by the creation of no less than nine chemical elements which are not to be found on our earth, and of which one, plutonium, is one of the most important sources of atomic energy. It will, we hope, not be very long before this artificial element will help to relieve the coal and oil shortage of the world.

There is still some doubt about the best way of placing these newly discovered elements in the table of the periodic system. Professor Glenn Seaborg, who was the leader of the team which discovered most of the transuranium elements, likes to place the elements from actinium on as a second rare earth group under the lanthanum series. It is felt, however, by other chemists, that the discovery of the new transuranium elements does not give any fresh information on the chemistry of the elements up to uranium, which are very satisfactorily placed in the usual table of the periodic system. Table II shows the arrangement of the periodic system which I think does full justice to the present state of our knowledge. If you compare this table with the previous one based on Moseley's work (Table I) you will see that the six gaps between hydrogen and uranium have been filled, thanks to the discovery of the naturally occurring elements 72, 75 and 87, and to the artificial production of elements 43, 61 and 85; and that the transuranium elements are written in such a way as to make it clear that they are not higher homologues of rhenium, etc., but a group of their own, just as the rare earths are, in a different way.

Theoretical chemistry today exists only as a part of physics; but that of course does not mean that the physicist can take over the experimental side of chemistry as well. Not only is the whole practical application of chemistry entirely alien to the physicist's training, but also in most purely scientific problems the approach of the chemist is different from that of the physicist and has certainly a value of its own. If the chemist gratefully admits that the deeper understanding of his science is due to the work of the physicist, he can at the same time point out with pride that many of the greatest advances in physics have been made on the basis of chemical discoveries. We have met with an outstanding example, the periodic system. When, in 1913, Moseley for the first time was able to determine with certainty the number of possible chemical elements between hydrogen and uranium, he was astonished to find that almost all of them had already been discovered by the analytical chemists and, as we know today, three of the six missing elements they could not possibly find by any skill as these elements do not exist on our earth. Another similar instance was the discovery of

TABLE II

Group

Period	1	2	3	4	5	6	7	8	9	10	11	12	13	14	15	16	17	18
I																	1 H 1·0080	2 He 4·003
II	3 Li 6·940	4 Be 9·02											5 B 10·82	6 C 12·010	7 N 14·008	8 O 16·0000	9 F 19·00	10 Ne 20·183
III	11 Na 22·997	12 Mg 24·32											13 Al 26·97	14 Si 28·06	15 P 30·98	16 S 32·066	17 Cl 35·457	18 A 39·944
IV	19 K 39·096	20 Ca 40·08	21 Sc 45·10	22 Ti 47·90	23 V 50·95	24 Cr 52·01	25 Mn 54·93	26 Fe 55·85	27 Co 58·94	28 Ni 58·69	29 Cu 63·54	30 Zn 65·38	31 Ga 69·72	32 Ge 72·60	33 As 74·91	34 Se 78·96	35 Br 79·916	36 Kr 83·7
V	37 Rb 85·48	38 Sr 87·63	39 Y 88·92	40 Zr 91·22	41 Nb 92·91	42 Mo 95·95	43 Tc 99	44 Ru 101·7	45 Rh 102·91	46 Pd 106·7	47 Ag 107·880	48 Cd 112·41	49 In 114·76	50 Sn 118·70	51 Sb 121·76	52 Te 127·61	53 I 126·92	54 Xe 131·3
VI	55 Cs 132·91	56 Ba 137·36	57–71 Rare Earths*	72 Hf 178·6	73 Ta 180·88	74 W 183·92	75 Re 186·31	76 Os 190·2	77 Ir 193·1	78 Pt 195·23	79 Au 197·2	80 Hg 200·61	81 Tl 204·39	82 Pb 207·21	83 Bi 209·00	84 Po 210	85 At 211	86 Rn 222
VII	87 Fr 223	88 Ra 226·05	89 Ac 227	90 Th 232·12	91 Pa 231	92 U 238·07	93 Np 237	94 Pu 239	95 Am 241	96 Cm 242	97 Bk 243	98 Cf 244						

* Rare Earths

VI 57–71	57 La 138·92	58 Ce 140·13	59 Pr 140·92	60 Nd 144·27	61 Pm 147	62 Sm 150·43	63 Eu 152·0	64 Gd 156·9	65 Tb 159·2	66 Dy 162·46	67 Ho 164·90	68 Er 167·2	69 Tm 169·4	70 Yb 173·04	71 Lu 174·99

isotopy by Soddy; the conception arose from the proof provided by analytical-chemical work, that some radioactive elements are so similar to each other or to stable elements that they cannot be separated by the usual laboratory methods. Many physicists, including Rutherford, were for some time reluctant to admit that there was something more behind this failure than "rotten chemistry".

If we want to add one more example where analytical chemistry paved the way to an important progress in physics we may remember the fission of uranium. It was again mastery of analytical chemistry which led Otto Hahn, and only following him the physicists, to the recognition that an entirely new type of atomic disruption was effected by the impact of neutrons on uranium.

It is also to be expected that in future, in a similar way, the boldness of the chemists—proceeding on evidence of sometimes rather crude chemical experiments—will lead to initial hypotheses which only later are confirmed by more refined physical experiments in a theoretically more straightforward way. One of these developments seems already well under way. Studies on the abundance and weights of the many nuclides known today have led to the assumption that there is some periodicity in their internal structure. Further empirical confirmation of this model, especially the rough agreement of the observed spins with expectations derived from it, has overcome the initial theoretical objections of physicists to any such model. Today the idea of a shell structure is getting more and more to the fore in speculations about the building-up of the nuclei.

Although the experimental methods of chemistry and physics remain different, there is no longer any dividing line between the sciences. Long ago Bunsen used to say: "A chemist who is not a physicist is nothing"; now, with equal right, we may say: "A physicist who is not a chemist is nothing". Today there is only one fundamental science of the inorganic world, of which chemistry, physical chemistry, chemical physics and physics are just different chapters.

This merging of physics and chemistry has in many ways greatly simplified our general outlook, and it is in my opinion quite unjustified if we hear every now and then complaints that the modern development of theoretical physics has complicated matters. It is true that the chemist is no longer permitted to picture his atoms as solid balls held together by irreducible chemical forces and that, in his theoretical explanations, he, as well as the physicist, has to rely on mathematical symbols which are not capable of representation in space by models taken from macroscopic experience. But was it really true that the old picture was more intelligible? A little philosophical reasoning shows that the apparent simplicity of the cruder materialistic explanations was quite deceptive; nobody was ever able really to understand the interaction even between two colliding molecules. This was shown by the German philosopher Eduard von Hartmann as long ago as 1902 in a very remarkable book, and the still more penetrating studies of modern philosophers about the nature of scientific explanations surely agree with this result. So if today there is some complaint about the dry and abstract character of theoretical physics and chemistry, and in comparison the old days of naive realism appear to some like a paradise, I think we must admit that it was nothing but a fool's paradise which we should be glad to have left at last. We see much more sharply today where the boundaries lie for the human mind to any understanding of the world, and our more agnostic outlook should not be considered as a retrograde step compared with the naive attitude of the nineteenth century.

One point certainly will be admitted by everybody, that the study of inorganic and physical chemistry today is at least as fascinating as it was a hundred years ago. Those of us who are approaching the end of the span during which they can hope to take part in scientific research will sympathize with the words uttered by one of the greatest amongst the French chemists and physicists of that period. Gay-Lussac died in 1850. In his last words he expressed regret to have to go just when science became so curious: "C'est dommage de s'en aller; ça commence à devenir drôle". Today we have the same feeling, that we are just witnessing a new start, and that with this most interesting period the real fun is just beginning.

4 | John Newlands and the Periodic System

Fifty years ago* died John Alexander Reina Newlands, to whom eleven years earlier the Royal Society had presented their Davy Medal "for his Discovery of the Periodic Law of the Chemical Elements". Although the recognition of this law was one of the greatest advances in the whole history of science, one looks in vain for any reference to Newlands in many chemical textbooks. The Royal Society itself is not quite free from responsibility if other scientists are given greater prominence in connection with the periodic law, because five years before they gave the Davy Medal to Newlands they had bestowed the same honour on Dmitri Mendeleeff and Lothar Meyer "for their discovery of the periodic relations of the atomic weights", without even mentioning the name of Newlands. Whom shall we then consider as the real discoverer of the periodic system?

Like many other great achievements, the insight into the mutual relationships of the chemical elements was reached gradually, and a complete historical record would have to name, in addition to Newlands, Mendeleeff and Meyer, at least six other chemists—Döbereiner, Pettenkofer, de Chancourtois, Dumas, Odling and Gladstone—and to a certain extent it will always be a matter of opinion whose contribution ought to be considered as the most important one. Not so long ago a well-known French chemist, G. Urbain, wrote in one of his books that the Russian Mendeleeff, who is usually regarded as the most noteworthy of this whole group of scientists, had done little but extend in a somewhat questionable fashion the fundamental idea of the Frenchman Dumas. Urbain's astonishing attitude will probably be considered by most chemists as an example of misplaced patriotism; while the action of the Royal Society in honouring two foreigners before their own countryman had at least the merit of being dictated by a desire to be absolutely impartial.

* On July 29th 1898. [Ed.]

41

As a matter of fact, it is not difficult to understand why Newlands was for a while completely overshadowed by Mendeleeff. It is true that he had seen several years earlier than Mendeleeff that the most natural grouping of the chemical elements is one based on their atomic weights; he had also come to the correct conclusion that from the conflicting values of atomic weights then in use only those based on the calculations of the Italian chemist Cannizzaro could serve as a reliable basis of such a system; finally, in one paper he had already made an attempt to predict the atomic weights of undiscovered elements—a most impressive undertaking for which usually Mendeleeff alone is given credit. But these ideas were published by Newlands in several short papers scattered over a period of four years (1863 to 1866) and showed no steady improvement; for example, the interesting gaps for missing elements just mentioned, which he had left in his 1864 table, were no longer there in the 1866 presentation. When he read this latter paper to the Chemical Society, one of the Fellows suggested that an order according to the initial letters of the elements might give similar regularities. This silly remark has since been quoted again and again as a proof of how far Newlands's colleagues were from grasping the importance of his ideas; but at the same meeting another Fellow of the Society, J. H. Gladstone, made the very judicious criticism that any discovery of a new chemical element, which was by no means unlikely, would destroy Newlands's analogies since in the absence of empty places it would make a complete reshuffle necessary.*

When in 1870 Mendeleeff's very comprehensive paper appeared and was immediately followed by the long-postponed publication of Lothar Meyer's equally important article, all previous attempts at a systematization of the chemical elements were quite naturally eclipsed. Nevertheless one must not forget that Newlands was undoubtedly the first who showed that by arranging all known elements in the order of their atomic weights a classification was obtained in which elements of similar properties followed each other at regular distances. As this is the fundamental idea of Mendeleeff's and Meyer's periodic systems, it is to be regretted that the grant by the Royal Society of the Davy Medal to Newlands came only as a sort of afterthought. On the other hand, most historians of science

---

* It may be worth noting that there is some uncertainty about the state of Newlands's ideas at the time when Mendeleeff's paper appeared, since his work had for some time been too unpopular to secure publication. Thus, in *Chemical News*, **20,** 288 (1869) under the heading "To Correspondents", we read: "John A. R. Newlands, F.C.S.—Declined with thanks. Such purely theoretical speculations occupy more space than we can now spare." "The Editor's regrets" were then apparently expressed publicly. [Ed.]

will subscribe to a pointed remark made by Helmholtz on a somewhat similar occasion; in the course of the dispute about Robert Mayer's share in the discovery of the law of conservation of energy Helmholtz recommended that questions of priority ought to be decided not simply according to the date of the first publication, but that the maturity of the papers should also be taken into account. To a certain extent the action of the Royal Society in honouring first Mendeleeff and Meyer can be justified by Helmholtz's argument.

Even after the appearance of Mendeleeff's article, Newlands returned on several occasions to the problem of the classification of the chemical elements, mainly to remind chemists of his earlier papers on this subject. He did this always in a very modest fashion, by simply quoting the relevant passages. In 1884 he collected all his contributions to the periodic system in a little booklet. However, theoretical speculations like these played only a small part in Newlands's professional life; he taught chemistry for a number of years at schools and at the City of London College, was then chief chemist at a sugar refinery (where he was responsible for various improvements in the process), and finally he became an analytical and consulting chemist in independent practice. Together with his brother, B. E. R. Newlands, he wrote a *Handbook for Sugar Growers and Refiners*. In his twenties he had fought under Garibaldi for the liberty of a people to which he was related through his mother. His death in 1898, when he was only sixty-one, as the consequence of an attack of influenza, came as a shock to the many friends of this "kindly courteous man".

If we want to honour Newlands's memory on the fiftieth anniversary of his death, we can hardly do better than remind readers that his idea of the periodicity of the chemical elements has steadily grown in scientific importance; today not only chemists but also experimental and theoretical physicists are constantly making use of such systematized tables of the elements. We shall, therefore, conclude this article by describing an arrangement which incorporates the latest discoveries.

This will be all the more appropriate as an essential feature of all the modern tables is the assignment of a number to each element; and this is just the one point in which Newlands was in advance even of Mendeleeff and Lothar Meyer. Meyer liked to arrange the elements on a continuous curve; this was criticized by Mendeleeff because it could mislead one into thinking that there was everywhere room for intermediate elements. Mendeleeff's tables with their horizontal and vertical lines made it clear that only a strictly limited number of chemical elements could be placed; but he still ascribed to the actual figures of the atomic weights an exaggerated importance. Newlands, however, used the sequence of the atomic weights only for the purpose of finding the "ordinal number" of each element, and expressed the "law of octaves" (i.e. the periodicity) in terms of these ordinal numbers; in 1866 his table ended with element No. 56, in 1875 with No. 63. These tables, in which prominence is given to the numbers of the elements, not to their weights, look astonishingly modern; it was not before 1897 that ordinal numbers were again introduced in the periodic system by Rydberg; but only after 1913, when the Rutherford–Bohr theory of the atom had been developed, the deep physical significance of these ordinal numbers, now usually called atomic numbers, could be understood; they represent the number of positive electric charges of the atomic nuclei. In giving them prominence over the atomic weights Newlands had been guided by a remarkably sure instinct.*

---

* Newlands's "Law of Octaves" as published in a letter to *Chemical News*, 18th August, 1865.

To the Editor of the *Chemical News*

SIR,—With your permission, I would again call attention to a fact pointed out in a communication of mine, inserted in the *Chemical News* for August 20, 1864.

If the elements are arranged in the order of their equivalents, with a few slight transpositions, as in the accompanying table, it will be observed that elements belonging to the same group usually appear on the same horizontal line.

No.	No.	No.	No.	No.	No.	No.	No.
H 1	F 8	Cl 15	Co & Ni 22	Br 29	Pd 36	I 42	Pt & Ir 50
Li 2	Na 9	K 16	Cu 23	Rb 30	Ag 37	Cs 44	Tl 53
G 3	Mg 10	Ca 17	Zn 25	Sr 31	Bd 38	Ba & V 45	Pb 54
Bo 4	Al 11	Cr 19	Y 24	Ce & La 33	U 40	Ta 46	Th 56
C 5	Si 12	Ti 18	In 26	Zr 32	Sn 39	W 47	Hg 52
N 6	P 13	Mn 20	As 27	Di & Mo 34	Sb 41	Nb 48	Bi 55
O 7	S 14	Fe 21	Se 28	Ro & Ru 35	Te 43	Au 49	Os 51

(Note—Where two elements happen to have the same equivalent, both are designated by the same number.)

It will also be seen that the numbers of analogous elements generally differ either by 7 or by some multiple of seven; in other words, members of the same group stand to each other in the same relation as the extremities of one or more octaves in music. Thus, in the nitrogen group, between nitrogen and phosphorus there are 7 elements; between phosphorus and arsenic, 14; between arsenic and antimony, 14; and lastly, between antimony and bismuth, 14 also.

This peculiar relationship I propose to provisionally term the "Law of Octaves".

I am, &c.

JOHN A. R. NEWLANDS, F.C.S.

Laboratory, 19, Great St. Helen's, E.C., August 8, 1865.

TABLE I. SHORT-PERIOD SYSTEM OF THE CHEMICAL ELEMENTS

Period	Group I a	Group I b	Group II a	Group II b	Group III a	Group III b	Group IV a	Group IV b	Group V a	Group V b	Group VI a	Group VI b	Group VII a	Group VII b	Group VIII a	Group VIII b
I														1 H 1·0080		2 He 4·003
II	3 Li 6·940		4 Be 9·02			5 B 10·82		6 C 12·010		7 N 14·008		8 O 16·0000		9 F 19·00		10 Ne 20·183
III	11 Na 22·997		12 Mg 24·32			13 Al 26·97		14 Si 28·06		15 P 30·98		16 S 32·066		17 Cl 35·457		18 A 39·944
IV	19 K 39·096	29 Cu 63·54	20 Ca 40·08	30 Zn 65·38	21 Sc 45·10	31 Ga 69·72	22 Ti 47·90	32 Ge 72·60	23 V 50·95	33 As 74·91	24 Cr 52·01	34 Se 78·96	25 Mn 54·93	35 Br 79·916	26 Fe 55·85 27 Co 58·94 28 Ni 58·69	36 Kr 83·7
V	37 Rb 85·48	47 Ag 107·880	38 Sr 87·63	48 Cd 112·41	39 Y 88·92	49 In 114·76	40 Zr 91·22	50 Sn 118·70	41 Nb 92·91	51 Sb 121·76	42 Mo 95·95	52 Te 127·61	43 Tc 99	53 I 126·92	44 Ru 101·7 45 Rh 102·91 46 Pd 106·7	54 Xe 131·3
VI	55 Cs 132·91	79 Au 197·2	56 Ba 137·36	80 Hg 200·61	57–71 Rare Earths*	81 Tl 204·39	72 Hf 178·6	82 Pb 207·21	73 Ta 180·88	83 Bi 209·00	74 W 183·92	84 Po 210	75 Re 186·31	85 At 211	76 Os 190·2 77 Ir 193·1 78 Pt 195·23	86 Rn 222
VII	87 Fr 223		88 Ra 226·05		89 Ac 227		90 Th 232·12		91 Pa 231		92 U 238·07		93 Np 237		94 Pu 239 95 Am 241 96 Cm 242	

* Rare Earths

Period															
VI 57–71	57 La 138·92	58 Ce 140·13	59 Pr 140·92	60 Nd 144·27	61 Pm 147	62 Sm 150·43	63 Eu 152·0	64 Gd 156·9	65 Tb 159·2	66 Dy 162·46	67 Ho 164·90	68 Er 167·2	69 Tm 169·4	70 Yb 173·04	71 Lu 174·99

Table II. Long-Period System of the Chemical Elements

Group

Period	1	2	3	4	5	6	7	8	9	10	11	12	13	14	15	16	17	18
I	1 H 1·0080																	2 He 4·003
II	3 Li 6·940	4 Be 9·02											5 B 10·82	6 C 12·010	7 N 14·008	8 O 16·0000	9 F 19·00	10 Ne 20·183
III	11 Na 22·997	12 Mg 24·32											13 Al 26·97	14 Si 28·06	15 P 30·98	16 S 32·066	17 Cl 35·457	18 A 39·944
IV	19 K 39·096	20 Ca 40·08	21 Sc 45·10	22 Ti 47·90	23 V 50·95	24 Cr 52·01	25 Mn 54·93	26 Fe 55·85	27 Co 58·94	28 Ni 58·69	29 Cu 63·54	30 Zn 65·38	31 Ga 69·72	32 Ge 72·60	33 As 74·91	34 Se 78·96	35 Br 79·916	36 Kr 83·7
V	37 Rb 85·48	38 Sr 87·63	39 Y 88·92	40 Zr 91·22	41 Nb 92·91	42 Mo 95·95	43 Tc 99	44 Ru 101·7	45 Rh 102·91	46 Pd 106·7	47 Ag 107·880	48 Cd 112·41	49 In 114·76	50 Sn 118·70	51 Sb 121·76	52 Te 127·61	53 I 126·92	54 Xe 131·3
VI	55 Cs 132·91	56 Ba 137·36	57–71 Rare Earths*	72 Hf 178·6	73 Ta 180·88	74 W 183·92	75 Re 186·31	76 Os 190·2	77 Ir 193·1	78 Pt 195·23	79 Au 197·2	80 Hg 200·61	81 Tl 204·39	82 Pb 207·21	83 Bi 209·00	84 Po 210	85 At 211	86 Rn 222
VII	87 Fr 223	88 Ra 226·05	89 Ac 227	90 Th 232·12	91 Pa 231	92 U 238·07	93 Np 237	94 Pu 239	95 Am 241	96 Cm 242								

* Rare Earths

Period															
VI 57–71	57 La 138·92	58 Ce 140·13	59 Pr 140·92	60 Nd 144·27	61 Pm 147	62 Sm 150·43	63 Eu 152·0	64 Gd 156·9	65 Tb 159·2	66 Dy 162·46	67 Ho 164·90	68 Er 167·2	69 Tm 169·4	70 Yb 173·04	71 Lu 174·99

Tables of the periodic system are so well known that only a few explanatory remarks seem necessary for the two considered here. They concern the elements technetium, promethium, astatine, francium, neptunium, plutonium, americium and curium, which are still missing in most tables available today but which have been included in ours.*

If we look at a table of the periodic system drafted a few years ago, we shall find that the last element shown in it, uranium, has the number 92, but that to several previous numbers no elements have been assigned. The most correct tables left the places 43, 61, 85 and 87 empty while some others filled one or two of the vacancies with the symbols of spurious discoveries. According to our present-day knowledge, the position is briefly as follows.

The discovery of element 43 was claimed by Noddack, Tacke and Berg in Berlin in 1925, but their preliminary announcement was never followed up by a more convincing paper; nevertheless the proposed name, masurium (symbol Ma), derived from Germany's eastern province, was put into many tables. So far the element 43 has not been found in any naturally occurring mineral, but it was artificially produced by Perrier and Segrè in 1937 by bombarding element 42, molybdenum, with deuterons or with neutrons in the cyclotron. Another method for obtaining element 43 is the fission of uranium, in the course of which all the elements between No. 30, zinc, and No. 63, europium, are formed in different amounts. Today several isotopes of 43 are known; the most stable one has a half-life of 4×10^6 years and an atomic weight of 99. Perrier and Segrè suggested for element 43 the name technetium (symbol Tc), because of its artificial production.†

The story of the discovery of element 61 is very similar to that of 43. In 1926 Harris, Yntema and Hopkins, of the University of Illinois, believed they had found it among other rare earths, and the name illinium (symbol Il), proposed by them in honour of their State, was widely accepted; but they were unable to substantiate their claim, and a very careful search by the greatest authority in the field of rare-earth chemistry, the Austrian industrialist Auer von Welsbach, proved that the element to be expected between neodymium and samarium does not exist in the minerals in which the presence of illinium had been announced. However, as stated

* It will be noticed that the Table II, the "long-period system", is identical with Table II of Chapter 3 (p. 38), except that the latter contains the additional elements 97 and 98, which were not known when the present paper was written. [Ed.]

† It is of interest that element 43 has since been discovered in stars of spectrum-type S. [Ed.]

before, it is formed as one of the many fission products of uranium and was isolated and identified by Marinsky and Glendenin who worked during the recent war on atomic energy problems in the team of Professor Coryell of the Massachusetts Institute of Technology. One isotope of element 61 with atomic weight 147 is fairly long-lived; its half-life is 3·7 years. Marinsky and Glendenin recommended the name promethium (symbol Pm), the allusion being that just as Prometheus brought fire from the heavens to earth, science has now succeeded in harnessing for the use of mankind another cosmic force, atomic energy.

Element 85 seems to exist as a rare branch product in the natural radioactive series; but its preparation and chemical study were only possible after one of its isotopes had been artificially made by the bombardment of bismuth with alpha-rays. The credit for this achievement goes to Corson, MacKenzie and Segrè; they put forward the name astatine (symbol At), with reference to the instability of the new element (the Greek "astatos" meaning "unstable"). The half-life is only 7·5 hours; the atomic weight is 211.

Element 87 was discovered in 1939 by Mlle. Perey in Paris as a minor disintegration product in the actinium series, and has also been artificially produced from heavier elements. Its name will be francium (symbol Fr). The natural product has the atomic weight 223 and is very short-lived, its half-life being only 21 minutes.

The extensive study of the behaviour of element 92, uranium, under bombardment with neutrons and other particles has led to the discovery that several elements with ordinal numbers higher than 92 can be obtained which do not exist on the Earth. So far four of these "transuranium" elements have been identified; their proposed names and symbols as well as the atomic weights and half-lives of their most stable isotopes are as follows:

Atomic Number	Name	Symbol	Atomic weight	Half-life
93	Neptunium	Np	237	$2·25 \times 10^6$ yrs
94	Plutonium	Pu	239	$2·4 \times 10^4$ yrs
95	Americium	Am	241	500 yrs
96	Curium	Cm	242	150 days

The names of the first two elements after uranium are taken from Neptune and Pluto, the planets beyond Uranus in the Solar System; as no planet beyond Pluto is known the names of elements 95 and 96 have been chosen for their geographical and personal connotations.

The discoverers of these four new elements are McMillan, Seaborg and several other American physicists and chemists who have been working with them in the universities of California and Chicago.*

The eight new element-names mentioned have not yet been officially sanctioned, and in view of a few rival claims (especially for element 61) it may still be some time before an international agreement is reached. It seems, however, not unsafe to predict the eventual acceptance of the names given above, and we have, therefore, inserted their symbols in our tables.

Innumerable forms of the periodic system have been tried since the days of Newlands, Meyer and Mendeleeff, but we believe that all real advantages of any of these diverse attempts are incorporated in one or other of two comparatively simple tables. Table I (p. 45) is the usual "Mendeleeff table", somewhat modernized; the fundamental idea of Table II (p. 46) has occurred from time to time independently to a number of chemists and it goes, therefore, under different names, but is, in fact, to be found already in Mendeleeff's earliest publications as an alternative. We prefer, therefore, to distinguish the two basic forms as the "short-period table" and the "long-period table". The first is especially useful to demonstrate the valency regularities of the chemical elements and is, therefore, favoured in chemistry textbooks; the latter is frequently more suitable for discussions on subjects of theoretical physics. We recommend having both simple tables at hand, and not to bother with complicated schemes which try to unite the specific advantages of the short- and the long-period representations with the help of elaborate geometrical designs, colours, movable parts, or steric models.

A final word may be said about the way in which we have placed the transuranium elements. From their chemical behaviour it must be concluded that they are not higher homologues of the elements rhenium, osmium, iridium and platinum, but all very similar to uranium. We have, therefore, not assigned them to definite places under the elements 75 to 78 but have written them as a continuous group together with uranium. This is similar to the treatment of the rare earth elements, which, however, for reason of space, are taken out of the framework of the table altogether and written as a coherent group, beginning with lanthanum, at the bottom. It ought to be mentioned that, for theoretical reasons, Professor Seaborg believes that it is justified to speak of a second

---

* Longer-lived isotopes of elements 94, 95 and 96 have been discovered since 1948, when this paper was first published. [Ed.]

rare-earth group which begins already with element 89, actinium, and extends at least as far as element 96, curium; he calls elements 89 to 96 the "actinide series", just as the elements 57 to 71 are often named, after their first member, the "lanthanide series", and he recommends writing both groups in parallel lines at the bottom of the periodic table. However, it seems to us that the similarity between the elements of the so-called actinide series is not nearly great enough to justify this comparison with the rare-earth group, and that it would be a mistake to obscure the obvious correspondence between actinium and lanthanum, thorium and hafnium, protactinium and tantalum, uranium and tungsten. For instance, the increase in the maximum valency from three to six is as regular if we pass from actinium to uranium as it is from lanthanum (and the other rare earths) to tungsten; this and other valuable information embodied in the traditional form of the periodic table would be lost if we were to isolate elements 89 to 92 as members of a second rare-earth group. For this reason the arrangement in our tables of the elements 89 to 96 differs from that adopted recently in several publications by Seaborg and others.

BIBLIOGRAPHY

Obituary note on John A. R. Newlands, *Nature*, **58**, 395 (1898).

Seaborg, G. T., "The Transuranium Elements," *Science*, **104**, 379 (1946).

Seaborg, G. T., "Plutonium and other Transuranium Elements," *Chem. Eng. News*, **25**, 358 (1947).

Paneth, F. A., "Radioactivity and the Completion of the Periodic System," *Nature*, **149**, 565 (1942).

Paneth, F. A., "The Making of the Missing Chemical Elements," *Nature*, **159**, 8 (1947).

5 | A Tribute to Lothar Meyer on the Centenary of his Birth

A hundred years ago, on the 19th of August, 1830, Lothar Meyer was born. German chemists have every reason to commemorate this day. In Lothar Meyer they honour a man who in a full, straightforward and purposeful life made most important contributions to the advancement of chemical knowledge—as an experimental and theoretical chemist, as a literary man through his masterly book *The Modern Theories of Chemistry*, and as a popular and much revered teacher at the university. The general public, however, is mainly interested in one of his discoveries, the one which has made his name world-famous—the discovery of the periodic system of the chemical elements.

Lothar Meyer's share in this discovery has been much discussed and much disputed. We need not go into this, for since the Royal Society in 1882 bestowed the Davy Gold Medal on him and at the same time on the Russian chemist Dmitri Mendeleeff for "Investigations into the Classification of the Elements", there has been no question that the two scientists developed their ideas completely independently until they resulted in the years 1869 and 1870 in the well-known, almost simultaneous publications. Also, we need have no hesitation in allowing Mendeleeff precedence in one essential point. "I readily admit," wrote Lothar Meyer later, referring to Mendeleeff's prediction of the properties of then undiscovered elements, "that I lacked the boldness to formulate such far-reaching conjectures as Mr. Mendeleeff pronounced with confidence." The confirmation of these predictions which followed within a surprisingly short time through the discovery of the elements gallium (1875), scandium (1879), and germanium (1886), has naturally made Mendeleeff's name especially widely known. On the other hand, it is not too much to claim that the origin of the discovery lay deeper in the case of Lothar Meyer than in that of Mendeleeff. The latter needed a suitable and unambiguous system of the elements when he wrote his *Foundations of Chemistry*; he found it in a classification based on atomic weight. What mattered to him was the strict validity of this "periodic law" and he frequently turned with surprising violence against any sort of speculation which would have seen in it an indication of the existence of a primordial matter common to all elements. The starting point of Lothar Meyer's considerations was the question: "Are the chemical atoms fundamental particles or are they themselves compounds of atoms of a higher order?" He has proved to have been quite justified in regarding even the few relations known in his time between the atomic weights as "arguments for the composite structure of the atoms", and it was in his search, stimulated by these considerations, for further laws regulating their relationships that he too discovered the natural system of the elements. This system has remained essentially unchanged since the days of Meyer and Mendeleeff, and nowadays stimulates not only chemists but especially theoretical physicists to repeated consideration of its significance. This is due not only to its serviceability as a principle of classification, but also to the inexhaustible contribution which it makes to a true understanding of the structure of the atoms and of "atoms of a higher degree"; that is, to the very question which occupied the enquiring mind of Lothar Meyer from the very beginning of his work on the system of the elements.

As in so many instances in the history of science, one cannot help regretting that he did not live to see the victory of the idea which even in the last edition of his *Theories of Chemistry* he only ventured to indicate cautiously. Lothar Meyer died on the 11th of April, 1895.

6 | Chemical Elements and Primordial Matter: Mendeleeff's view and the Present Position*

In yesterday's session of the Congress, Professor Bajkov discussed Mendeleeff's scientific work and especially his greatest achievement, the drawing up of the periodic system of the elements. The ever-increasing interest which has been shown in the periodic system in recent years is due not only, as in Mendeleeff's time, to the fact that it is the foundation of chemical theory, but even more to its significance for the problem of the structure of the chemical elements, of their formation and their disintegration, of their artificial synthesis and transmutation—in short, for the question of "primordial matter", to use the historic expression for this whole nexus of problems. Indeed, some now hope to apply the principles of the periodic system even to the solution of the puzzle of the composition of the atomic nucleus, a problem which Lord Rutherford, in a recent lecture to the London Chemical Society, in honour of Mendeleeff, described as the task of the future.[1]

It is of considerable psychological interest that Mendeleeff himself took a definitely negative attitude towards this line of development, the beginnings of which were appearing even in his day. He denied that the periodic system could have any significance for the question of the structure of the chemical elements, and on numerous occasions argued emphatically against the hypothesis of one primordial matter. At a time when the periodic system had just been brought to light, such an attitude was indeed not surprising, since Mendeleeff did not want his discovery to be discredited by having it put on the same level as a philosophic conception handed down from antiquity. He was understandably offended when the great French

---

* In view of the importance in this article of the distinctions which are drawn between apparently similar concepts, care has been taken to preserve consistency in translation according to the following scheme, any departure from which is indicated by a footnote: *Urmaterie*, primordial matter; *Materie*, matter; *Urbestandteile*, primary constituents; *Urstoff*, primary substance; *Stoff*, substance; *Stoffbegriff*, concept of matter; *Grundstoff*, basic substance; *einfacher Stoff*, simple substance. [Ed.]

chemist, Berthelot, mentioned the periodic system in one breath with Prout's hypothesis and the alchemical and Greek speculations;[2] he therefore tried to draw the dividing line between the periodic system and the idea of primordial matter as sharply as possible. I would like to prove this by a few verbatim quotations from his writings, though I regret that I am not able to read the original publications in the Russian language; I have to rely on German and English translations which, however, may be taken to be reliable in the majority of cases.* With regard to a few dubious points, Professor M. Bloch (Leningrad) has been kind enough to explain to me the exact meaning of the Russian original.

Of the primordial matter Mendeleeff states, not without some justification: "We see that all which is imperfectly worked out, new and unexplained . . . has been used to justify it".[3] He therefore attached great importance to the statement that "the periodic law . . . has been evolved independently of any conception as to the nature of the elements; it does not in the least originate in the idea of a unique matter; it has no historical connection with that relic of the torments of classical thought".[4]

This very definite assertion, which is in complete agreement with Mendeleeff's later attitude to this question, has often been overlooked. As late as 1921 Émile Meyerson, the distinguished French epistemologist, wrote with regard to the discovery of the periodic system: "Il eût été absurde de rechercher des relations entre les propriétés des éléments, si l'on n'avait pas eu au fond l'idée de l'unité de la matière".[5]

While we thus have no difficulty in understanding the emphasis which Mendeleeff placed on the experimental basis of the periodic system and its independence of the concept of primordial matter, it is nevertheless very surprising that he even denied that the periodic system could, conversely, give any support to the idea of a composite nature for the chemical elements, which he assumed to be the ultimate entities, not susceptible of further philosophical analysis. Still adhering to this point of view in the last publication available to me, he wrote in the preface to the seventh edition of his textbook (November 1902): "The more I have thought on the nature of the chemical elements, the more decidedly have I turned away from the classical notion of a primary matter, and from the hope of attaining the desired end by a study of electrical and optical phenomena".[6]

* When quoting passages from Mendeleeff's textbook I refer to the most recent foreign edition, i.e. the English translation of the 7th Russian edition: *Principles of Chemistry*, Longmans Green, London, 1905.

In many passages in the book he returns to a discussion of the relationship between chemical elements and primordial matter. "By many methods, founded both on experiment and theory, has it been tried to prove the compound nature of the elements. All labour in this direction has as yet been in vain, and the assurance that elementary matter is not so homogeneous (single) as the mind would desire in its first transport of rapid generalization is strengthened from year to year."[7] The periodic law "affords no more indication of the unity of matter or of the compound character of our elements than the law of Avogadro".[8]

"The results of my labour in the study of matter show me two . . . properties in matter: (1) the mass which occupies space and evinces itself in . . . weight, and (2) the individuality expressed in chemical transmutations and most clearly formulated in the notion of the chemical elements."[9]

"For me the conceptions of the chemical elements and what (beyond any atomic theory) we consider as their atomic weights belong to those primary conceptions of all natural science, like those of mass or quantity of matter."[10]

Towards the end of his life, in 1902, Mendeleeff wrote an "Attempt towards a Chemical Conception of the Ether" (English translation: Longmans Green, London, 1904). In this strange treatise he regards the universal ether as the lightest element (its atomic weight is assumed to amount to one millionth part of that of hydrogen). His guiding principle was, as he says himself, a certain striving towards unity: "In endeavouring to clothe the conception of the 'ether' with a chemical dress, and so render it an actual, real possibility in harmony with the purely realistic periodic law, I think I am serving the cause of unity in natural philosophy".[11] Anyone else would have been tempted to regard this lightest chemical element at the same time as the primordial matter from which the other elements are built up. But Mendeleeff turned at once against even this form of Prout's hypothesis: "I cannot admit this." "I do not see that such an admission would in any way facilitate or simplify our understanding of the substances and phenomena of nature." "It is simpler to admit the germs of individuality in the material elements than elsewhere."[12]

Mendeleeff's determined rejection of this notion becomes all the more surprising when one compares it with the attitude of Lothar Meyer who had simultaneously and independently discovered the essential features of the periodic system of the elements. It is generally known that the decisive success in the early history of the periodic system was the exact prediction of the properties of then unknown elements which were later to be discovered. This outstanding achievement was Mendeleeff's alone. Lothar Meyer himself has emphasized this: "I readily admit that I lacked the boldness to formulate such far-reaching conjectures as Mr. Mendeleeff pronounced with confidence".[13] On the other hand, Lothar Meyer did from the beginning regard as crucial the question whether the chemical elements were simple or composite. At the time he was almost alone amongst chemists in indulging in this interest, as he emphasized in his book, *Modern Theories of Chemistry*. "Chemistry has rarely sought out, but has usually by-passed or completely avoided, the answering, indeed even the posing of the problem of the character of the atoms."[14] In this respect Lothar Meyer for his part was bolder than the majority of his colleagues, including Mendeleeff. From the beginning he declared it to be his conviction that "the existence of some sixty or even more fundamentally different kinds of primordial matter is intrinsically not very probable".[15]

Compare this "intrinsically not very probable" of Meyer with the various pronouncements of Mendeleeff that for him the individuality of the chemical elements seemed an ultimate, not further reducible, postulate. You will then not doubt that here a contrast in fundamental philosophical attitudes is revealed; for the experimental data available to the two scientists were practically identical. We know today that further developments in this field have justified Meyer's and not Mendeleeff's view. I need not remind this audience of the spectacular success of experiments based on the assumption that chemical elements are built up of primary electrical constituents, which is designed to afford an explanation by mathematical deduction, on the basis of a very restricted number of suppositions, of the individual differences between the elements and of their relations as expressed in the periodic system—experiments initiated by J. J. Thomson, the recent developments of which are primarily connected with the names of Rutherford, Bohr and Pauli.

Does this mean that Mendeleeff would today change his views about the fundamental significance of the individuality of the elements? There can be no doubt that he would give due recognition to the weight of evidence adduced by physics, for in spite of his strongly personally coloured views on many questions (such as electrolytic dissociation) he never lacked appreciation of the arguments of his opponents. Yet I believe that something very essential in his fundamental philosophical tenets would have remained untouched by the progress in physics and could be successfully defended even today; and it is just these "philosophical principles of our science" which he regarded as the main substance of his textbook.[16] I would like to explain what seems to me the fundamental characteristic of his philosophical views concerning the chemical elements. Such an investigation is of particular interest nowadays, when we frequently hear it said that chemistry ought, and is destined, to be merged in physics. The case of Mendeleeff seems to me to illuminate particularly aptly a fundamental difference between the principles of the two sciences, a difference which explains the, at first sight, surprising attitude which he adopted in this matter.

First we have to determine exactly what Mendeleeff means when he regards the individuality of the chemical elements as an ultimate reality, like the concept of mass. Needless to say, he does not refer to the properties of, for example, one particular metal, which disappear as soon as the metal forms a chemical compound. It is worth pointing out that Mendeleeff in numerous passages makes a distinction between "simple bodies" and "elements": "A simple body is something material, for instance, a metal or metalloid, endowed with physical properties and the ability to show chemical reactions. To the concept of the simple body corresponds the molecule consisting of one or several atoms . . . On the other hand, element is a term for those material constituent parts of simple and composite bodies which determine their physical and chemical behaviour. The concept corresponding to element is the atom."[17]

Mendeleeff seems to me to have tried to introduce here a very important epistemological distinction which astonishingly enough has received very little attention in German and English literature. (There are, however, some French chemists, such as G. Urbain,[18] who have made it their own.) The reason why this distinction has been so little noticed seems to be, on the one hand, that the terms used by Mendeleeff are not very appropriate, and that, on the other hand, by coupling them to the pair of concepts, *molecule* and *atom*, he seems to have missed the essential point. It is hardly possible in chemistry to introduce a contrast between elements and simple bodies, as the definition of the element since Lavoisier is based on the simple body.[19] It seems to me even less apt simply to equate the terms element/atom and simple body/molecule, respectively; for, apart from the fact that there are simple bodies whose molecules are single atoms, molecules and atoms belong indubitably to one and the same group of scientific concepts, while the essential difference between element and simple body (in the Mendeleeffian sense of the words) lies in their belonging to quite different spheres in epistemology.

In a lecture three years ago I attempted to define more precisely the epistemological status of the chemical concept "element", and especially to do justice to the double meaning that Mendeleeff had in mind. As the lecture is not easily accessible,* I would like briefly to recapitulate some points from it.

Whenever philosophers—or, as is more frequently the case, theoretical physicists—engage in epistemological speculation about the modern non-biological sciences, they usually take into account physics only; there are, however, certain peculiarities appertaining to the chemical concepts. Like all other sciences, chemistry started with a naively realistic view of the world which it gradually found itself forced to modify; what is characteristic of chemistry is that it has not progressed so far in introducing these modifications as, for instance, physics.

Indeed it is part of the essence of its fundamental concepts that they have kept a considerable "naively realistic residue".

Let us consider from this point of view the concept of matter on which rests the whole edifice of theoretical chemistry and which is fundamental for the concept, element, with which we are here concerned. It is well known that the aim of physics has long been the reduction of sensory qualities to quantitative terms; nature is assumed to be without quality, and it is only to our perceptions that such properties as sound, taste, smell, and so on can be attributed. If, however, we tackle the problem of the nature of matter† somewhat more thoroughly with the tools of epistemological criticism, it appears—as has repeatedly been demonstrated—that not only can none of the properties of matter perceptible to the senses be assumed to exist in nature, but that the concept itself evaporates altogether. The position of the Greek atomists, who regarded size, shape, and motion as real, but colour, smell, etc. as phenomena—a point of view which was taken up again by Locke in his distinction between primary and secondary qualities—constitutes only an arbitrary halt in this process of dissolution, though it serves the purposes of the natural sciences very well. The subjective nature of the primary

---

* "Die erkenntnistheoretische Stellung des chemischen Elementbegriffs", in *Schriften der Königsberger Gelehrten Gesellschaft*, Naturwissenschaftliche Klasse, VIII, No. 4. Niemeyer Halle a.S. 1931. It has been republished in English translation in *The British Journal for the Philosophy of Science*, XIII, pp. 1, 144 (1962) as "The Epistemological Status of the Chemical Concept of Element". [Ed.]

† Here, as in all passages in which the *Stoffbegriff* is being discussed, *Stoff* is translated as *matter*. [Ed.]

qualities which this view ascribed to the things themselves was demonstrated in the idealistic systems of philosophy (Berkeley, Hume, Kant) and even advocates of transcendental realism, convinced of the existence outside ourselves of a universe which can be recognized in some degree, find themselves forced, if they follow the atomistic train of thought to its logical conclusion, to declare that matter is "not something real but only a phenomenon in and for consciousness", produced by the joint action of neighbouring forces.[20]

It is of particular interest that, independently of these philosophic considerations, progress in theoretical physics has of necessity also led to a complete dissolution of the concept of matter. The era of the classical kinetic theory of matter has long passed; molecules and atoms are no longer solid spheres, the space allotted to them is filled only by electrical forces which emanate from the positive nuclei and negative electrons. One might thus be inclined to regard nuclei and electrons as the last relics of the old concept of matter, if modern quantum mechanics did not force upon us the assumption that the motions of these particles do not take place in the three-dimensional space imaginable by us but in multi-dimensional spaces. This deprives us of the last chance to hold on to the familiar concept of matter in any sense whatsoever; any possibility of visualizing it is left behind, and at the same time the possibilities of predictive calculation reach heights never previously scaled. Here physics harvests the fruit of a tree planted centuries ago. Beginning with Galileo, greater and greater importance was attached to mathematical formulation; the success of this methodology encouraged still further progress on the same route, and it is not surprising that present-day physicists, in a manner somewhat similar to that of the old Pythagoreans, see the true essence of the world in mathematical relations.[21]

Chemistry has not joined in this course of development. If colour, taste, smell and so on are to be called secondary qualities, then it is just these secondary qualities that concern chemistry; and in many cases it is by far the simplest way to act as if the secondary qualities were properties of the substances themselves. In the case of taste and smell, for instance, the objectively real preconditions for their existence are still shrouded in almost complete obscurity; since, however, in chemistry they play as important a part now as formerly in the characterization of substances, the chemist has no choice but to attribute, in a simple naively realistic way, the properties of taste and smell to the substances themselves. Indeed, nobody objects to talking of the salty taste of sodium chloride, or of the nasty smell of hydrogen sulphide. I need give no further proof that here we are still standing with both feet on the ground of naive realism without, indeed, as I would like to emphasize, feeling any disadvantage from this philosophic ambiguity. Even in the case of that "property of substances" which can most easily be reduced to quantitative terms—that of colour—we usually dispense with them for the purposes of chemical characterization: cinnabar "is" red, gold "is" shiny. A more exact numerical statement introducing the various constants would indeed be possible in such cases, but would usually be too complicated.

For those less familiar with chemistry, let us briefly elucidate the significance for this science of the secondary qualities. For the purpose of characterizing substances, chemical analysis makes use of all properties perceptible by the senses. The optical ones rank first; seeing plays such a pre-eminent part in chemistry that the Polish epistemologist, Kozlowski, even went to the length of declaring: "la chimie est le résultat de la différence qualitative des impressions visuelles",[22] in which statement admittedly we would not like to follow him. The importance of olfactory perceptions in chemistry need not be specially mentioned: the frequent occurrence of characteristic smells has given it a bad name in the widest circles. Taste is made use of more rarely than formerly for the identification of substances, but those in one important group, the acids, continually remind us of it by their name. The "decrepitation" of some salts when they are being heated, the "crackling" of silicic acid when rubbed, the "creaking" of tin ("Zinngeschrei"), and so on, are examples of the use of auditory perceptions in chemistry, just as the "warm touch" of gold, the "slipperiness" of skin wetted with a lye, the feel of a "greasy substance", are concepts, familiar to any chemist, from the sphere of touch. Further, the synthesis of certain chemical substances is pursued solely because of their secondary qualities. The value of a dye (forgive me for pointing out the obvious!) rests in its colour, the importance of the "liquefaction of coal" lies in the fact that the solid carbon and the gaseous hydrogen are turned into a liquid fuel.

We can follow up this predominance of the secondary qualities in chemistry on the psychological side. It is no accident that the great chemists especially are reported to have had a special talent for the observation of material properties. No one who reads the classical book of Bunsen on flame reactions can be in any doubt that he had the ability to perceive very subtle colour distinctions. In Liebig's biography we find that his memory for smells enabled him, years later, to recognize a substance which he had handled and smelt but once. Of von Baeyer it is known that he was able to follow the progress of reactions of interest to him from simple experiments in test tubes without complicated apparatus and measuring tools. These examples could be multiplied *ad lib*. How different from this is the typical physicist, especially the theoretical physicist! In the founders and leaders in this science the joy in mathematical abstraction preponderates; it happens only very rarely, as for example in the case of Boyle, that the talents for theoretical thinking and for practical work in the laboratory are united.

Mendeleeff certainly belonged to that type of scientist that takes pleasure in the variety of phenomena, in the secondary qualities. This shows in many passages in his writing, as for instance when he states: "For chemistry, matter is an entire world of life, with an infinite variety of individuality both in the elements and in their combinations".[23] (We might mention incidentally that the vividness of his perceptions and the visual emphasis in his thinking are supposed to have shown themselves in the anatomy of his brain when dissected, especially in the outstanding development of the left parietal region.)[24]

To denote the pre-eminent importance of secondary qualities in chemistry we shall use a word introduced by the German philosopher Fechner;[25] he uses the term "Daylight View" for the world as apprehended by naive men (and the chemist!), in which colour, smell, sound and so on exist objectively, in contrast to the "Night View" of physics, which regards all these phenomena only as illusions and seeks to explain them by reducing them to some kind of mathematical terms. We may say that the chemist in his descriptions tries to keep to the "Daylight View".

Chemistry, however, is not only a descriptive but also an interpretative science. For the description of substances it may obviously be possible to confine oneself in this simple way to the point of view of naive realism, but is it possible to go so far as to explain chemical changes in this way? This leads us to the general question whether a scientific theory can be constructed on a basis of qualitative explanations.

The history of science knows of one spectacular attempt in this direction—the physics of Aristotle. His attitude in epistemological questions is mainly determined by his opposition to the atomists. He would have nothing to do with their distinction between an objective real world, in which only primary qualities existed, and a world of illusion, that of the secondary qualities. He was an adherent of naive realism. From the point of view of the development of physical knowledge we must say that the atomists looked deeper and created a much more solid foundation for the natural sciences. Malebranche has some justification for objecting that Aristotle's physics is really only logic. In the field with which we are concerned, in chemistry, it has failed completely; even with the greatest ingenuity it is not possible to explain the formation of a chemical compound on the basis of Aristotelian principles.[26] We must not, however, overlook the fact that not only the abstract logic of scholasticism, but also practical alchemy, clung for centuries to the physics of Aristotle in its essential points and even achieved some successes which I may assume to be known to this audience. The fundamental qualities recognized by Aristotle were humidity and warmth (and their opposites) and those of the alchemists were combustibility, resistance to fire, and volatility, represented by the principles of sulphur, salt and mercury.

Even in later times, important attempts at qualitative explanations were made in the natural sciences. The phlogiston theory was a purely qualitative doctrine, and its contributions to the development of chemistry are nowadays probably undisputed (though Mendeleeff personally held a different opinion, and called it "metaphysical and metachemical").[27] Indeed, qualitative theories have proved fertile even in the soil of more modern physics; it is interesting to note that Carnot based his principle on the assumption of a "heat-stuff" (caloric) although he was already inclined to regard heat as a kind of motion. And when Lavoisier, whose decisive arguments were of a quantitative type, had drawn up his first table of elements, he had kept the qualitative principles not only in the case of the light- and heat-substances but also in the case of oxygen ("Sauerstoff"—the acid substance); this latter was for him the carrier of acid properties, just as phlogiston had been the carrier of combustibility. Still nearer to our own times, Liebig emphasized that we tend to look for a colouring principle to account for every striking colour.[28] In his time, when most pigments were inorganic, one expected to find the colouring principle in a definite substance; nowadays the same thought appears in a more subtle form in our belief that we understand the colour of an organic compound when we have ascertained the presence in it of a certain "chromophoric group". And when we endow a metal alloy with the property of lightness by the addition of a light metal, and with the property of toughness by some other addition, then we are remarkably close to the old qualitative explanation of the alchemists.

This is the side of chemistry which the physicist and the philosopher usually ignore, or at least do not appreciate; yet the endeavour to forbid the use of qualitative explanations in the exact sciences is quite arbitrary. I think that even nowadays nothing could more aptly be said of it than the statement of Boyle in his Physiological Essays: "I consider then, that generally speaking, to render a reason of an effect or phaenomenon, is to deduce it from something else in nature more known than itself; and that consequently there may be divers kinds of degrees of explication of the same thing. For although such explications be the most satisfactory to the understanding, wherein it is shown, how the effect is produced by their more primitive and catholick affections of matter, namely, bulk, shape and motion; yet are not these explications to be despised, wherein particular effects are deduced from the more obvious and familiar qualities or states of bodies, such as heat, cold, weight, fluidity, hardness, fermentation, &c. though these themselves do probably depend upon those three universal ones formerly named. For in the search after natural causes, every new measure of discovery does both instruct and gratify the understanding; though I readily confess, that the nearer the discovered causes are to those, that are highest in the scale or series of causes, the more is the intellect both gratified and instructed."[29] (There is no necessary connection, but yet complete harmony, between this evaluation of the secondary qualities and Boyle's clear inclination towards a "Daylight View". He states for instance that snow is white and burning coal hot, even if nobody sees or feels it.[30])

We accept Boyle's view that the qualitative explanation is not quite so satisfactory as the quantitative one; we may even add that it unmistakably harbours great dangers since it can easily be abused and become completely worthless from a scientific point of view. Suffice it to mention the doctrines put forward about a hundred years ago by German natural philosophers (e.g. Schelling or Oken). Even after the collapse of these schools the danger was not overcome; it would be easy to adduce modern examples, such as the Marburg Neo-Kantian School and its more or less distant adherents.

After what has been said, we may take it as established that chemistry can be naively realistic, not only as a descriptive and comparative science (like mineralogy and zoology) but, to a certain modest degree, even when it becomes explanatory. But in its own peculiar field, in the interpretation of the formation of a chemical compound, naive realism fails, as we shall see in a moment; here we must abstract completely from the qualities perceptible by the senses. The important question therefore arises whether chemistry in this case must adopt the point of view of physics. We have seen earlier that the road taken by physics leads to the complete dissolution into mathematical formulae of the reality of the world around us. On the other hand, however, we have accepted the qualities perceptible by the senses as a valid principle of explanation for chemistry in some cases, and it would therefore be admissible to adopt an intermediate position. Which is the most suitable for chemistry?

That chemical changes cannot be explained on the basis of naive realism becomes at once evident if we consider the well-known law of the conservation of the chemical elements. It is fair to say that this theory is nowadays accepted by all chemists, even though formerly liberties were occasionally taken with its interpretation; e.g. St. Clair Deville and Ostwald put forward the view that it did not imply anything more than that chemical elements could be recovered from their compounds. Mendeleeff too makes some concession to this point of view when he says: "the composition of a compound is the expression of those transformations of which it is capable".[31] The realism of our present-day view of nature—indeed even the language of chemical symbols—admits only, however, of the interpretation that the (atoms of the) elements are actually present in the compounds. We shall therefore keep to the strict sense of the law of the conservation of the chemical elements.

That such attempts at re-interpreting the clear principle of the conservation of the chemical elements should arise at all, was possible only because, after Lavoisier, the epistemological meaning of the concept, element, fell into oblivion amongst chemists. The old atomists had known that natural laws were valid not for the world of naive realism but for a transcendental world without sensory qualities. ("Transcendental" is here used in the sense given it by Eduard von Hartmann, i.e. "outside the sphere of consciousness".) Even the alchemists were convinced that their three principles, salt, sulphur, and mercury, must not be thought of as endowed with the qualities of the substances of the same names perceptible by the senses, but represented transcendental principles; these three principles (or, alternatively, the four elements of the Peripatetics) could be regarded as constant only in the context of a world deprived of all sense qualities, and only on these terms are the elements of Lavoisier constant too. In introducing his definition of "element", Lavoisier had, however, made a few rather unfortunate comments on the metaphysics he had successfully defeated, and in this connection one finds even in many modern books such assertions as: "If one compares the elements of Boyle (and Lavoisier) with those of the Aristotelians and their principles, one easily sees that as concepts they are completely different. The new elements are taken to be the actual substances occurring in nature, whilst the old ones implied the properties embodied in these substances."[32]

If one believes this, then those grotesque difficulties arise which have misled philosophers and chemists as recently as when, for instance, John Stuart Mill thought that the laws of chemistry violated the principle of "composition of causes",[33] or when Berthelot found the difference between the properties of common salt and those of the constituent elements of sodium and chlorine so incomprehensibly great that he felt obliged explicitly to refute the view that a third element (with less divergent properties) was present in common salt.[34]

Mendeleeff too seems to have believed too strictly in the overthrow of metaphysics by Lavoisier, and to have shared his allergy to the inheritance of the Greek philosophers. (Not very astonishing in the case of a person so alien to classical teaching that he uses the term "torments of classical thought"!) This is the only probable explanation of his above-mentioned predilection for the erroneous view of Ostwald that chemical formulae indicate only possible changes; and possibly the only reason why he compares the difference between elements and simple bodies with that between atoms and molecules instead of clearly stating that, even after Lavoisier's reform, the chemical element represented a transcendental principle just as it had before his time.

In my lecture referred to above, I endeavoured to demonstrate in greater detail how closely Lavoisier's—and consequently our present-day—concept of the element resembles the maligned "metaphysical" principles of the philosophers and alchemists. I considered it helpful to distinguish the two senses in which the expression "chemical element" is used by the terms *simple substance* and *basic substance*. I suggested that we should use the term "basic substance" whenever we want to designate that which is indestructible in compounds and simple substances, and that we should speak of a "simple substance" when referring to the form in which such a basic substance, not combined with any other, is presented to our senses. We cannot ascribe any particular qualities to an element as a basic substance, since it contributes to the production of the infinite variety of qualities which it exhibits both when alone and when in combination with other basic substances; as a simple substance it can be characterized, without infringing scientific exactitude, in terms of its properties, as we have shown earlier for matter ("Stoff") in general. With the concept of the simple substance we may remain within the realm of naive realism. When we are concerned with the basic substance, however, we cannot disregard its connection with the transcendental world without getting involved in contradictions.

Following Lavoisier, it is common even today to define an element as "a substance which cannot be reduced to simpler ones by any chemical process".[35] This definition takes as a criterion for the elements that they can be produced as simple substances which cannot be decomposed any further; their great significance for the whole of chemical doctrine lies, however, in the assumption that these same entities which produce the phenomena of "simple substances" serve in the transcendental, objectively real sphere of nature as "basic substances" not only for the formation of simple but also for that of compound substances. The fundamental tenet of chemistry, that the elements persist in compounds, applies only to the basic substances that cannot be apprehended by our senses; any other interpretation makes the assertion meaningless. And although we demand in principle that every element should be producible as a "simple substance", yet the discovery of many elements (such as for instance, fluorine or radium) was established with complete certainty by the sheer necessity to assume transcendental new "basic substances" in exactly the same way as the transcendental alchemical principles were justified.[36]

If we keep to this distinction between "basic substance" and "simple substance" when referring to the two aspects of the concept of the chemical element, then we begin to understand why we must avoid referring to the coupled concepts, atom and molecule, in this connection; atom and molecule both belong to the transcendental world, and must never be conceived, in a naively realistic manner, as endowed with qualities perceptible to the senses. Mendeleeff is hardly justified in saying "the characteristics of the material substances, such as silver, for example, or of any other body, remain unchanged in every subdivision from the largest masses to the smallest particles and consequently these characteristics must be properties of the particles".[37] Epicurus had already realized that understanding of a chemical compound cannot be reached unless all sensible qualities are denied to the smallest particles of the substances. I have pointed out the significance of Epicurus' epistemological theory for an understanding of this problem in the lecture mentioned above,[38] and shall not repeat it here.

Once one has realized that, in the generally recognized usage of chemistry, the basic chemical substances are transcendental, without any measurable sensible qualities, then their reduction to one primordial matter becomes a natural and logical process. Mendeleeff's resistance was no doubt rooted in the predilection of the chemist for the "Daylight View". This is however compatible only with the "simple substances" and not with the "basic substances" which (like most concepts of the interpretative, and unlike those of the descriptive, sciences) are condemned to the "Night View". Fechner too had no doubts on this matter.[39]

This reduction of the basic substances to a primordial matter has essentially been accomplished by present-day physics. Admittedly we have not succeeded, as has been hoped since the times of the pre-Socratic philosophers, in reaching a single primary substance, but need, according to the present stage of our knowledge at least four* basic bricks—the neutron, the positive and the negative electron, and the neutrino. (We may imagine the proton as formed by one neutron plus a positive electron plus a neutrino.)

Even if, from the point of view described, we no longer share Mendeleeff's objection to one (or four) kinds of primordial matter, the question still remains whether it is necessary or advisable for chemistry to hark back so far in its interpretative principles. We have already emphasized that the attitude of chemistry to the problem of matter is essentially different from that of physics. Every science must decide for itself on the units with which it builds, and the deepest foundation is by no means necessarily always the best for the purpose. To take but one example: anatomy usually does not go back to the unit of histology, to the cell (although there are, of course, borderline subjects), but works with bones, muscles, sinews and so on. In spite of its striving after physical causal explanations of single events, biology does not renounce the use of qualitative principles of explanation for the understanding of general processes such as heredity; indeed, it cannot yet dispense with teleological considerations.[40]

The essential process of chemical reasoning has been no more influenced by the reduction of the chemical elements to the neutron, neutrino, etc., than the foundations of anatomy by the invention of the microscope. Obviously this does not apply to physical chemistry and to other subjects on the borderline between chemistry and physics, but in general one may well say that the immense field of

* The number of fundamental particles now recognized is much greater than four, and changes rather rapidly. [Ed.]

non-theoretical chemistry has remained astonishingly untouched by the spectacular successes of modern physics. We may add, "fortunately"! Some of you may know the saying of a famous Göttingen mathematician: "Physics is much too difficult for the physicists".[41] If chemistry were forced to base itself on modern theoretical physics, then most of us would have to admit that "chemistry is much too difficult for the chemists".

As Boyle guessed long ago,[42] the chemical elements are only *relatively* constant; that is, they remain unchanged in *chemical* transformations. Nowadays we know that they are composite in two senses: they consist of a mixture of isotopes, and the atoms of every isotope are built up from simpler constituent particles. Since, however, in chemical reactions there is neither an unmixing of the isotopes nor any change in the essential parts of the atoms, the law of the conservation of the elements is valid in *chemistry*.

Conviction on this point permits us, in complete agreement with Mendeleeff, to regard the chemical elements as our ultimate building blocks. If we investigate the foundations of chemistry as an independent science, then indeed we do not come up against those primary qualities which for centuries were regarded as the ultimate principles in physics, viz. size, shape, and motion (which are really quantities, since they can be determined numerically); neither do we encounter the four qualities of modern physics mentioned above (the neutron, the two types of electron, and the neutrino), but only these eighty-nine chemical basic substances. If, following Locke, we call primary qualities those intrinsic in the substances, then we must recognize eighty-nine primary qualities as the basis of chemistry. It is really astonishing that in the discussion of primary qualities in philosophical literature, so far as I know, the chemical elements are never mentioned. This seems to me but an additional confirmation of the statement made above, that professional philosophers have so far been little concerned with the foundations of chemistry. From the philosophical point of view, hardly any expression for the chemical elements could be more apt than "primary qualities".

The number of eighty-nine will possibly soon be increased somewhat by the discovery of one or more of the missing elements within the periodic system, or of elements beyond hydrogen or uranium.* But even eighty-nine may seem to some a surprisingly high number for the primary qualities of a science. Against this I would like to emphasize firstly, that physics too has been less successful than was

* The gaps have since, of course, been filled, and the periodic system is now known to extend some way beyond uranium. [Ed.]

previously hoped in the reduction of the number of primary qualities, and that today it cannot go below four qualitatively differentiated elementary constituents; the ideal of one primordial matter
is not sufficient for the laws and equations of physics. Secondly,
what matters is not the greater or lesser number of the principles
assumed in the transcendental world, but the fact that this number
is not infinite but limited. The Viennese epistemologist Schlick[43]
has argued that it would constitute a progress in science if the subjective colour sensations which different people experience in
various circumstances could be coordinated with constant transcendental qualities, but that this would still be unsatisfactory for
science as long as an infinite number of shades of colours were matched
by an infinite number of transcendental qualities. In the realm of
optics the decisive progress consisted in the reduction of qualitative
to quantitative differences. In chemistry the course of progress was
different: it was not (direct) reduction to differences in quantity,
but a reduction to a limited number of transcendental qualities to
which the infinite number of chemical substances could be related.
This number has, since Boyle's time, very gradually risen from
roughly ten basic substances clearly recognized as constant to eighty-
nine, which is the present estimate.

It may be astonishing to some that chemistry, a science with such
a clear predilection for the "Daylight View", has to work with the
assumption of transcendental qualities, to which no properties perceptible by the senses can be ascribed. But the justification for this
choice of conceptual system lies here, as always in science, in the
facilities it affords for the formulation of laws. Amongst these the
laws of conservation always have a special importance in the sciences.

Schiller defined the activity of the scientist poetically: "He looks
for the familiar law amongst the awesome phenomena of chance,
he looks for the steady pole amongst the fleeting appearances" (er
"sucht das vertraute Gesetz in des Zufalls grausenden Wundern,
sucht den ruhenden Pol in der Erscheinungen Flucht").[44] To put
it more soberly and more concisely, what matters is "to discover the
one objective world in the welter of subjective data".[45] Just as the
formulation of the concepts of energy and momentum is based on the
laws of the "conservation of energy" and the "conservation of
momentum", so the assumption of eighty-nine transcendental basic
substances is justified by the law of the "conservation of the elements
in all chemical transformations".

By their occurrence either separately or in combination, these
transcendental substances produce the sensible qualities of the

simple substances and chemical compounds. Chemistry cannot and does not seek to give an explanation of how this happens; that is where theoretical physics on the one side and physiology and psychology on the other side take over.

Even today chemistry is the theory of the chemical elements. The dissolution of these elements into their constituent parts is necessary only in relatively few branches close to physics as is shown, for example, in the undiminished freshness of Mendeleeff's *Principles of Chemistry*, a book which every chemist may read with great profit even today. Mendeleeff once said that the chemical elements could be compared to the axioms in geometry; perhaps it would be still better to remember the etymological sense of the word "element". Element means "letter"[46]; the elements are the eighty-nine letters of chemistry from which all its words are formed.* Letters can be dissolved into strokes and dots, but language is as little interested in this process as chemistry in the dissolution of the elements into the four primordial matters of physics. In an article published recently it was said: "La pensée du chimiste nous paraît osciller entre le pluralisme d'une part et la réduction de la pluralité d'autre part".[47] Rather than calling it oscillation, it seems to me that it would be better to speak of simultaneous development in different branches. The reduction to unity (or quadruplicity) has been successfully achieved by physics; chemistry, however, will probably preserve, as long as there is a science of chemistry in the present meaning of the word, a plurality of its basic substances in complete agreement with the doctrine of its old master, Dmitri Ivanovitch Mendeleeff.

REFERENCES

1. Lord Rutherford, *J. Chem. Soc.*, 642 (1934).
2. Berthelot, M., *Les Origines de l'Alchemie*, Paris, p. 312, 1885. (It is interesting to note that leading French chemists are even now lukewarm in their appreciation of Mendeleeff's achievement. See, for example, G. Urbain, *Les Disciplines d'une Science*, Paris, pp. 85–95, 1921.)

* The English language allows of an illuminating extension of this analogy which is not possible in German since that language contains no words which are single letters. In English, A, I, are units for the composition of words and also words themselves. In the former capacity they correspond to "basic substances", and in the latter to "simple substances". As mere letters they have no meaning, though they contribute to the infinite number of meanings of the words in which they occur. ("We cannot ascribe any particular qualities to an element as basic substance, since the basic substance contributes to the production of the infinite variety of qualities which it exhibits both when alone and when in combination with other simple substances"); as words they have meanings ("as a simple substance it can be characterized, without infringing scientific exactitude, in terms of its properties"). [Ed.]

3. Faraday Lecture, *J. Chem. Soc.*, 643 (1889); *Principles of Chemistry*,* London, II, p. 497, 1905.
4. Faraday Lecture, *J. Chem. Soc.*, 644 (1889); *Pr. of Chem.*, II, p. 498.
5. Meyerson, Émile, *De l'Explication dans les Sciences*, Paris, I, p. 309, 1921.
6. *Pr. of Chem.*, I, p. XIV.
7. *Pr. of Chem.*, I, p. 20.
8. Faraday Lecture, *J. Chem. Soc.*, 644 (1889); *Pr. of Chem.*, II, p. 498.
9. *Pr. of Chem.*, II, p. 30.
10. *Pr. of Chem.*, II, p. 33.
11. *Pr. of Chem.*, I, p. XV.
12. *Pr. of Chem.*, II, p. 522.
13. Meyer, Lothar, *Ber. Deut. Chem. Ges.*, **XIII**, 259 (1880).
14. Meyer, Lothar, *Die modernen Theorien der Chemie*, 5. Auflage, Breslau, p. 129, 1884.
15. *ibid.*, p. 134.
16. *Pr. of Chem.*, I, p. VIII.
17. *Annalen der Chemie u. Pharmazie*, p. 8, 1871; Supplementband, p. 133.
18. Urbain, G., *loc cit.* The comments (p. 75 ff.) on the concepts "element" and "simple substance" clearly betray the influence of Mendeleeff.
19. Cf. further comment in reference 34.
20. Hartmann, E. v., *Grundriss der Erkenntnislehre*, Bad Sachsa, p. 73, 1907.
21. See, for example, Sir James Jeans, *The Mysterious Universe*, Cambridge, p. 127 ff, 1930.
22. Kozlowski, W. M., *Bibliothèque du Congrès International de Philosophie*, Paris, III, p. 529, 1901.
23. *Pr. of Chem.*, I, p. XI.
24. Bechterew, W. V. und Weinberg, R., *Anatomische und Entwicklungsgeschichtliche Monographien*, herausgegeben von P. P. Roux, Leipzig, no. 1, 1909.
25. Fechner, G. T., *Die Tagesansicht gegenüber der Nachtansicht*, Leipzig, 1879.
26. See Lasswitz, K., *Geschichte der Atomistik*, Leipzig, I, p. 237, 1890.
27. *Pr. of Chem.*, I, p. XV.
28. Liebig, J. v., *Chemische Briefe*, 3. Brief.
29. *The Works of Robert Boyle*, Birch Edition, London, I, p. 308, 1772.
30. *ibid.*, III, p. 22.
31. *Pr. of Chem.*, I, p. 23.
32. Benrath, A., *Chemische Grundbegriffe*, Berlin, p. 26, 1920.
33. Mill, J. S., *A System of Logic*, London, Book III, Chap. VI, 1843.
34. Berthelot, M., *De la synthèse en chimie organique* (Leçons de chimie, Paris, p. 149 ff, 1861.) (Berthelot realized that Lavoisier's purely empirical definition of the concept "element" was incomplete. *La révolution chimique, Lavoisier*, Paris, p. 148 ff, 1890.)
35. On the introduction of the phrase "by any chemical process" into Lavoisier's definition see *Handbuch der Physik*, Springer, Berlin, XXII, p. 440, 1933.
36. See the lecture mentioned (*British Journal for the Philosophy of Science*, **XIII**, 1, 144, 1962).
37. *Pr. of Chem.*, II, p. 472.
38. *Loc cit.*, p. 110 ff.
39. Fechner, G. T., *op. cit.*, p. 238.
40. See Meyerhof, O., *Betrachtungen über die naturphilosophischen Grundlagen der Physiologie*, Berlin, 1933.

* Referred to hereafter as *Pr. of Chem.*

41. See, for example, *Naturwissenschaften*, **X,** 70 (1922).
42. Boyle, R., *The Sceptical Chymist*, Everyman's Library, London, p. 104.
43. Schlick, M., *Allgemeine Erkenntnislehre*, Berlin, p. 241, 1918.
44. Schiller, F., *Spaziergang*.
45. Schlick, M., *op. cit.*, p. 237.
46. Diels, H., *Elementum*, Leipzig, 1899.
47. Bachelard, G., *Le Pluralisme cohérent de la Chimie moderne*, Paris, p. 3, 1932.

7 | Auer von Welsbach

On the 1st of September of this year* the birthday of the most famous of Austrian chemists, Freiherr Carl Auer von Welsbach, was celebrated in the solitude of the Carinthian Mountains. Equally distinguished in science and in technology, he has lived for years in his castle of Welsbach in almost complete retirement, owing to hearing difficulties and recently total deafness. Difficult of access, like the castles of fairy tales, his residence contains unique treasures—the quantity and purity of the rare earths in the private laboratory of the lord of the castle cannot be matched anywhere in the world.

Those who wished to pay a personal tribute to the scientist on his seventieth birthday had thus to make up their minds to travel to Carinthia and to be transported by car from the last station of the railway up to the heights on which the castle stands. Perhaps nothing could show more plainly the popularity and the high esteem in which this scientist is held than the number of well-wishers from all over the world who arrived, to his complete surprise, on the morning of the first of September in the park of his castle in order to congratulate him—official representatives of the Austrian authorities, representatives of the Federation of Industries, representatives of scientific corporations, deputations from universities and technical high schools, and delegates from the most varied societies. Though oral communication with the scientist was difficult, the honorary diplomas, tributes and documents which were handed to him spoke a silent, but none the less convincing, language. In addition to the honorary diplomas of the University of Graz and the Technical High Schools of Vienna and of Karlsruhe bestowed on him on previous occasions, he received the honorary doctorate of the University of Freiburg and of the Technical High School of Graz as well as honorary membership of the Senate of the University of Heidelberg. All these distinctions seemed to give the scientist genuine pleasure, but perhaps most of all a special birthday present devised by the German

* 1928. [Ed.]

Auer Gasglühlicht Gesellschaft. Its two representatives presented two large crystal vases which radiated a peculiar light, one a violet hue, the other an equally unusual green. These were the first pieces of glass dyed with the rare earths neodymium and praseodymium— discovered by Auer in 1885—to be produced in a glass works. The German Chemical Society's tribute to its honorary member was in the form of an address; as this document gives a survey of the various branches of activity in which Auer has achieved outstanding success and shows at the same time the high esteem in which he is held by his colleagues for his personal qualities, we would like to reproduce it here verbatim:

"Dear Freiherr Auer von Welsbach! One and a half decades have passed since the German Chemical Society bestowed on you the highest distinction at its disposal—an Honorary Membership. Since that time we have looked upon you with pride as belonging to our Society in a very special sense, and so this day, on which you complete the seventh decade of your life, is a welcome opportunity for us to celebrate this anniversary with you in spirit and to recall your life and work up to this landmark in your career. Only rarely has it been given to the genius of one man to fertilize both departments of our science, pure research and its industrial applications, to such an outstanding degree and to reap such a rich harvest in both of them. Your name is known, even to the lay public, as that of one of the leading technologists of our time. The invention of the gas-mantle named after you opened up a new path in the lighting industry, and it was this invention alone which made it possible for gas to compete with the electric lighting technique emerging at that time. Even today gas lamps are used in innumerable variety in all continents, and in spite of the decades of work which scientists and technicians have devoted to its further development, the principle of the gas lamp as discovered by you is still used without change when gaseous or liquid fuel is used for lighting purposes. But the electric lighting technique also owes to your inventive genius an important stimulus. It is you who succeeded in making osmium filaments, and thus produced the first practically usable metal filament lamp. That was the foundation from which later the incandescent lamp industry developed the tungsten filament lamp and gave it a dominant place. In yet a third field your insight into technical possibilities has proved brilliantly successful. The pyrophoric alloys of iron and rare earths invented by you have spread all over the world in lighters of many kinds.

These were no accidental successes which you achieved in the field

of industry: it was your untiring application that overcame the
innumerable difficulties offered by the refractory nature of the
materials and the resistance of the inert world: the fertile soil from
which grew your great inventions was, and still is, work in the
scientific laboratory.

While your practical successes have made your name world-
famous, your discoveries in pure science ensure that you will always
be ranked among the greatest masters of inorganic chemistry, and
we honour in you a true descendant of your teacher Bunsen, in whose
footsteps you also followed in your spectroscopic work. In one of
the most difficult subjects, the rare earths, you can point to the highest successes. You have introduced subtle new methods into the
analytical chemistry of the rare earths, and thus opened up new
and undreamt of paths to methods of separation. You have succeeded in proving that didymium consists of two elements, to which
you have given the names, praseodymium and neodymium. Similarly science owes to you the first realization that the old ytterbium
also is not homogeneous, but contains a second element, cassiopeium.*
Thus you have increased the number of chemical elements known to
us by two, a success which even earlier generations of chemists, who
were still opening up new territories, would have regarded as extraordinary, but which must be ranked even higher since in your days
the territory had been so thoroughly explored by chemical techniques, while the aid of X-ray spectroscopy was not yet available.

Since the discovery of radioactive substances, some of which are
placed amongst the rare earths because of their chemical reactions,
you have put the incomparable experience which you possess in
this branch of chemistry into the service of a new type of research.
Of the many precious radioactive substances which you extracted
from large quantities of raw material in concentrations previously
unknown and whose further investigation you left to the Vienna
Radium Institute, we would mention only your sample of thorium,
especially rich in ionium: we do so because, with the exception of
the familiar radiogenic leads, this is the only substance for which it
has been possible to confirm experimentally the variations in combining weight predicted by isotopic research.

This leads us to that aspect of your work which scholars from many
countries remember on this day with special gratitude, your in-
variable willingness to help others in their research whenever
necessary. Theoretical interest in problems of atomic structure nowadays centres on the rare earths to which only a few specialists had

* Now known as lutetium. [Ed.]

7

paid attention before you made them the subject of your special studies and, in this field, substances of a high degree of purity are a prerequisite for many fundamental investigations. As a result of years of toil you have produced the whole series of rare earths in incomparable purity, and wherever a scientific colleague has applied to you for a sample of your treasures for scientific purposes, you have granted his wish most generously. Not only in Austria and Germany, but also abroad, the number of researches carried out with rare earths of your provenance is most impressive, and certain advances of equal importance for chemistry and physics would not have been possible without your unselfish assistance.

Thus today we honour in you not only the undisputed master in science and technology, but also a man who has actively encouraged the investigations of others and who has always been ready to sink his own arduous investigations in the general scientific effort—one whose modesty and reserve, manifested throughout his life, distinguishes him as much as does the superiority of his abilities and the brilliance of his own famous works. In this disinterested service to science, no less than in the achievements which have made your name immortal, you are our model and our guide, and our wish today is that you may long continue in undiminished vigour to be the pride of German chemical science and of the German Chemical Society."

8 | Egon von Schweidler

Egon Ritter von Schweidler, formerly professor of physics in the University of Vienna, died on February 12, 1948 in his country home near Salzburg. His death has not hitherto been recorded in *Nature*.

Schweidler's name is familiar to all workers in radioactivity as the co-author of a manual of radioactivity which surpasses the well-known French and English standard works in this field by the range it covers and the completeness of its documentation; the two editions of 1916 and 1927 have been most valuable to generations of physicists and chemists. It was written in collaboration with Stefan Meyer, with whom Schweidler's name is linked also in numerous experimental papers on radioactivity. Another field in which he worked as an experimental physicist and was an acknowledged authority is atmospheric electricity.

It was, however, a contribution to theoretical physics by which Schweidler exerted the strongest influence on the development of science. At the International Congress on Radiology held in Liège in 1905, he read a paper in which he gave the statistical interpretation of Rutherford and Soddy's law of radioactive disintegration. He showed that the statement that, per unit of time, it is always the same fraction of a radioactive substance which disintegrates, can be true only if the law of large numbers makes its levelling effect felt and obscures the deviations; but these must become obvious as soon as the number of atoms under observation is reduced sufficiently. These "Schweidler fluctuations" were soon verified by experiment, and thus the chance character of the process of disintegration directly demonstrated.

This erratic behaviour of single atoms seemed in 1905 to be something completely out of step with the rest of physics and confined to radioactive disintegration. However, in 1917 Einstein used an analogous interpretation of the emission of light from an excited atom, and it is well known what a predominant role statistical interpretations now take in quantum mechanics. The credit must go to Schweidler, however, for having recognized the first case in a fundamental paper which, in his history of physics, von Laue calls "a step forward of incalculable importance".

Schweidler was born in Vienna on February 10, 1873; he was a student, a lecturer, and an assistant professor there before he was called to the chair of physics in Innsbruck. This he occupied from 1911 until 1926 when he returned to Vienna as director of one of the physics institutes there. This position he held until his retirement in 1939. He was a member of the Vienna Academy of Sciences and for several years also general secretary and vice-president.

The atomistic school of Vienna, famous for such names as Loschmidt and Boltzmann, has lost in Schweidler another worthy representative.

9 | Stefan Meyer

The science of radioactivity is more than fifty years old and the number of scientific workers who can claim a share in its early development is by now exceedingly small. One of the best known died on December 29.* He was Stefan Meyer, for many years director of the Vienna Radium Institute and the author of a fundamental treatise on radioactivity.

Meyer was born in Vienna in 1872 and educated in the flourishing school of atomic physics there; for some time he was assistant in Boltzmann's institute. The decisive events for his scientific development were, however, the discoveries of Henry Becquerel and Pierre and Marie Curie in Paris. It was only one year after the discovery of radium that he began to experiment on the magnetic deflexion of its rays, in collaboration with his life-long friend E. v. Schweidler. From those days right to the end of his life his interest in radioactivity never flagged, and his influence was widely felt, not only through his own researches but also thanks to his unceasing efforts to foster international collaboration in this field. At the beginning, Austria was the only country possessing the raw material for radium production; when the Curies asked for it, the Austrian Government sent several wagon-loads to the French workers at a nominal price; and when later Ramsay and Rutherford needed "large" quantities of radium salts, these were lent to them by the Vienna Academy of Sciences for indefinite periods. In these decisions, Meyer was always consulted as one of the very few experts in this new field.

Meyer's organizing ability was given full scope when in 1910 the Vienna Academy received from a private donor the means for the erection and equipment of an institute devoted to the study of radium. Although for some years the chief position was nominally held by a senior member of the Academy, it was Meyer who made the plans

* 1949. [Ed.]

and, from the start, was the acting director. He took the same interest in the chemical as in the physical side of radioactivity; to mention only one example, the late Otto Hönigschmid was given facilities in the Vienna Radium Institute for his famous atomic weight determinations of radium, uranium, thorium, ionium, and uranium and thorium lead.

It is impossible to give details here of the many papers on radio-activity Meyer himself has published. In almost every year the *Mitteilungen aus dem Institut für Radiumforschung* contained one or two of them; but even that does not give the full impression of his activities because many of the papers by younger scientists were suggested by him and carried out under his eyes, without his name appearing anywhere. He was always happy if he could add a new number to the *Mitteilungen*; he was a mild, in a few cases perhaps too mild, critic of the contributions of the younger generation; but a glance over the titles and authors of the four hundred and fifty-odd *Mitteilungen* published up to now will reveal at once how much fundamental progress in the physics and chemistry of radioactive substances is due to research work carried out in Meyer's institute.

So long as it was humanly possible, Meyer tried to be informed about everything that was published on radioactivity. Impressive witness to his success in this line are the two editions of the *Radio-aktivität* he published, together with Schweidler, in 1916 and 1927; neither in the French nor in the English literature was there a manual available containing such a wealth of detailed, carefully documented information.

From the institution of the International Radium Standard Committee Meyer was a very active member, and in 1938, after the death of its president, Lord Rutherford, he became his successor. The Second World War paralysed the activities of the Committee; but when three years ago efforts were made again to agree on inter-national regulations for the standardization of radioactive sources Meyer took a lively interest in them. Letters he wrote to colleagues up to a few days before his death were full of valuable information about previous international negotiations, and wise counsel as to how to overcome the present difficulties.

Meyer's activities as director of the Vienna Radium Institute came to an abrupt end in 1938 when the Nazis seized power in Austria; being of Jewish descent, he was dismissed. He did not leave the country but retired to his house in Upper Austria where he was fortunate enough to live unmolested, thanks to the loyalty of friends and to the courage and devotion of his daughter, who had become a

Norwegian by marriage. Several brochures which have since appeared, about the theory of vision and about musical instruments, and a few theoretical contributions to the *Mitteilungen* (written jointly with his daughter), show that even in retirement his mind was constantly active.

All those who at any time have worked in Meyer's institute, as his assistants or as guests, remember with deep gratitude his never-failing kindness. It was perhaps the most outstanding feature of his personality.

10 | Memories of the Early Days of the Vienna Radium Institute: The Preparation of Bismuth Hydride

Last autumn, Professor Stefan Meyer told me of plans to celebrate, in October 1950, the fortieth anniversary of the Vienna Radium Institute. In his characteristically charming way he invited me to make a contribution to the proposed anniversary publication, for which he himself suggested the theme: I was to recall the days in which the existence of gaseous bismuth hydride was definitely established.

It was with great pleasure that I agreed because this seemed an opportunity to give expression to the respect and gratitude felt by all his pupils and co-workers for the scientific founder of the Radium Institute in the evening of his life. He was not destined to live to enjoy the anniversary. Since, however, I hear from the present Director of the Institute, Professor Karlik, that the celebrations are to take place, although they will be overshadowed by mourning for the doyen of Austrian research in radioactivity, I shall try to fulfil the promise given to Professor Meyer and bring together a few of the facts concerning the discovery of bismuth hydride. The experiments have long since been described, but Professor Meyer was of the opinion that this occasion afforded an opportunity to tell the story of the surprises experienced as a result of the mistaken assumption on which these experiments were based.

The discovery of bismuth hydride is an instance of a not infrequent phenomenon which, however, does not seem to have a name in any language except English. I refer to *serendipity*, "the faculty of making happy and unexpected discoveries by accident". (The rather complicated explanation of this word can be found in the Oxford Dictionary, from which this definition is taken.) My experiments were intended to show that polonium forms a volatile hydride, a fact which could be of interest to scarcely anybody except specialists in radio-chemistry. The result was the discovery of a method to produce bismuth hydride, a compound for which many chemists had searched in vain for many years.

My experiments with polonium were directly related to those of our

English "Prisoner-of-War". In 1915 Robert Lawson had attributed the surprisingly high volatility of polonium to a hypothetical polonium hydride. If this compound existed, then it followed that it must be possible to produce it in larger quantities than before by a straightforward synthetic process and to study its properties. In 1917 Professor Otto Hönigschmid had succeeded in obtaining my release from military service and secondment to his Department of Chemistry in Prague in order to assist him in the teaching of inorganic chemistry. This gave me the opportunity, at least during the holidays, after an interval of several years, of again undertaking experiments of my own. With the simple apparatus available the problem of polonium hydride seemed a suitable subject. From my notes I gather that I started these experiments in the Radium Institute on September 30, 1917, and that as early as October 13 I had the impression that the decomposition of a polonium–magnesium alloy was resulting in the production of detectable amounts of polonium hydride. On October 16, however, I had to go to Prague. I took some polonium with me and in my rather limited free time there I was able to repeat and confirm the experiments.

On December 6th I was back in Vienna and spent most of my time in the Radium Institute. Soon it could no longer be doubted that by decomposing a polonium–magnesium alloy by acids and simultaneously passing a current of gas over it, it was possible to transport polonium at room temperature through pipes of considerable length into an electroscope. It was difficult to prove, however, that we were not dealing here with a dust cloud or a spray of particles of the metal or the solution. Filters of glass wool or cotton did not prevent the passage to the electroscope, but even this did not seem to be an absolutely conclusive proof in view of the invisibly small quantities involved. At this point, it occurred to me to conduct a parallel experiment with the active deposit of thorium. It was considered impossible to produce a gaseous hydride of lead or bismuth, and I therefore expected that, in contrast to the analogous experiments with polonium, no activity would appear in the electroscope from the decomposition of an alloy of magnesium and thorium B and thorium C.

As I had only the Christmas holidays at my disposal, I started the decisive experiments on Boxing Day; even during the period of my Prague appointment I remained, as an assistant of the Radium Institute, in possession of all the keys. To my great disappointment, the electroscope showed a strong activity. This seemed to prove that, in all my experiments, in fact only the transport of spray and not of a gaseous chemical compound had been involved. One thing, however, was astonishing: the activity in the electroscope soon decreased considerably, much more rapidly than one would have expected if equilibrium amounts of thorium B and thorium C had been carried over as spray.

The half-life seemed to be about one hour, but I had to interrupt the measurements owing to a dinner engagement. As soon as I was free again, shortly before midnight, I returned to the Radium Institute and found that by then practically the whole activity had disappeared; thus only thorium C and no thorium B had been transported by the gas current through the filter into the electroscope.

The interpretation was obvious. The absence of thorium B excluded the possibility of a purely mechanical effect. The fact, however, that thorium C behaved like polonium proved that not only this new element but also the well-known and often investigated bismuth was capable of forming a gaseous compound with hydrogen.

In the second half of January, my teaching duties started again in Prague, but before my departure the conclusion based on the experiment described had been sufficiently confirmed by further experiments so that, on January 29th, Hofrat F. Exner could present to the Imperial Academy of Sciences in Vienna two preliminary papers from the Institute for Radium Research: (1) "On bismuth hydride" and (2) "On polonium hydride". In these papers, as well as in the subsequently more detailed publications, the experiments proving the existence of bismuth hydride are described purely factually without mention of the erroneous expectations which led to their being undertaken.

Indeed, scientific publications should not be encumbered by incidental anecdotes. In the present anniversary number, however, containing a collection of personal memories of the Vienna Radium Institute, it may not be inappropriate to describe the historical course of the experiments and the line of thought followed in them.

It is not claiming too much to call this a case of serendipity, for the success went considerably beyond the original target aimed at. The production of polonium and bismuth hydride showed the way for similar experiments with tin and lead, and the experience of the use of metal mirrors in glass tubes which was gained with the hydrides led to a method for demonstrating the existence of short-lived organic radicals and thus to the discovery of free methyl and ethyl. No one followed these developments with greater interest than Professor Meyer, who always liked to recall that this whole branch of scientific work originated in the Vienna Radium Institute in the winter of 1917–18.

I I | A Tribute to Frederick Soddy

The first International Conference on Radioisotopes in Scientific Research seems an appropriate occasion upon which to consider our debt to Frederick Soddy. The duty to clarify his picture is specially incumbent on us, as it is the tragedy of his life that members of the younger generation may know him only as the person who adopted the term "isotope" and, perhaps, as the author of provocative statements in economics and other fields far remote from science. The number of those who knew Soddy in his creative period is dwindling.

In fact, the whole science of radioactivity owes to Soddy infinitely more than the coining of the household word which is the unifying tie of this Conference.

First, I would like to recall that the fundamental theory of radioactive disintegration was developed by Rutherford and Soddy. From experiments carried out during 1901–3 at the McGill University in Montreal by the physicist Rutherford and the chemist Soddy, they drew the conclusion that the emission of the Becquerel-rays (as they were called in those days) was accompanied by chemical transmutations; in a vague way such a hypothesis had been considered before as one of several possibilities, but the French school in particular had favoured other explanations. Anybody who studies the original papers will easily recognize the decisive part the chemist must have played in this joint work; some of the arrangements are, from the point of view of experimental chemistry, models of a scientific investigation. Nevertheless, in later books Soddy's name sometimes no longer appears in this context; to Rutherford is attributed the sole merit—illustrating the old truth, well known to students of the history of science, that great reputations tend to absorb the smaller ones—although Rutherford himself always gave full credit to his colleague.

Their ways, however, soon parted. Soddy's name immediately appeared again in connection with an experiment of the greatest significance: the proof that in the process of radioactive disintegration by alpha-rays helium is evolved in sufficient quantities to be identified spectroscopically. This time the team was Ramsay and Soddy: the study of such small quantities of rare gases is so difficult that in those days Ramsay's laboratory in London was the only place where the necessary experience was available, but the radioactive technique—then quite new to Ramsay—was clearly Soddy's contribution. Anybody who knows from Ramsay's later publications on radioactive transmutation, after Soddy had left, how incapable he was of taking the precautions necessary in this field, will credit Soddy with the clean and convincing conduct of experiments in which he later proved himself so much more adept than Ramsay.

So far, Soddy's name had been linked with those of senior and already very famous investigators. He came fully into his own during the ten-year tenure of a lectureship in physical chemistry at the University of Glasgow, where he devoted himself to radiochemistry proper, that is, to the study of the chemical behaviour of the radioactive substances. Such work had been going on in many laboratories, but the published results were frequently erroneous and no attempt had been made at a comprehensive survey. By far the clearest presentation of the new subject was given by Soddy in 1911, in a small volume called *The Chemistry of the Radioelements*. Here, for the first time, the phenomenon of the chemical inseparability of those substances which today we call isotopic was stressed as something fundamentally new and important. More than that, a connection was indicated between the positions that a radio-element occupies in the disintegration series and in the periodic table; the first part of the important "radioactive displacement law" is already contained in this book, namely, the rule that emission of an alpha-particle means shifting down by two places in the periodic table. The second part of the law, namely, that emission of a beta-particle leads to the production of an element one place higher in the table, was pronounced three years later, almost simultaneously, by Fajans and Soddy; the experimental basis for this statement had in the meantime been safely laid, largely through the systematic efforts of Soddy's laboratory. In the course of various researches the inseparability of some radio-elements from other elements had independently been found by Svedberg, by Boltwood, by Hahn and others, but it is Soddy's outstanding merit to have undertaken a special investigation in order to clarify this mysterious phenomenon; here he was ably helped by a Scottish student with the name of A. Fleck, now Sir Alexander Fleck, chairman of Imperial Chemical

Industries, Ltd. Their well-planned analytical work contributed decisively to the recognition of the validity of the displacement law and thereby to the understanding of the physical cause of isotopy. It was fitting that Soddy should christen this phenomenon, and that, in 1921, he should be awarded a Nobel Prize.

After these brilliant successes in his scientific efforts—I have not time to mention other excellent papers by Soddy—everybody would have expected him to become the leader of a strong British school of radiochemistry, in a position perhaps similar to that of Rutherford on the side of physics. Soddy's books (*The Interpretation of Radium* and others) were eagerly read; they showed didactic and literary qualities of the highest order and seemed to add to his qualifications for a successful teaching career. But nothing of this sort happened. True, after a few years at Aberdeen, Soddy was called to Oxford as professor of inorganic and physical chemistry, but little scientific work emerged from his laboratory there, no school of radiochemistry was formed, and in 1936 he gave up his chair and retired into private life. How is this surprising eclipse of Soddy as a scientific worker to be explained? To help us understand it, something must be said about his character.

Science was never the only concern in Soddy's life. He had a deep interest in social questions, and whenever he suspected that injustice was being done to a certain group, or that something was wrong in the social structure, he fought it in the most uncompromising way. I had an opportunity to see this side of his nature as early as 1913 when I had the privilege of learning the then current methods of gas microanalysis under his guidance in Glasgow. Scottish Sundays would have left me rather lonely if Soddy had not introduced me to the hospitable house of his parents-in-law, Dr. and Mrs. Beilby. Incidentally, I read recently in the *Proceedings of the Chemical Society* that on that house a tablet is to be fixed, recalling that there, about 1912, the name "isotope" was invented. This date is certainly too early; in the many discussions to which I had the pleasure of listening in the first half of 1913, this word was never used. According to Soddy's own story, it was a little later supplied to him by a school teacher, a lady to whom he had explained that the substances to be named occupied "the same place" in the periodic table. (The term made its first public appearance in Soddy's letter to *Nature* of December 4, p. 399, 1913.)

It is very unfortunate that in recent years this clear scientific meaning has been obscured by the indiscriminate use of the word "isotope" for any radioactive substance. If no relation to another substance occupying the same place is involved, the designation "radio-element" or "radionuclide" ought to be used. One substance in isolation can no more claim to be an isotope than an only child can be a brother.

I remember very clearly having heard Soddy's heated arguments, in Dr. Beilby's house at 11 University Gardens, in favour of home rule for Ireland and votes for women, the two main political topics of those days. Later he took a deep interest in political economy; to the theory of money he devoted several publications in which he expressed very radical views. Objections from acknowledged experts in this field he used to brush aside with the remark that chemical experts did not accept his views on isotopes either when he first pronounced them. There was, however, the difference that in chemistry he could present such convincing facts that resistance was overcome within a few years. In economics he met with no such success, and he became more and more embittered about this failure.

Nearer home, he tried to introduce reforms into the structure of the University of Oxford; he considered some aspects of the college system, as, for example, the independent teaching of physical chemistry in several small and poorly equipped college laboratories, as outmoded. He was a declared admirer of some features of the German university system. However, he was not good at waiting or satisfied with slow progress, but was always inclined to suspect unpardonable indolence or even ill-will. After he had left Oxford some developments went in the direction desired by him, just as votes were given to women and independence to Ireland. But Soddy did not wait. Never satisfied by a compromise, he manoeuvred himself more and more into the position of an opponent and critic without influence; finally he resigned, and Britain lost the hope many had certainly cherished that this great man and his pupils would establish a permanent school of radiochemistry.

After his retirement Soddy had little contact with colleagues and followed the further development of the science he had helped so much to launch with growing distrust. He resented especially the dominant role physics assumed in radioactive research. Apart from the general trend—physics has invaded other branches of chemistry as well—it was Soddy's own premature retirement which accelerated this shifting of the centre of gravity. He had been the only man in Great Britain who could to a certain extent have kept the balance. Instead he was, in his later years, inclined to believe in dark scheming on the part of physicists who did not want to acknowledge the merits of chemists. But anybody who ever had the opportunity of knowing the generous character of Rutherford and his readiness to admire and enjoy good scientific work, wherever it was done, will be quite unable to accept Soddy's occasional bitter remarks. It is most regrettable that these unfounded grievances of an old and disgruntled Soddy have found their way into recent books.

The reasons for Soddy's tragic scientific isolation in later years are to be found in his own personality. He was gifted in many, perhaps too many, ways. He was such a good writer of English prose that it was all too easy for him to give his polemical essays the sting he wished. Once, when he had solved a problem of stereometry, it amused him to publish it in verse. An occasional excursion into the history of chemistry instigated him to the best vindication known to me of the strong claims of William Higgins, as opposed to those of John Dalton, to be the originator of the chemical atomic theory. His special gift for technical constructions made him for long periods exchange the laboratory for the workshop. There are many other examples which could be quoted to illustrate the richness and variety of his talents.

Rutherford once said in a lecture that he was naturally in favour of simple explanations in physics, being a simple person himself. Now, Frederick Soddy was not a simple person. He was a very complex personality, not easy to approach, living a rather solitary life, especially after the early death of his charming and devoted wife; but he was a great idealist, always ready to fight against what he deemed morally wrong, without any consideration of his own personal interests. Very kind and helpful to young and struggling people, he was suspicious of nearly everyone in authority and power. If he had lived, on September 2, 1957, he would have completed his eightieth year. It is fitting, at a conference to discuss the scientific applications of isotopes, to remember the man who was the first to see the general theoretical importance of what had been until then scattered observations. Let us honour the memory of a brilliant intellect, an experimenter second to none among the founders of radiochemistry, and an uncompromising champion of his ideals.

Thomas Wright and Immanuel Kant

FOREWORD

Immanuel Kant was born at Königsberg, where he remained throughout his life, never leaving his native province. Thomas Wright was born in County Durham and lived there for most of his life, never apparently (apart from a brief sea-trip to Amsterdam and back) leaving the British Isles. Through the vicissitudes of fortune, Paneth moved from a Chair at the University of Königsberg to a Chair at the University of Durham, and, he being what he was, the result was inevitable.

The accident by which Kant's thoughts were so strangely influenced by Wright is told in this Section. Wright's name was already familiar to Paneth through his interest in Kant, but before finding himself in the county to which Wright belonged, his knowledge of the astronomer's career—like that of everyone else, even in Durham itself—was of the slightest. Almost all the facts related here, including the discovery that the "Westerton Folly" was in fact Wright's observatory, were unearthed by Paneth himself, and it is entirely owing to his efforts, and to those of others inspired by him, that we are now able not only to form a reasonably clear picture of Wright and of his connection with Durham, but also to reach a just estimate of his achievement and its relation to the subsequent work of Kant for which it provided the impetus.

Paneth gave several addresses on Wright and Kant, both in England and in Germany, the titles of which are included in the Bibliography (p. 282). They show, of course, the development naturally resulting from the gradual progress of his investigations, and no one of them gives the whole story. On the other hand, the repetition

8

which a reproduction of all of them would involve would have been excessively tedious. It has therefore been thought advisable to form a single essay by taking the article in the *Durham University Journal* (No. IX, 21 of the Bibliography) as a basis, and inserting in the appropriate places the additional material contained in later publications. The account given here is, excepting a very occasional connecting phrase, entirely in Paneth's own words, nothing having been written in German that was not already available in English, and no fact of importance is omitted.

Chapter 13 is a description, written by Paneth for *Nature*, of the celebrations which he organized at Durham to commemorate the 200th anniversary of the publication of Wright's *Original Theory*.

<table>
<tr><td>I2</td><td># Thomas Wright of Durham and Immanuel Kant</td></tr>
</table>

Lovers of eighteenth century German fiction may remember the charming figure of Jean Paul's "little schoolmaster Wutz". An enthusiast for newly published books, but too poor to buy them, Wutz could only procure the booksellers' annual lists; whenever one of the titles appealed to him he composed the book he thought the author might, or should, have written, whereupon the volume obtained its proper place in his private library.

Some forty years before Jean Paul created this character, such a procedure had actually been adopted in the far eastern corner of Germany. A young scientist, Immanuel Kant, a former student of Königsberg University, was making a modest living as a private tutor on a nobleman's lonely estate between this town and the Russian border. In 1751 he happened to read in a German journal a summary of an *Original Theory or New Hypothesis of the Universe* just published in London. Although greatly interested, he made apparently no attempt to secure a copy; instead he began to think out his own system, and when he had finished his *Universal Natural History and Theory of the Heavens* he had to admit in the Preface his inability "exactly to define the boundaries" between his hypothesis and that of the Englishman, or to "point out in what details he had merely imitated his sketch or had carried it out further". And for a long time it seemed that his book, in truly Wutzian fashion, had been written for the author alone; for, although printed in 1755, it was not to be released to the public for several years to come, on account of the publisher's bankruptcy and the sealing-up of all his stock; and when at last its sale was authorized, nobody paid any attention to it.

The end of the story, however, is quite different. Kant returned to his Alma Mater, for fifteen years a "Privatdozent" and, from 1770 onwards, as a professor. He turned more and more away from science (in Helmholtz's opinion principally owing to the lack of research facilities in Königsberg), although right to the end of his academic career he still gave regular lectures on scientific subjects. His own investigations in later years were mainly concerned with epistemological questions, and when, in 1781, at the age of 57, he published the *Critique of Pure Reason*, his reputation as a philosopher was quickly established. Enhanced by further contributions to theoretical and moral philosophy, his fame not only survived him, but grew steadily until his name became firmly established as one of the greatest in the history of philosophy. His collected works are now to be found in every large library all over the world; they contain his *Natural History of the Heavens*, now universally considered a very important contribution to astronomy, and enshrined in it is the name of the man whose treatise he had read about in early life, and to whom he gives all the credit for having inspired him: Thomas Wright of Durham.

Most students of Kant are, therefore, familiar with this name, although they may appreciate even less than Kant himself how much, or how little, of his cosmological theory is due to his predecessor. Thus to somebody coming from the "city of pure reason" to Durham it may be something of a surprise to find the name of Thomas Wright so little known here even in university circles. There can be hardly any doubt that but for Kant's acknowledgement Wright would be entirely forgotten today; his life and books had no other detectable influence on the development of astronomical knowledge. But did he deserve this fate? Can he shine only by reflection, like the dark celestial bodies, or does he possess some luminosity of his own? It ought to be possible to settle this question by studying his achievements far away from the brilliancy of the Kantian sun.

Thomas Wright was born in September 1711 at Byer's Green, a small village about six miles to the south-west of Durham City, the son of a carpenter of some means. Restricted in the choice of a profession by an impediment of speech, he learned some mathematics, became an apprentice to a clockmaker, and in leisure hours applied himself to the study of astronomy. For a while he made mathematical instruments with a London firm. Later he opened a school for teaching mathematics and navigation at Sunderland, and published by subscription, with the approbation of the Admiralty, in 1734 a work on navigation, called *Pannauticon*. His reputation in this field led in 1742 to an invitation by the Imperial Academy of St. Petersburg to become Professor of Navigation there; he preferred, however, to remain in England and to continue the sort of life which he had in the meantime found to be most congenial to him, that of a private instructor in noble families. Kant spent nine years of his youth in a similar position and was, at least according to his own judgement, no success; Wright, on the other hand, seems to have enjoyed greatly the opportunities thus offered to him of mixing with the aristocracy and sharing their pleasures; and since his official

FIG. 2. Thomas Wright. (Reduced from an engraving in quarto which is prefixed to a few copies of *Clavis Coelestis* and of the *Original Theory*.)

duty in most cases was "to teach the mathematicks to the ladies of the family" we cannot expect this to have been a full-time job. His notebooks give some insight into the variety of his engagements. We learn that, within a year or so, he "travelled to the Earl of Bristol's, in Suffolk, to wait upon the honourable Miss Hervey; that he was introduced to Lord Cornwallis to teach his daughters geometry; that he hunted with the Earl of Halifax; spent three months at Wrest to teach the ladies to survey (the duchess surveyed all the pleasure-grounds, and made a plan of them which was engraved); that in London, in 1740, he dined almost every day with the Duke and Duchess of Kent; taught the honourable Miss Talbot and Lady Sophia Grey, afterwards lady of Dr. Egerton, bishop of Durham", etc. "So acceptable had Mr. Wright rendered himself to people of fashion."

In the year 1746 Wright went to Ireland where for several months he stayed "under the patronage of Lord Limerick and the bishop of Raphoe", collecting drawings for his *Louthiana*, a description of antiquities in this part of Ireland, published in 1748. In 1750 his *Theory of the Universe* appeared; and in 1756 he began to build a house at his birthplace, Byer's Green. He retired there in 1762, and died, unmarried, in 1786. He was survived by one daughter.

These and many more biographical details can be found in "A Sketch of the Character of Mr. Thomas Wright, late of Byer's Green Lodge, in the County of Durham" which appeared anonymously in *The Gentleman's Magazine* for 1793 (Vol. 63, pp. 9 and 126). The author claims to have collected the material from Wright's own notebooks and manuscripts; his identity is revealed by a remark made by Professor Chevallier of the University of Durham to Professor De Morgan (see the latter's article on Thomas Wright quoted below); it is a Mr. George Allan of Darlington, who is mentioned in the sketch as the purchaser of Wright's "collection of prints, mathematical instruments and other valuable articles", as well as of the coppers of several of Wright's plates. Professor Chevallier obtained the information possibly from a younger relative of George Allan, R. H. Allan, in reply to the letter he addressed to him in a search for Wright's manuscripts, as it seems. Parts of this letter are reproduced in W. H. D. Longstaffe's *History and Antiquities of Darlington* (Darlington and London, p. XV, 1854) and, less complete, in W. Fordyce's *History and Antiquities of the County Palatine of Durham* (Newcastle-upon-Tyne, p. 588, 1857). Fordyce appends to the paragraph on Byer's Green a long footnote on Thomas Wright which is essentially an abbreviation of the biographical sketch in *The Gentleman's Magazine* (containing even the same misprints, though altering the sentences), but adds a few details. We learn, for example, that Wright's manuscripts were sold by Sotheby in December 1844; the coppers of Wright's plates seem to have had a similar fate already in 1822.

The biography in *The Gentleman's Magazine* is "embellished with an elegant Portrait of Mr. Thomas Wright", engraved "in his middle state of life at his own expense".*

---

* There is no doubt that Wright himself is responsible for the choice of the Ouroboros Serpent as frame to his portrait, for this tail-eating snake, familiar to students of alchemy

Since all these sources of information, so far as Wright's life is concerned, are based on his own notebooks or on personal observation—George Allan is known to have been one of his friends—they are probably generally reliable though not free from mistakes. A bad error is the addition of the letters F.R.S. to Wright's name both in Fordyce and in Longstaffe. Wright was never elected a fellow of the Royal Society, as a glance through the Society's Record (4th edition, 1940) reveals.* More serious still is the misfortune that George Allan was not a scientist but an antiquary. Of Wright's one outstanding contribution to astronomy, his *Theory of the Universe*, all he has to say is that it is "illuminated with a great many plates"; and next to nothing can be learned from his article about Wright's earnest occupation with science, while all his various mechanical devices for popularizing astronomy and amusing their lordships and ladies, such as a 16 feet long "section of the creation", a "system of planetary bodies" (in brass with a radius of 190 feet) or the invention of an "astronomical fan for the ladies", are admiringly enumerated.

To obtain a correct idea of Wright's scientific standard in astronomy we have to turn to his two books: *Clavis Coelestis being the Explication of a Diagram entituled a Synopsis of the Universe or, the Visible World Epitomized* (London 1742), and *An Original Theory or New Hypothesis of the Universe founded upon the Laws of Nature and solving by Mathematical Principles the General phaenomena of the Visible Creation; and particularly the Via Lactea. Comprised in Nine Familiar letters from the Author to his Friend* (London, 1750).†

The first is a popular introduction to astronomy, with two folding plates printed from coppers 36 inches by 24 inches. In the Preface

---

as a symbol of the unity of matter ($\overset{\text{\textasciimacron}}{\epsilon}\nu$ $\tau\grave{o}$ $\pi\tilde{a}\nu$), appears as circumference also on plates in *The Use of the Globes* and the *Original Theory*, surrounding in the latter the solar system and in the former a conglomeration of several systems, thus symbolizing the unity of the Universe. As a frame to a microcosm it is certainly unusual. Still further away from its proper meaning is the Ouroboros in a variation of Wright's portrait on a copper-plate print prefixed to a copy of the *Clavis Coelestis* in the library of Durham Observatory (see Fig. 2); the serpent is no longer embracing the picture but plays at its bottom like a puppy which has caught its own tail. This last debasement of the great Egyptian symbol is due to the artistic effort of G. Allan, Thomas Wright's biographer.

* Thomas Wright had friends amongst the fellows of the Royal Society and communicated to this body some of his scientific achievements; for instance, drawings referring to an eclipse in two long sheets. It might be worth while, when conditions are more favourable than now [1941, Ed.], to examine the Society's archives for Wright relics, and to collect the references to him in their Proceedings.

† Wright's book *The Use of the Globes* (London, 1740) need not concern us here as its relation to astronomy is only slight. It was composed in fulfilment of a contract with John Senex, F.R.S., to serve as an instruction for the use of the terrestrial and celestial globes offered for sale by Mr. Senex.

the author claims that the work has "several Things to recommend it besides Usefulness; in particular the seldom failing Plea of Novelty, and that both as to Matter and Manner; not only great Part of the Subject, being quite new (in a Tract of this Kind) but also the Method of treating it, viz. clearly and plainly". This claim seems to be justified; one can imagine that a similar way of presenting his subject, and adorning it with quotations from Milton, Dryden's *Ovid*, etc., was used by Wright to make his oral instructions palatable to his non-professional pupils. In a table of the "Comets that have been duly observed" he is in a position to include one whose elements he had computed himself, based on his own observations.

The second of Wright's astronomical books is the one in which we are principally interested. The title already indicates that here he is aiming much higher: an *original* theory or *new* hypothesis of the universe, solving particularly the phenomenon of the Milky Way. Let us state at the outset that this claim too is not at all exaggerated. For the first time in the history of astronomy the view is expressed here that the fixed stars are not distributed at random in space, but mainly concentrated in a flat disk; that the Sun with his planets is situated somewhere not too far from the disk's centre, and that, therefore, for us many more stars are visible in the direction of the disk's plane than in any other. As they are too numerous to be seen separately they appear to the naked eye as a luminous circle on the sky—the Milky Way.

The explanation given here by Wright of the galaxy as an optical phenomenon, following from, and thus revealing, a disk-like distribution of the visible stars, is contained in the seventh letter, and illustrated by a diagram (Fig. 3). The wording of the crucial paragraph is rather clumsy and involved, and the author at once proceeds to much wilder speculations in which the Universe appears as a combination of concentric shells; the Eye of Providence is seated in the Centre and becomes, therefore, clearly visible on the plate depicting the Universe in cross section.

It was, perhaps, a blessing in disguise that the very careful abstractor who reviewed the book for a Hamburg periodical, the *Freye Urtheile und Nachrichten zum Aufnehmen der Wissenschaften und der Historie überhaupt* (Year 8, Part 1, Jan. 1, 1751) was, to his regret, unable to include the copper plate prints and had consequently to omit those passages which could not be presented without reference to the diagrams. Wright's convincing explanation of the nature of the galaxy stands out all the clearer in the translator's account. It was this summary which Kant happened to read, and

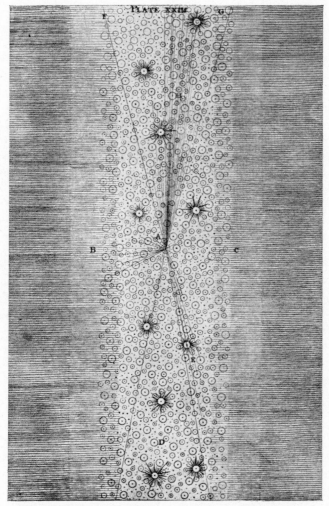

FIG. 3. Diagram of the Milky Way.

which became the starting point of his own cosmological speculations. W. Hastie, Professor of Divinity at Glasgow University, was fortunate enough to discover a manuscript copy of this article—the journal *Freye Urtheile* has long ceased to exist—and all interested in the question of the relation of Kant to Wright are indebted to him for having added it to his translation of Kant's *Cosmogony* (Glasgow, 1900).*

* All our quotations from Kant's *Cosmogony* are taken from this perfect translation.

It is now easy to realize that some obvious similarities between the books of Kant and Wright are nothing but coincidence. For instance, Wright frequently quotes long passages from English poets like Dr. Young, Milton, Addison and Pope; no clear reference is made to this peculiarity in the Hamburg summary, and if Kant too adds poetical lines, some of them taken from Addison and Pope, it only shows the generality of this habit and the wide extent of Kant's reading. For similar reasons it hardly needed Wright's example to induce Kant to emphasize the complete harmony of his system with correctly understood religious conceptions; even if that had not been his own firm conviction (which we have no reason whatever to doubt), a work of this kind could not have been published in the Germany of Kant's days without such assurances. How careful he had to be on this issue is clearly shown by the preface in which he tries "to remove the objections which seem to threaten his position from the side of religion"; by the dedication of his work to no less a person than "the most serene, the most powerful king and lord, Frederick, King of Prussia"; and by the anonymity which he maintained for a while.

The one fundamental point where Kant clearly accepts the lead given by Wright is the explanation of the appearance of the Milky Way, with all its implications for a "systematic constitution of the Universe". The entire "First Part" of Kant's treatise is essentially an exposition of Wright's ideas. We do not intend to mention here minor features which he adds to his precursor's picture, e.g. his views on the nebulous patches in the sky, since the discussion of their merits from the point of view of modern astronomy would occupy too much space. We should like, however, to point out one essential difference: the style. Wright was apparently very fond of engraving. The value of his *Louthiana* naturally lies in the illustrations; his *Clavis Coelestis* consists of two (awkwardly large) plates with explanations; and in preparing his *Original Theory of the Universe* he must have spent a great amount of time, labour and money on the execution of the 32 plates. All these figures are very carefully drawn and some reach an artistic effect. Wright is said to have been an accomplished engraver himself, and must at least have closely supervised the workmen he employed for this unusual sort of picture. In sharp contrast to the attention given by him to the copper plates stands the sometimes astounding lack of precision and clearness in his writing; actually he is hardly able to put into words his own explanation of the appearance of the Milky Way, in spite of the help of one elaborately drawn figure. Kant's exposition, unaided by any diagram, is incomparably clearer.

It is, however, only in the "Second Part" that Kant comes entirely into his own, giving here the "Reasons for the Theory of a Mechanical Origin of the World". It is the explanation of his famous cosmogony which in textbooks is frequently, but very unsatisfactorily, referred to as the "Kant–Laplace hypothesis". Laplace, without knowledge of Kant's scientific papers, developed in 1796 a somewhat similar hypothesis on the origin of the solar system; superior in mathematical precision, but in other respects much less complete, and in its assumptions as to the first stage—a gaseous nebula instead of Kant's swarm of particles—different, and hardly more probable.

We cannot indulge here in a discussion of Kant's cosmogonical speculations as they have no connection with Thomas Wright. It ought, however, to be emphasized that for Kant they were far more important than all he had learned from Wright. This explains the sentence by which he introduced in the "First Part" the new theory of the Milky Way: "It was reserved for an Englishman, Mr. Wright of Durham, to make a happy step with a remark which does not seem to have been used by himself for any very important purpose, and the useful application of which he has not sufficiently observed". The useful application Kant has here in mind is nothing less than the interpretation of the present "systematic constitution" of the Universe by a history of its development in time, in other words the introduction into stellar astronomy of the fundamental conception of evolution.

It was one of Kant's deepest convictions throughout the whole of his life that in every science a full understanding needed knowledge of the past. While it was only in the nineteenth century, through Lamarck and Darwin, that evolutionary theories in biology became more widely known and "evolution" as a general technical term was popularized by Herbert Spencer, Kant must be regarded as the first who introduced this idea not only into scientific astronomy, but also into modern biology. In a remarkable footnote in his *Anthropology* (a course of lectures delivered frequently during his professorship at Königsberg, and eventually printed) he stated that, for special reasons given there, man must have changed fundamentally in the course of time. This remark, he adds, leads far: "for instance" to the idea that, in a future natural revolution, orang-utangs or chimpanzees might acquire human form, and the organs for speech and the use of intelligence. This "for instance" seems to invite the attentive reader to try the past instead of the future—a possibility which Kant was careful enough not to mention himself.* If in this

* Cf. Kant's confession in a letter to the Berlin philosopher Moses Mendelssohn that

application to the animal origin of man his real opinion necessarily remains somewhat in the dark, there are (in the *Critique of Judgement*) passages dealing with the less dangerous topic of the origin of animal species, where he declares himself wholeheartedly in favour of a mechanistic theory of descent from a "common primordial mother" ("gemeinschaftliche Urmutter"). Putting it quite generally (in his treatise *On the Different Human Races*) Kant states: "It is clear that in addition to a knowledge of the objects in the physical world as they are now, a realization of their past state is desirable, and also of the series of changes through which they had to pass in order to reach everywhere their present state". Instead of "Naturbeschreibung" we need a separate, and so far hardly existing science, "Naturgeschichte".

This passage ought to be kept in mind when interpreting the meaning of the title of Kant's book here under consideration: *Allgemeine Naturgeschichte und Theorie des Himmels*. "Naturgeschichte" is not meant in the usual sense, which is the same as that of its English equivalent "Natural History", but in the special Kantian connotation just discussed. To save lengthy commentaries in translations it might be advisable to introduce here Spencer's term and to render the title by: "Universal Theory of Celestial Evolution". It would then at once become obvious that the main subject is quite different from Wright's.

There is one other passage where Kant draws a dividing line between his views and those of Thomas Wright. From the Hamburg account he had seen that Wright had finished his work with speculations about the centre of the creation, concluding: "Since we must allow it to be far superior to any other point of situation in the known universe, it is highly probable there may be some one body of siderial or earthly substance seated there, where the Divine Presence or some corporeal agent full of all virtues and perfections more immediately presides over His own creation." Such a materialistic conception could hardly appeal to the philosopher in Kant. "We shall leave it to Mr. Wright of Durham", he says, "to determine what is the nature of this foundation stone of the whole creation, and what is to be found upon it." In the "Third Part" of his book Kant himself gives sufficient rein to his imagination to venture conjectures about the nature of the inhabitants of other planets. When, in 1791, a new edition was prepared, to be printed together with a German

---

he would never say anything that he did not think, although he was "thinking many things with the clearest conviction and to his great satisfaction which he would never have the courage to say".

translation of Sir W. Herschel's treatises, Kant did not allow this "Third Part" to be included because of its too hypothetical character; as a young man he was less strict, but even then a localization in space of moral principles was more than the future author of the three *Critiques* could permit.

Another basic difference beween Wright and Kant might be mentioned, as it has apparently not been noticed before. Wright's conception of the universe can be seen from several of his plates. The many star systems he assumed to exist are always depicted as enclosed by spheres or, in cross-section, by circles (in the latter case the "Eye of Providence" may be discerned in the centre of each), and many readers may have wondered what he meant by these boundaries of the star systems (see Fig. 4).* No explanation is given in the *Original Theory*, but he drew a similar diagram for an earlier work, *The Use of the Globes*, and here he stated that his scheme was "founded upon This Hypothesis, That the Stars are so many Suns; that each of these Stars or Suns is attended (as ours is), by a proper number of Planets and Comets; and that each hath a gravitating Power independent of each other", so that "these several Systems cannot interfere with one another". From this passage it is clear that Wright meant by the enveloping spheres represented on his plates the boundaries of the independent forces of gravitation.† This queer idea shows very strikingly what a gap there was between his natural philosophy and that of Kant, who assumed the validity of Newton's law throughout the whole universe, attraction being "unlimited and universal", reaching "to all the distance of nature's infinitude".

Among the many diagrams in Wright's book there are two which are meant not only to be illustrations in a qualitative way, but to help professional astronomers in their studies on the positions of

* In astronomical literature instead of "worlds" or "systems" the expression "universes" or "island universes" frequently occurs. Recently Professor F. C. Leonard of the University of California has protested against it (*Publications of the Astronomical Society of the Pacific*, Vol. 51, No. 302, August 1939): "The word 'universe' does not, logically or etymologically, admit of the plural form. Accordingly the expression 'island universes' (instead of 'island galaxies'), which has been current in astronomical parlance and literature ever since the time of the philosopher Kant, who in effect introduced it, is to be condemned as being both illogical and improper." It would be astonishing if Professor Leonard were right, and Kant, perhaps the most powerful logician the world has seen, had to be blamed for the invention of an illogical term. Actually he never uses the word universe in the plural. He speaks of a plurality of worlds ("Welten", or "Weltordnungen", or "Weltgebäude") in the one Universe ("Universum"). The ugly expression "island universes" seems to be due to W. Herschel who is known to have been a poor writer. Professor Hastie, in his Kant translation, has two or three times the plural of universe where Kant says "Weltgebäude" or "Weltordnungen".

† A similar idea had previously been held by Copernicus. [Ed.]

stars. Wright firmly believed that the "fixed" stars were moving, and in order to enable future astronomers to establish this fact beyond doubt he made an attempt to transmit to them the relative

FIG. 4. "A finite view of Infinity."

positions of the main stars in the Pleiades and in Perseus exactly as they appeared to him. As his fine pictures of these constellations, mentioned above, were obviously not suitable for the delicate task, he supplemented them by geometrical drawings. From Fig. 5, which represents the Pleiades, can be seen the way in which he connected the stars by many straight lines; he considered their positions as the corners of regular triangles, and hoped that any future movements of the stars could easily be detected by the disappearance of such regularities as shown in his plates. It is rather strange, but very

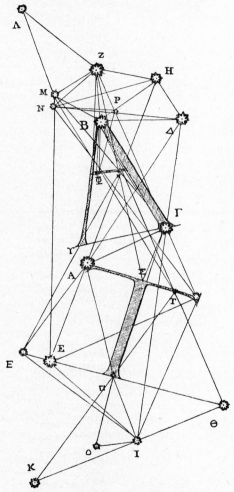

Fig. 5. Diagram of the Pleiades.

characteristic, that he relied entirely on engraved plates for such difficult comparisons, and did not trouble to give numbers for the positions of the stars he had observed. Moreover, if the Pleiades should move as a group—as they actually do—their relative positions would not show any variation from his drawings.

Wright was obviously always happy if he could exchange the pen for the engraving tool; the figures he drew were of no real value for the purpose of observing star movements, but we may perhaps see in them an inkling of the decisive help which today the infinitely more exact photographs of the stars give to astronomy. When modern observatories store thousands of photographic plates for future comparisons they do in principle exactly what Thomas Wright intended with his laboriously prepared copper plates.

To do justice to him and to his peculiarities as an author we must not forget the kind of readers he had to reckon with. The subscribers to his book were the same gentlefolk whom he taught orally as an instructor, and this may explain not only the unnecessarily large number of illustrations but also his habit, so distracting to modern readers, of constantly interrupting his scientific discussion by theological digressions, exhortations, and quotations from poets. The scientific contents of the *Original Theory* could easily have been presented on less than half of its eighty-four pages, and Wright's interesting views on various astronomical questions would then have stood a better chance of being noted by his scientific contemporaries. He was probably completely "original" only in his explanation of the Milky Way, but it is certainly noteworthy that in his book he inclines also to the modern interpretation of Saturn's rings as consisting of small particles. Some writers on astronomy give him credit for the conjecture that "could we view Saturn thro' a Telescope capable of it, we should find his Rings no other than an infinite number of lesser Planets, inferior to those we call his Satellites". Kant, however, who discusses the theoretical difficulties, following from Kepler's law, which beset the assumption of a solid ring, mentions that as early as 1705 Cassini had suggested that Saturn's ring might be a swarm of small satellites. It is quite likely that Wright too, who cared less than Kant for exact references, had seen Cassini's paper. On the other hand, it is possible that he had no forerunners in his interpretation of the nebulae as systems similar to the galaxy, and that this was one of the points in which he influenced Kant— although the Hamburg abstract which the latter saw does not make Wright's opinion clear. In any case, Kant's main argument for this interpretation of the nebulae, viz. their appearance as elliptical figures, is not to be found in Wright's book.

It remains for us briefly to trace the gradual acceptance of Wright's views on the Milky Way by other astronomers.* As

---

* The only other contemporary reaction we have found is a letter in *The Gentleman's Magazine* for 1751 (Vol. 21, p. 315) criticizing several minor points in the *Original Theory*.

mentioned before, his book influenced nobody but Kant, and for a long time Kant's remained equally unknown. Quite independently the German physicist and philosopher J. D. Lambert expressed similar ideas in his *Cosmological Letters* published in 1761; they obtained some popularity but were apparently as unknown as Wright or Kant to W. Herschel when he began to investigate the distribution of the stars by a long series of carefully planned observations. The results were summarized in two papers he submitted to the Royal Society in 1785 in which he proposed a model of the stellar system whose essential feature was its flatness; Herschel assumed it to extend in the direction of the Milky Way five times as far as perpendicularly to this plane.

Herschel is universally recognized as the founder of sidereal astronomy, a science which has grown enormously since his days. The one fundamental fact, however, which he discovered, the disk-like form of the stellar system constituting our galaxy, is still considered as correct in all essential features. And this is just the picture of the universe first proposed by Thomas Wright in his *Original Theory* of 1750!*

For historians of astronomy it was easier to discover Kant and Lambert as forerunners of Herschel than Wright; the latter's name, if mentioned at all, was added only on the strength of Kant's

---

Although the writer ("S.L.") addressed it to Wright personally, no reply from the latter appeared in the Magazine.

* In a later lecture ("Die Erkenntnis des Weltbaus durch Thomas Wright und Immanuel Kant"—"The Elucidation of the Structure of the Universe by Thomas Wright and Immanuel Kant", *Kant-Studien*, Vol. 47, No. 4, 1955/56) Paneth said: "Herschel . . . does not quote his predecessors Wright and Kant anywhere; in the case of Kant this is not astonishing, but it would nevertheless be worth while investigating whether Herschel did not perhaps see Wright's book. In 1760 and 1761 he was employed as music master for the band of the Durham militia, and frequented the houses of that set of landed proprietors who as subscribers provided the financial basis for the publication of Wright's *Original Theory*. As it is also known that even then Herschel was greatly interested in books of this type, it must be regarded as probable that Wright's strikingly gorgeous book did at some time fall into his hands. Whether, however, he remembered it when he later arrived at the same conclusion by quite a different route, is another question; it is known that he rarely quoted his predecessors."

An instance of serendipity has since led to the discovery by Dr. Thomas Sharp of the following remark as item 452 in "A Catalogue of Valuable Printed Books comprising . . . the library . . . of Sir William, Caroline and Sir John Herschel", put up for sale by Sotheby on March 3rd 1958:

Wright (Thomas) An Original Theory or New Hypothesis of The Universe, folding plates, pencil note on page 19, in the hand of Sir William Herschel, half calf, Herschel Library stamp on title, 4to, 1750.

The pencil note reads: "Now proved to be 95 millions". This evidently refers to the distance of the Sun in miles, and since this value was first derived from observations at the Transit of Venus of 1769, the note must have been written after that time. [Ed.]

reference to him. In 1837, however, a second edition of the *Original Theory* was prepared in the United States by the well-known naturalist, C. S. Rafinesque; he wrote in the "Preface of the American Editor": "Our worthy Author has met with total neglect at the hands of his blinded countrymen. We have not yet found him quoted anywhere, and a Philosopher and Astronomer, equal to Plato, Copernic, Newton and Herschel, was to this day nearly unknown, until we found his work, and determined at once to restore him to life and fame."

Rafinesque was right that in England Thomas Wright was completely forgotten. He was mistaken in the hope that his own effort would bring fame to him (his inconspicuous little brochure, published in Philadelphia without any plates, is today of greater rarity than Wright's impressive volume, at least in England, where the British Museum seems to possess the only copy). Rafinesque was carried too far by his enthusiasm in putting Thomas Wright on a level with the greatest names in astronomy, and he did not know that, long before his days, some of Wright's ideas had induced Immanuel Kant to compose in his East Prussian solitude his own theory of the universe, in which he gives full credit to the inspiration received from Wright.

In 1848, Professor De Morgan of University College London re-published in *The Philosophical Magazine* (Vol. 32, p. 241) extracts from Wright's *Original Theory* and submitted that "his name ought to be enrolled in the list of discoverers". One point in which De Morgan fails is the description of Kant's relation to Wright; while continental writers like Arago (Paris), Humboldt (Berlin), and Struve (St. Petersburg) were not familiar with Wright, De Morgan knows of Kant's astronomical work only through Struve and is under the impression that it extends Wright's only in two minor points; he does not seem to be aware of the fact that it is a treatise on cosmic evolution. In 1895, in a new attempt to make Wright's name better known, an address was delivered by Professor Sampson of the Newcastle College of Science* to the Society of Antiquaries of Newcastle upon Tyne; a brief abstract of it is printed in their *Proceedings* (Vol. 7, p. 99). It rests mainly on De Morgan's authority. Richer in material, although mainly focused on Kant, and very well balanced in its judgement, is Professor Hastie's Introduction to his above-mentioned translation of Kant's astronomical writings.

In Allibone's *Dictionary of English Literature* Wright is included, but

---

* Professor R. A. Sampson, F.R.S. (1866–1939), later Astronomer Royal for Scotland. [Ed.]

as a sort of "split personality", the author of *Louthiana* being presented as different from the Thomas Wright "of Durham". In the *Dictionary of National Biography* the paragraph on Thomas Wright ("stated to be 'of Durham' ") is partly based on Allibone's *Dictionary* and partly on the British Museum catalogue; its author does not seem to know the biographies in *The Gentleman's Magazine* or in Fordyce, nor the abstract of the former given by Professor De Morgan in the *Philosophical Magazine*; Wright is primarily mentioned as the author of *Louthiana*, and the importance of the *Theory of the Universe* is not indicated by a single word.

Since the information to be gained from these two biographical standard works is so meagre, it is not too astonishing that references to Wright in astronomical literature are rare, and often beside the point. Many well known textbooks do not mention his name at all, and others do so in the wrong place. As a typical example we may quote the recently published *Astronomy* (New York, 1935) by F. R. Moulton, the co-author of the well-known Chamberlin–Moulton planetesimal theory. Wright's name appears in this excellent textbook only in the section "Hypotheses of Wright and Kant Respecting the Origin of the Planets" in which we read: "Thomas Wright, of England, and Immanuel Kant, of Germany, neither of whom was an astronomer, made bold attempts to reconstruct the past history of the solar system and of the stars". We have seen, however, that Wright dealt exclusively with the present state of the world; so he must not be mentioned in any connection with the evolutionary hypotheses of either Kant or Laplace, but as a precursor of the elder Herschel. It is gratifying to see how well Alexander von Humboldt, in his *Kosmos*, lives up to his reputation of encyclopaedic knowledge by his very brief but perfectly correct reference to Wright's merits. "What Wright, Kant and Lambert, by conclusions based on reasoning, had anticipated about the general system of the world and the distribution of matter in space, was studied by Sir William Herschel by the safe procedure of observation and measurement." Deservedly Wright is heading here the list of these illustrious men.

In a minor point even Humboldt's statement does not do full justice to Wright; although not going so far as Moulton by denying him explicitly the name of an astronomer, it ranges him in opposition to practical astronomical workers. We know, however, from passages in his *Clavis Coelestis* and *Original Theory*, and from a few contributions about comets to *The Gentleman's Magazine* for the years

1742 and 1748, that he was an enthusiastic observer of the stars. Allan's biographical sketch provides no information as to the instruments Wright was able to use, but from himself we hear occasionally that he saw a celestial object through a "tube of two convex glasses", a "very good reflector", a "one Foot reflecting Telescope", and even a "five Foot Focus Reflector". One of the finest plates in his *Original Theory* depicts a part of the Milky Way as seen through a telescope, and is a very interesting prelude to the illustrations with which readers of popular astronomical books have been lavishly treated since the invention of telescopic photography. Near the end of his life, living then in very comfortable circumstances, Wright planned the erection of a private observatory and built for this purpose not far from his house a small tower with gothic windows, but died before its completion. The tower still stands, on the highest point of Middleston (near Bishop Auckland), and must have puzzled many by its perfect uselessness (Fig. 6).*

It is not without interest to ask on this occasion how much Kant knew from his own observations about the starry sky. Probably not more than can be seen with the naked eye; we do not remember any reference to a telescopic observation made by himself, and it is doubtful if he ever had any opportunity for it. The university observatory at Königsberg, made famous by its first director, F. W. Bessel, was only founded six years after Kant's death, and in East Prussia scientifically interested persons in possession of telescopes were certainly not so frequent as in the England of Thomas Wright. In eighteenth century Italy, France, and England natural philosophy, on Newtonian lines, was a hobby with elegant men and, especially, women. Witness, e.g., the wide circulation of Count Algarotti's *Neutonianismo per le Dame*; the well-known part played not only by Voltaire but, independently, by his hostess in the castle of Cirey, the Marquise du Chatelet, in answering the question set for competition by the Paris Academy about the nature of heat; and Thomas Wright's great success as a tutor of fashionable ladies. Kant, in spite of his, in many respects, very progressive and liberal ideas, was himself no less opposed to this sort of feminism than his countrymen. By way of contrast to Thomas Wright's persistent efforts to teach noble ladies mathematics and astronomy we should like to quote here Kant's opinion in middle life (from his *Observations on the Feeling of the Beautiful and Sublime*): "It will not be necessary for women to know more of the cosmos than is necessary to make the aspect of

---

* The author wishes to thank Dr. G. H. Christie for placing at his disposal his local knowledge, and his car, for a photographic excursion to Thomas Wright's residence.

the sky touching to them on a fine night, after they have grasped, to a certain extent, that there are more worlds, and on them more creatures of beauty, to be found".

Durham City seems to have been nearer to Kant's than to Wright's opinion on this point. In the summer of 1740 the latter visited the North of England and then proved, as his biographer sadly remarks,

Fig. 6. Westerton Folly, which Wright built and proposed to fit up as a private observatory.

the truth of the saying "a prophet has no honour in his own country". He published "proposals for a Course of Lectures of Natural Philosophy at Durham; which exhibition held him five weeks, but was very thinly attended". Amongst the names of his listeners as recorded by his biographer there is no lady. Durham seems to have appreciated him better as an adviser on questions of artistic taste; according to a statement by Professor Chevallier, the ornamental battlements with finials upon the western towers of the Cathedral have been executed in accordance with a design by Wright.

Allan, the author of Wright's obituary notice, also gives hardly any information about Wright's serious studies. All he has to say in praise of the *Original Theory* is just: "it is illuminated with a great many plates"; but he was at least interested in these plates and, as we have said, purchased the original coppers out of Wright's estate. He also bought his collection of pictures and prints, but a peculiar misfortune seems to have prevented the survival of any of these relics. Allan's collection passed into the possession of the Newcastle Literary and Philosophical Society, and it is not unlikely that they contained books and pictures, perhaps also instruments, from Thomas Wright's house, but a fire destroyed much of the Society's property in 1893, and nothing relating to Wright can be found there today. His house in Byer's Green is still standing, no longer as the elegant residence of a retired gentleman but as three small flats; it is closely surrounded by cheap houses which take the place of Thomas Wright's beloved gardens and orchards. In his days no house was less than a hundred yards from his own. The west terrace on which he liked to dine in the open air has also vanished, so that it is not very easy to recognize in the drab "Byer's Green Hall" of today (see Fig. 7) the eighteenth-century residence of which he himself once gave a glowing description in a letter to a friend. Still less has survived of the "composition of dials" Thomas Wright erected on the pier at the mouth of Sunderland harbour; it must have been a substantial piece, because he received a gratuity of 20 guineas for it, and a description was published at the expense of the town; but the pier was reconstructed in 1786, and nothing is known about the fate of Thomas Wright's sundials.

One structure, however, seems to have been preserved exactly in the state in which Thomas Wright left it: the "gothic tower on one of the highest hills in the country", as he calls it (see Fig. 6), which we have already mentioned. It belongs to the little village of Westerton, two miles distant from Wright's residence in Byer's Green. It was meant to become his private observatory, but was never used as such. Most likely it was never used for anything, if we disregard its service as an observation post during the last war. This seems to be implied by the name "Westerton Folly" under which it is known locally, by the great difficulty encountered in an endeavour to discover its present owner and to get access to it, and by its complete emptiness. The spiral wooden staircase within lacks a few steps and is far from safe, but whoever climbs to the top of the tower will be surprised by the magnificent view it commands of the surrounding countryside, with Durham Cathedral in the distance. Its place was certainly well chosen.

The University of Durham is celebrating the 200th anniversary of the publication of Thomas Wright's *Original Theory* by an exhibition of his books, one of them existing only as a single copy recently purchased for Durham, and the unveiling of a memorial tablet at his observatory tower. It is also hoped to invite speakers from other universities to give addresses on Thomas Wright and the general

Fig. 7. Wright's home, Byer's Green Hall.

scientific background of his time. Nobody will try to follow Rafinesque and put Thomas Wright on the same level as Newton, but it is felt that too few people still know exactly what Wright's merits are, and that his *Original Theory* has become a not unimportant link in the history of astronomy. What Rafinesque valued most, the florid passages in Wright's last letter on theological and moral principles, are just those which Kant treats with hardly concealed irony and dismisses briefly as "fanatical enthusiasm". Neither Rafinesque nor Wright's friend Allan could "restore him to life and fame", because what they admired, and what no doubt Wright himself considered important, was either irrelevant or could not stand serious criticism. On the other hand, his one great idea, the explanation of the Milky Way, does not seem to have occupied his thoughts in later years; he never returned to it, and the "useful applications" quite obviously escaped him. It was only Kant who saw them, and who could therefore tell what was of permanent value in Wright's book.

BOOKS PUBLISHED BY THOMAS WRIGHT

Pannauticon, The Universal Mariner's Magazine, 1734. A treatise on navigation, sponsored by the Navy and published by subscription. Strangely enough, no copy and not even a record of this book could be found in any library, although the list of subscribers (printed in *Clavis Pannautici*) is rather long and one of them ordered no less than nine sets.

As an introduction to this presumably large volume Wright published at the same time a small booklet:

Clavis Pannautici, or a Key to the Universal Mariner's Magazine, 1734. The only copy that could be traced belongs to Durham Observatory. On the title page the author is given only as T.W., Student in Astronomy, but the full name is printed at the end of the dedication to the King.

The Universal Vicissitude of Seasons, 1737. This book seems to exist only in the one large copy, which originally belonged to Bishop Thurlow of Durham and is since 1948 in the possession of the Durham University Library. Diagrams and ornaments are most carefully drawn and coloured by hand, so that this curious and impressive work, in spite of the use of copper plates, is nearer to a manuscript than to a printed book.

The Use of the Globes, 1740. A small book written at the request of John Senex, F.R.S., to serve as an instruction for the use of his terrestrial and celestial globes. Now rare.

Clavis Coelestis, Being the Explication of a Diagram entituled a Synopsis of the Universe: or, the Visible World Epitomized, 1742. A popular introduction to astronomy, with four large plates, each almost exactly 2 × 3 ft. These plates are of such an awkward size that some libraries (for instance in London those of the Royal Society and the Royal Astronomical Society) possess only copies of the book without any figures; others have copies which contain some of the plates, usually folded and badly damaged. Durham Observatory owns a copy, from the library of Bishop Thurlow, in which three of the four plates, which contain several figures, have been carefully cut and bound with the book. Moreover, thanks to the expert and friendly help of Mr. Cyril E. Kenney, London, the Durham University Library was able recently to acquire a set of the four plates in the original size and in perfect condition; as one of them cannot be cut into smaller figures, it is missing even in the otherwise excellent copy just mentioned. Since this plate seems to be practically unknown, it is reproduced here (Fig. 8). In very small letters (not visible in the

FIG. 8. Comparison of the various astronomical systems. Engraving by Thomas Wright for *Clavis Coelestis*.

reduced size) Thomas Wright is mentioned as the engraver; it certainly does credit to his skill.

Louthiana, 1748. A description of the antiquities in the Irish county of Louth. Some of the illustrations are signed by Wright. This became his most popular book and copies exist in many libraries; not all of them contain the list of subscribers. A second edition appeared in 1758.

An Original Theory, or New Hypothesis of the Universe, 1750. Wright's most important publication. Three copies in Durham libraries; a few in other libraries and in private hands. An "American edition" was published with notes by C. S. Rafinesque, but without any plates, in 1837.

Universal Architecture—Book I. *Six Original Designs of Arbours*, and Book 2. *Six Original Designs of Grottos*, 1755. Already in 1860 both books were described as scarce. A copy is preserved in the New York Public Library.

The Longitude Discover'd without use of Graduated Instruments, 1773. This work is mentioned in Wright's Newcastle manuscripts, Volume III. The New York Public Library owns a copy of this rare book.

MANUSCRIPTS BY THOMAS WRIGHT WHICH ARE KNOWN TO BE STILL IN EXISTENCE

In the custody of the British Museum are three of Wright's manuscripts, viz.

1. *The Early Journal of Thomas Wright of Durham* (British Museum ADD.MSS. 15627). This manuscript was the main source for two not very satisfactory biographies (Bibliography* No. 1 and 8). It has been edited twice (Bibliography No. 6 and 15).

2. *Observations on . . . Remains of Antiquity . . . Taken on a Tour through England* (British Museum ADD.MSS. 15628). According to Mr. E. Birley, Durham University, some of the drawings contained in this work and in the Wright letters which are in the possession of the Royal Society are still of considerable value to archaeology, since in Wright's days many of the objects were better preserved than they are now, and he depicted them very carefully.

3. *Observations on . . . Remains of Antiquity in Ireland* (British Museum ADD.MSS. 33771). This was meant as a sequel to *Louthiana*. The manuscript was practically ready to go to the printer, but was never

---

* The Bibliography referred to in this list of manuscripts is that which immediately follows, not the main Bibliography on p. 273. [Ed.]

published. Some drawings from it are reproduced in No. 6 of the Bibliography.

The Newcastle Public Libraries possess *Eight volumes of various Thomas Wright manuscripts*, bound without any order. They contain scientific observations and theories, geometrical problems, archaeological notes, mythological essays, drawings, and poems by Thomas Wright and others. The authorship of these poems which are all written in his own hand is not always easily recognizable. (See *Durham University Journal, New Series*, Vol. 12, pp. 19 and 76, 1950.) Some of the contents are mentioned in No. 15 of the Bibliography.

Durham University Library has recently acquired the manuscript of *Pansophia, or an Essay towards a General Compendium of Universal Knowledge*. It tries to systematize all human activities. As frontispiece a tree of knowledge is drawn by pen.

The library of the Royal Society of London has a few *Letters by Thomas Wright* on astronomical and archaeological subjects, and the Royal Astronomical Society in London a calligraphic letter, "To the Excellencies the Lords Justices of the Kingdom of Ireland", in which Wright proposes to draw an accurate map of the ports, rocks, etc., of the shore of Ireland in the interest of navigation.

BIBLIOGRAPHY OF WRITINGS ON THOMAS WRIGHT

1. "A Sketch of the Character of Mr. Thomas Wright, late of Byer's Green Lodge, in the County of Durham" (*The Gentleman's Magazine*, **63**, 6 and 126, 1793). The author of this anonymous article, George Allan of Darlington, had been a friend of Wright's and could base his statements on Wright's unpublished manuscripts which he had acquired. His source is largely the British Museum Additional Manuscript 15627(see above), but he was able to add a few personal remarks and is about the only source of information for Wright's later years. The various paragraphs concerning Wright in the standard biographical dictionaries and topographical works (on Darlington, Bishop Auckland, the county of Durham, etc.) are mostly copied verbatim from this article. Wright's portrait, which is prefixed, is similar to the engraving reproduced in No. 10, but much cruder; it was probably copied from it.

2. "Mr. Wright's Description of his Villa at Byer's Green" (*The Gentleman's Magazine*, **63**, 213 1793). This very characteristic essay by Wright, written in the form of a letter to a friend, was published as an appendix to the above article. The manuscript of the essay

is still preserved in Volume VI of the Newcastle manuscripts, and a comparison shows that the printed article contains a few misprints.

That Wright's villa and its peculiar collections impressed occasional visitors is shown by a reference to which Mr. E. Birley has kindly drawn my attention. Thomas Pennant describes in his *Tour from Abston-Moor to Harrowgate and Brinham Craggs* (1804) a lunch he had in 1773 with Thomas Wright in his home, and the many interesting sketches shown to him there.

3. De Morgan, Augustus, "An Account of the Speculations of Thomas Wright of Durham" (*Philosophical Magazine*, (3), **32**, 241 1848).

4. Sampson, Ralph Allen, "Thomas Wright, the Durham Astronomer" (*Proceedings of the Society of Antiquaries of Newcastle upon Tyne*, VIII, 99, January 1895 to December 1896).

5. Hastie, W., *Kant's Cosmogony*, Glasgow, James Maclehose and Sons, 1900.

About the merits of De Morgan's, Sampson's and Hastie's contributions, see No. 9 (below).

6. Buckley, James, "The Journal of Thomas Wright, Author of Louthiana" (*Louth Archaeological Journal*, II, Part 2, 165 1909). Mainly an edition of Wright's autobiography, but containing also other biographical remarks.

7. Shapley, H. and Howarth, Helen E., *A Source Book in Astronomy*, McGraw-Hill, New York, 1929. In one chapter Thomas Wright's speculations on the structure of the Milky Way are reprinted, but unfortunately made unintelligible by the omission of the figure to which he constantly refers and the substitution of an unrelated one.

8. Gushee, Vera, "Thomas Wright of Durham, Astronomer" (*Isis*, **33**, 197 1941). This article fails to understand Wright's *Original Theory*. The portrait added shows no similarity with the authentic copper engraving in a Durham copy of *Clavis Coelestis* and seems to depict a much older man; it probably represents another Thomas Wright.

9. Paneth, F. A., "Thomas Wright of Durham and Immanuel Kant" (*Durham University Journal, New Series*, **2**, 111 1941; reprinted, somewhat abbreviated, in *The Observatory*, **64**, 71 1941). Deals mainly with the relationship of Kant's ideas to Wright's.

10. Paneth, F. A., "Thomas Wright of Durham" (*Endeavour*, **9**, 117 1950). Contains reproductions of a portrait of Thomas Wright and of illustrations from the *Original Theory*, and photographs of his house and observatory tower.

11. Paneth, F. A., "Thomas Wright's Original Theory of the Milky

Way" (*Nature*, **166,** 49 1950). A report on the bicentenary celebrations of the publication of the *Original Theory*, arranged by the University of Durham on June 2nd, 1950.

12. Paneth, F. A., "Thomas Wright and Immanuel Kant, Pioneers in Stellar Astronomy" (*Proc. Roy. Inst.*, **35,** 114 1951).

13. Paneth, F. A., "Thomas Wright and Immanuel Kant, Pioneers in Stellar Astronomy" (*Nature*, **167,** 1014 1951). Identical with the first part of No. 12.

14. Dingle, Herbert, "Thomas Wright's Astronomical Heritage" (*Annals of Science*, **6,** 404 1950). An address delivered in the University of Durham at its bicentenary celebration of the publication of the *Original Theory*.

15. Hughes, Edward, "The Early Journal of Thomas Wright of Durham" (*Annals of Science*, **7,** 1 1951). An edition of Wright's autobiography by an authority on the eighteenth-century history of northern England, with many explanatory notes and corrections of mistakes made by previous writers.

It is to be hoped that some day a comprehensive biography of Thomas Wright will be written. His work can best be studied at Durham, whose libraries possess copies of nearly all of his books, and many of his manuscripts, either in the original or in photostats.

13 | Thomas Wright's "Original Theory" of the Milky Way

A celebration in honour of Thomas Wright of Durham was held on June 2, 1950, in the Science Laboratories of the University of Durham. Different from most historical celebrations, its purpose was not to recall a memorable date in the life of a famous man but to direct the attention of wider circles to an astronomer much less known than he deserves to be. The *Encyclopedia Britannica* does not mention him at all, and paragraphs concerning him in biographical dictionaries are very meagre and inaccurate. Born in Byer's Green, a little village near Durham City, he spent most of his life there and called himself always Thomas Wright "of Durham"; so two hundred years after the publication in 1750 of his most important book, *An Original Theory or New Hypothesis of the Universe,* in which he gives an explanation of the Milky Way, the University of Durham made this attempt to revive his memory.

The celebrations were introduced by Professor H. Dingle, of University College London. In a lecture on "Thomas Wright's Astronomical Heritage", he examined carefully all sources of information which might possibly have influenced Wright in his astronomical conceptions and especially in his interpretation of the Milky Way. He came to the conclusion that all Wright's forerunners had considered the Milky Way as one of the constellations on the celestial sphere; that since Galileo this luminous band was known to consist of many stars, and that from one author—Dr. Derham, whom Wright mentions—he might have learnt that the strange appearance of the galaxy presented an unsolved problem; but the direction in which Wright found the explanation is not foreshadowed anywhere and his publication was in the fullest sense original.

Following the first speaker, Professor F. A. Paneth, of the University of Durham, discussed the two reasons for which Thomas Wright ought to be remembered in the history of astronomy. He was the originator of the idea of the disk-shaped universe; it occurred to him that if our Sun with its planets were situated in the interior of a flat stellar system, on purely geometrical grounds we would see many more stars when looking in the direction of the plane of the disk than in any other direction. In this case there would be in Nature no crowding together of stars in the Milky Way, but this celestial circle would only be an optical effect, due to the peculiar form of the stellar system to which we belong.

Essentially the same interpretation of the Milky Way was given thirty-five years later by W. Herschel, who, without any knowledge

FIG. 9. F. A. Paneth at dedication of Wright's Observatory.

of Thomas Wright's book, based it on the convincing results of his star-gauging in various directions of the sky. There can be no doubt that the priority of this fundamental idea belongs to Wright; but since his *Original Theory* had no direct influence on the development of modern astronomy, this historical fact alone would have not more than a limited interest for specialists. There is, however, a second, much stronger, argument for remembering Wright: his book was the spark which fired the imagination of Immanuel Kant to develop his famous theory of celestial evolution. This great scientific cosmogony would probably never have been written if Kant had not seen, by mere chance, an abstract of Wright's book in a German periodical. Wright's conception of the universe was purely geometrical, but Kant considered immediately the forces acting therein; the disk-like shape of the stellar system seemed to him proof of its rotation—a conclusion since verified—and the elliptical nebulae he interpreted correctly as external galaxies. (Kant was the first to use the word in the plural!) The idea of cosmic evolution which is the essential part of Kant's theory follows almost logically from Wright's assumption of the flat universe.

After the two lectures, an excursion was made to a strong stone tower at Westerton, about seven miles from Durham, which for more than a century has been known to the local population as the "Westerton Folly", its original purpose being completely forgotten (see Figs. 6 and 9). Now it bears a freshly fixed tablet with the inscription:

> This Observatory Tower was erected by
> **THOMAS WRIGHT**
> born at Byer's Green 1711, died there 1786
> To commemorate his treatise
> **THEORY OF THE UNIVERSE**
> published 1750, this tablet was placed here
> by the University of Durham, 1950.

An exhibition in the University of Durham Library of Thomas Wright's published works, of manuscripts or photostat copies of manuscripts from the British Museum, the Royal Society, the Royal Astronomical Society and the Newcastle Public Library, and of drawings and pencil sketches representing a great variety of subjects, gave visitors a good impression of the genius of this versatile and highly original man.

It is hoped that his autobiography, the manuscript of which is still extant, will be edited this year by a competent scholar;* it tells a very human, and in parts touching, story of a boy whose early love for the study of mathematics and astronomy was so much opposed by his father that he ran away from home, penniless, but carrying with him the load of all those books which his father had not burned. It narrates how, against many odds, he slowly succeeded in having his works printed and getting access to the houses of the nobility as a teacher of astronomy, which in those days was a fashionable hobby with the ladies. It finishes with the description of the stately house he built in his native village and in which he died in 1786, too isolated, it seems, to have heard before his end of Herschel's fundamental paper presented to the Royal Society a year earlier, which proved the correctness of Wright's idea about the nature of the Milky Way.

* See item 15 of the Bibliography of Writings on Thomas Wright (p. 119). [Ed.]

Meteorites

FOREWORD

Paneth's interest in meteorites probably arose from the realization that they afforded a very useful field for the application of his method of radioactive dating, but it is characteristic of his general approach that, having once been stimulated, it extended to all aspects of meteoritic research. These articles, while they illustrate the attraction which the larger cosmological and historical problems held for him, show at the same time the care which he spent on seeming trifles. He held accuracy to be no less important in small than in large matters. The discussion of Chladni's St. Petersburg visit, for example, was a detail which he was determined to settle before entering hospital, both for his own amusement and as a playful provocation to his colleagues. As he said, if he did not write it nobody would.

This article, like those on the Breitscheid meteorite and on the discovery of the Widmanstätten patterns, was published posthumously; the manuscript of the last-named, in German, under the title, "Die Entdeckung und frühesten Abbildungen der Widmanstättenschen Figuren", was completed by Paneth just before his death. The Editors wish to record their thanks to Mr. C. Fahy, of University College London, for the translation into English of the Italian text quoted in that article. Obscurities in it are due to the original printed version, which was a probably imperfect translation into Italian of Thomson's English.

There has been an interesting sequel to Paneth's work on this article. A brilliant conjecture by Dr. Otto Kurz, of the Warburg Institute, University of London, has led him to the discovery of the following facts:

1. William Thomson, born at Worcester, went to Oxford in 1776 at the age of 15. He was enrolled at Christ Church in 1778; became B.A. in 1780, M.A. in 1783, B.Med. in 1785, and D.Med. in 1786, and in that year was elected a Fellow of the Royal Society. In 1787 he is recorded as having lectured on mineralogy at Oxford. As with so many of his contemporaries, his interests were very wide. He corresponded with fellow-scholars on astronomy and botany; he enquired, for example, of Sir Joseph Banks: "Could you procure for me any of the malleable Mexican iron, at a moderate price?" (the meteoritic origin of this iron was then still unknown). In September 1790, however, his brilliant career came to a sudden end. He resigned from the Royal Society, as rumour put it, "for an offence which happily the public opinion in this country never forgives". He left Oxford, "never to return". Nothing further is heard of him.

2. Four years later we find, in Naples, "Guglielmo Thomson, professore in Oxford", who lived in the palace of General Acton, moved in the circle of the British ambassador, Sir William Hamilton, and was in close contact with Italian scholars. In the same year Soldani sent Guglielmo Thomson specimens of the stones fallen "from the sky" near Siena. Soldani had set out to prove that the stones had really fallen from the sky and were of atmospheric origin. Contemporary critics were sceptical, or downright hostile. Hamilton was convinced that the stones were of volcanic origin: Thomson was rather doubtful, but nevertheless spent months analysing the stones. In September 1794 he discovered in them minute quantities of "iron of perfect malleability" (they were stone, not iron, meteorites). By a fortunate coincidence a certain Captain Tiharsky, who was then in charge of the cannon foundry at Naples, was able to inform Thomson of certain meteorites from Croatia which also contained malleable iron. In 1808 Thomson published the paper, "Sul ferro malleabile trovato da Pallas in Siberia", which Paneth here brings to light.

There seems little doubt that these two persons are identical. Apparently William Thomson, on removing to Italy, translated his Christian name into the Italian form, and continued the researches which had interested him in England. It is to be hoped that further facts will come to light concerning this interesting investigator.

We are much indebted to Dr. Kurz for permission to include this information.

During his lifetime, Paneth amassed a considerable collection of meteorites which, unlike most collections, he wished to be made available for experimental research. Accordingly, an "F.A. Paneth Meteorite Trust" has been set up, the terms of which are given in Appendix II.

He also left a large collection of literature connected with meteorites, containing a number of rare items, which he wished to be made freely available for the use of competent persons interested in the subject. It has been carefully catalogued, with cross-references, and has since been supplemented by the Story Maskelyne collection of some 150 papers on meteorites, mainly issued during the period 1800–1900, and by the co-operation of current workers who have continued to augment it by offprints. Arrangements are being made for the housing of the whole collection in an appropriate place.

14 | The Origin of Meteorites

There are three classes of meteorites: irons, stones, and glasses. Reports of pieces of iron or stone falling from the sky have come down to us from times immemorial; the interpretation of certain small lumps of glass found on the surface of the Earth as meteoritic belongs to this century.

In discussing the origin of these bodies we have to proceed in two steps: first we have to make sure that they have actually fallen to the Earth from the atmosphere; then, if this is established, we naturally want to find out how they reached the atmosphere.

Although it is true that as far back as historical records go we find good, and sometimes astonishingly accurate, descriptions of falling meteorites, official science has only for about one hundred and forty years been convinced of the facts. Long before man learned to smelt iron ore he used meteorites for the manufacture of iron tools, often fully aware of the precious metal's celestial origin. To quote just one instance: in a list compiled by a Hittite king more than three thousand years ago, he states that his treasury contained gold from a certain city, silver, copper, and bronze from mines, and "black iron of heaven from the sky".

This early differentiation of iron from the earthly metals is certainly very striking, and it is one of the most astonishing facts in the history of science that this knowledge of the falling, and of the nature, of meteorites was completely lost in the early days of modern science. By the eighteenth century learned men became too enlightened to believe the stories of fiery bodies coming down from a cloudless sky and burying themselves, after loud explosions, in the ground. None of their ranks had seen the phenomenon for himself, but as no more than about five meteorites a year are observed to fall, it would have been an astonishing coincidence if scientists had just been on the spot; when, after a fall had occurred, the *corpus delicti* was shown to them, they usually declared it to be an ordinary stone, and that the eye-witnesses must have been mistaken. Leading in this scepticism was the French Academy of Sciences, then the highest known authority in all matters scientific. So strong was their influence that even such an original mind as Lavoisier, when a meteoritic stone (with the exact record of its fall) was given to him, failed to recognize its peculiar nature and preferred, in the report sent to the French Academy by him and two colleagues, to alter the statements of the witness to fit the explanation that a stone on the ground had been struck by lightning. This is perhaps the most surprising feature, that no record, however well substantiated, could shake the scientists in their denial. On one occasion a whole village, backed by the mayor, sent in a written and signed statement about the fall of a meteorite. The Paris scientists were deeply shocked at their credulity, and simply declared the described facts as "physically impossible".

Worse than that: meteorites in collections were discarded all over Europe as shameful relics of a superstitious past. The newly appointed curator of the Imperial Collections in Vienna, the eminent mineralogist I. von Born, discovered a drawer labelled "Stones fallen from Heaven", and, trained in the new school of thought, with a scornful laugh ordered their removal.

In order to understand such a stubborn scepticism we must remind ourselves that there were, of course, many mistaken ideas held by common folk about objects falling from the sky, and superstition was so abhorred by the scientific societies that they rejected every story which seemed to lend support to it. It needed certainly special qualities to discriminate in this field between invented miracles and faithful descriptions, and I always thought it a significant fact that the one man who succeeded in reviving the faith and interest of scientists in meteorites, E. F. F. Chladni, although well known as a physicist for his distinguished work on acoustics, was educated as a lawyer. When, in 1794, he published in Riga a German paper on meteorites, he had not seen a single one, far less witnessed a fall; he had, however, read reports, and his juridically trained intelligence detected, and defended, the trustworthiness of those accounts of eye-witnesses which dealt with real meteorite falls, as distinguished from superstitious fabrications.

Chladni—who, by the way, lived as a private man and never occupied any university position—did not at first succeed in changing the attitude of the official scientists, least of all in France. But heaven itself now took a hand in the game and showered in 1803 several thousand stones over a large part of the country not far from Paris. The Academy, on the request of the Ministry of the Interior, had to take notice and sent down their member Biot who investigated, and at last acknowledged, the reality of an occurrence of which many hundreds of people were witnesses. In collecting their reports as well as the stones he did a very sound and reasonable piece of work, although the praise showered upon him by his colleagues on his return, and the position he occupies in French scientific literature as the great explorer who discovered the existence of meteorites, may seem to us somewhat exaggerated.

To date there are reliable reports on the fall of only some 40 iron meteorites, and about 550 falls of stones (if we neglect those of which

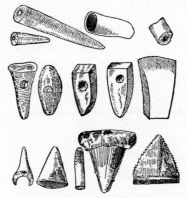

FIG. 10. Thunderbolts (after K. Gesner; 1565).

no specimens have come down to us). The meteorite collections in museums contain, however, irons from well over 400 other localities which were not observed to fall, but were simply found and recognized as meteoritic. Can we rely on this indirect evidence? Generally speaking, the assumption of an unobserved fall from the sky is a last-measure resource when all other explanations of the presence of an object somewhere on the surface of the Earth fail. Under the name of "thunderbolts" stone implements were supposed to have this celestial origin as long as people did not recognize them for the work of prehistoric man; they shared this distinction with belemnites and sharks' teeth, as can be seen for instance from the illustrations copied from a work by the famous Swiss naturalist Konrad von Gesner in the sixteenth century (see Fig. 10). The real meteorites were conspicuous by their absence from Gesner's pictures, and from those of his followers, of objects fallen from the sky.

Chladni's paper of 1794 is remarkable also in this respect. He draws attention to a large lump of metallic iron which half a century earlier a Cossack to his great astonishment had found in Siberia on the top of a mountain, far away from any place of iron smelting, and which later a scientific traveller, Pallas, had seen. Chladni knew Pallas's report on this mass (specimens of which can now be inspected in nearly every natural history museum) and, widely read as he was, he remembered a story (which the learned writer of the article himself emphatically refused to believe) of a big iron mass said to have fallen from the sky near Hraschina in Croatia in 1751. By the combination of careful criticism and bold speculation so characteristic of him, he arrived at the conclusion not only that this story was true, but that the origin of the erratic iron block in Siberia was the same: that it too had fallen from the sky!

Chladni was right in both respects. The careful investigation of the supposed meteoritic masses which he recommends at the end of his paper has been carried out, and since we know now that meteoritic irons have definite characteristics which distinguish them from terrestrial irons, the celestial origin of the Croatian and of the Siberian masses is proved beyond any doubt.

Stone meteorites are more difficult to identify, but as so many stones have been seen to fall, about 200 finds have by analogy been recognized as of meteoritic origin.

In the case of the third group of meteorites, the glass meteorites—or "tektites" as they are called, from the Greek word for a molten mass—we are in a less favourable position. There is not a single reliable report of a piece of glass falling from the sky, and it is, therefore, not astonishing that many scientists refused (and that some still refuse) to believe that the glasses of various size, shape, and colour which are found scattered over definite areas (in Bohemia and Moravia, Australia, Indo-China, and four or five other districts) are to be classed amongst the meteoritic bodies (see Fig. 11). This idea has "but little attraction to anyone at all acquainted with meteorites", to quote the words of a former keeper of the British Museum collections. But whether we like the idea or not, as long as all theories trying to explain the occurrence of these glass pieces either as products of human manufacture or as terrestrial formations can easily be disproved, there is no alternative left but to assume that they are of extra-terrestrial origin. We may use the same argument by which in 1803 the chemist de Fourcroy tried to convince his still sceptical colleagues in the French Academy of the reality of stone meteorites: "By eliminating the absurd or impossible one finds oneself compelled to adopt what would previously have appeared to be almost incredible". Only the hypothesis of a celestial origin can explain for instance that millions of rounded black pieces of a siliceous glass, of an average weight of one gram, are strewn over the central and southern part of the whole Australian continent, thus being distributed over an area of more than two million square miles, as shown by Dr. C. Fenner of the University of Adelaide.

Fig. 11. Glass meteorites.

While, even in the case of the tektites, it is fairly simple to prove that they must have come down from the atmosphere, the real difficulties of our subject begin when we try to answer the question: whence do meteorites reach the atmosphere?

It is only natural that as soon as the reality of meteorite falls had found official sanction, all sorts of theories were put forward about the origin of these heavy masses which so unexpectedly come out of the air. Chladni was from the beginning very positive that meteorites enter the terrestrial atmosphere as solid bodies from outside; in this respect he accepted views expressed as early as 1714 about the substance of fireballs by the great man whom this lecture commemorates, Edmond Halley (taking exception, however, to Halley's belief that their apparent motion was merely caused by the Earth's revolution). But for a considerable while this idea found no favour even with those who accepted Chladni's statement as far as the facts of the falls were concerned. The first French book on the new subject, written by Joseph Izarn in 1803 and dedicated (in the republican style of those days) to the "citoyen" Laplace, bears the telling title *Lithologie Atmosphérique*; Chladni's views are refuted and the theory expounded that meteorites are rocks, formed in the atmosphere out of metallic and stony vapours, which, as soon as they have consolidated, naturally fall to earth—a very strange idea to us, but not so unnatural in those days. The etymological connection between "meteor" and "meteorology" can remind us that falling stars and fireballs were likewise considered by most scientists of this period as atmospheric phenomena—"fiery" meteors, as opposed to the "aqueous" ones which we know as rain, snow, hail, and so on. Even Halley was in later years in favour of such an atmospheric theory of fireballs; he thought that "sulphureous Vapours" might "congregate" and, "gradually contracting themselves into a narrower compass, might lie like a Train of Gunpowder in the Ether, till catching fire by some internal Ferment" the "Flame would be communicated to its continued parts, and so run on like a Train fir'd".

A few years after Izarn's book (1812), when Bigot de Morogues wrote his comprehensive *Mémoire Historique et Physique sur les Chutes des Pierres*, the theory of the atmospheric production of meteorites had been recognized by most scientists as untenable. The fact that Laplace had declared it not impossible that they might have been ejected from the craters of the Moon was sufficient for some to take this origin for granted; others thought that in earlier, more vigorous days terrestrial volcanoes might have performed this feat. This hypothesis, according to which meteorites falling on the Earth are returning to their original home, appeared later in a modified form: the volcanic activity of the Earth was considered insufficient, but meteorites were supposed to be part of the material which left our Earth when the Moon was born. To another possible source pointed Olbers's idea, that the asteroids were scattered fragments of a planet once filling the gap between Mars and Jupiter; Chladni, for instance, thought it not unreasonable to consider meteorites as planetary fragments, although he favoured still more the opposite view that they were part of primordial cosmic matter which had failed to be incorporated in any of the big celestial objects. When, largely due to the work of Schiaparelli, the close relationship of meteor showers and comets was established, meteorites too were by many supposed to be of cometary origin. On the other hand, when it seemed proved that a large proportion of meteors are not connected with comets but arrive from interstellar spaces, the same distant place of birth was ascribed to meteorites; all the more so as it was frequently stated as a result of meteor observations that the brighter and bigger the fireball, the less doubt was permissible as to its extra-solar origin.

The number of theories proposed about the genesis of meteorites, of which the preceding paragraph is no complete record, is actually so great that already in 1886, in an address to the American Association for the Advancement of Science, H. A. Newton apologized for having no new hypothesis to give, because nearly all possible ones had already been put forth; but, he continued, "science may be advanced by rejecting bad hypotheses as well as by forming good ones". If an astronomer, and an authority on the subject, more than half a century ago could do no better than review ideas suggested before, it would certainly not be fair to expect a chemist of today to contribute something original. Besides, even if an author believes himself to be the first to advance a certain theory he may be mistaken; if the light of historical studies is thrown on "new" scientific conceptions, more frequently than not they bear out the truth of Goethe's saying: "Every bright thought has already occurred to somebody; the whole point is to think it again".

It is perhaps still too early to assign a definite birth-place to meteorites; but we may at least hope to be able to decide whether they originated in our solar system, or are "messengers from the world of the fixed stars". The first view has been advocated by geologists for the last seventy years; during the same period the latter was in favour with a great number of astronomers. The arguments of these two groups were so different that they usually confined themselves to stating their own and neglecting those of the opponents which were outside their interests. I shall try tonight to discuss equally those of the geologists as well as astronomers—helped, I am afraid, in this effort, only by the doubtful advantage that I am neither the one nor the other. I need hardly say how deeply conscious I am of the inadequacy of my training; my excuse for this attempt is the hope that such a wider survey may facilitate future discussions.

Let us begin with the geologists' arguments. They are all more or less based on the easiness with which the composition of meteorites can be explained by familiar geological principles. A French geologist, A. Boisse, was the first to point out, in 1850, that if we imagine all the iron and stone meteorites (and the various intermediate forms, the olivine-containing irons, the iron-rich stones, etc.) from the museum collections arranged in a sphere in concentric layers in the order of their specific gravities, this conglomeration would be a good model of the Earth's probable composition. The occurrence of meteorites of metallic iron had already by Chladni been linked with the assumption that the Earth's core consisted of this element. (If we remember that the whole idea of meteorites was then new to science we have a further reason to marvel at the insight displayed in his admirable paper of 1794 which seems to me to deserve a place in the well-known "Source Books" both of Astronomy and of Geology, but is not contained in either.) Boisse's view was accepted by the great French geologist A. Daubrée, and later backed by the authority of the Austrian geologist E. Suess in the one chapter of his famous *Face of the Earth* which deals not with the face but with the interior of our planet. He argued that such a similarity in composition conclusively proved that meteorites are fragments of an asteroid; as early as 1907 he had complained that there was *still* in some quarters a tendency to assume a cosmic origin of meteorites.

While at the time of their publication some of the conclusions drawn by these leading, and many other, figures in geology may have seemed a little rash to those holding other views, one must admit that all the refinements later introduced in their argument have fully confirmed and greatly strengthened it. The previous generation was satisfied when they had discovered that the same few elements were dominant in the Earth and in meteorites; we are now interested in the minor constituents as well. Chemical analysis, helped by X-rays, has been extended to most of the eighty-eight elements known to us, and it has invariably been found that their abundance, and their distribution amongst the main constituents of the meteorites, is just what might be expected if we assume that the composition of the original magma was very similar in both cases and only the geological history different—the Earth showing a more advanced differentiation than the meteorites. Physico-chemical studies, carried out by G. Tammann, V. M. Goldschmidt, and others, have proved that in the case of nickel and many other elements a real equilibrium between the molten iron and stone phases of the meteorites had been reached, corresponding to the chemical equilibrium which is supposed to have existed between the various liquid layers of the Earth.

But even a perfect analogy extending to all the minor chemical elements does not carry conviction to the mind of the modern geochemist so long as he is not certain that the isotopic constitution of the elements is the same in terrestrial and meteoritic material. This point can be tested, somewhat roughly, by determination of the combining weight of the elements, and more thoroughly by an investigation with the mass spectrograph. So far none of these methods, applied to the elements carbon, oxygen, silicon, chlorine, iron, cobalt, and nickel, has revealed the slightest difference. This may, of course, be only a consequence of the limited accuracy of our methods, and it is not improbable that very small differences will appear as soon as the measurements can be pushed one or two decimals further. We know that even on our Earth the isotopic composition of the element hydrogen varies according to the processes of fractionation to which it was subjected by nature, and, as recently shown by precision measurements of O. Nier, the same is true, to a much smaller extent, of the element carbon. So even minute differences between meteoritic and terrestrial elements, if established, would not rule out their common origin in the Sun, while, on the other hand, the very narrow limits to which variations in the isotopic composition seem to be confined, are certainly not in favour of the assumption that these isotopic mixtures have been generated quite independently; for we have reasons to believe that the atom-building processes depend on the temperature and history of the star in which they take place.

It is of special interest that even when radioactive elements from meteoritic sources were compared with terrestrial ones, no differences in isotopic composition could be detected; this has been shown on potassium from a glass meteorite by Hans Suess, and quite recently on uranium from a stone meteorite by Robley D. Evans and his co-workers. Since the isotopic ratio of a radioactive element varies in course of time, the identity of the isotopic composition points to a simultaneous creation of meteoritic and terrestrial potassium, of meteoritic and terrestrial uranium.

While the radioactive measurements just mentioned give only a comparison, and no clue as to the absolute time when the creation of the meteorites took place, it is well known that, by other radioactive methods, it is possible to determine ages in a geological sense, i.e. the time which has elapsed since the solidification of a mineral or rock. The application of such methods to meteorites seemed especially interesting when most astronomers believed that fixed stars had been in existence for 10^{12} to 10^{13} years, while the age of the Earth, and probably of the whole solar system, was not supposed to exceed 3.10^9 years. The examination of thirty iron meteorites showed that the age of none of them was of a higher order; this was certainly in very good agreement with the assumption of their genesis as part of the solar system, and seemed to make their interstellar origin unlikely. But while this work was in progress arguments in favour of a shorter lifetime of the universe accumulated, and I think I am right in saying that today few astronomers believe that a celestial object can be much older than our solar system.* So the absence of higher ages amongst the meteorites is no longer an argument against their extra-solar origin; this was quite rightly pointed out by the Estonian astronomer E. Öpik, whose work on meteors we are going to discuss later. (We need hardly emphasize, however, that we do not agree with his further statement that the interstellar origin of most meteorites can be taken for granted, and that their low age values, therefore, are experimental evidence for the "short" time scale of the universe.)

We have seen so far that recent laboratory work on meteorites has supported throughout the old conviction of geologists that these bodies have a genetic relationship to the solar system. Let us now consider the astronomical arguments.

Theoretically it should be a simple matter to tell from the velocity of a falling meteorite whether it was a member of the solar system; in this case its heliocentric velocity must not exceed 42 km per sec, the value for a body describing a parabola round the Sun. But unfortunately the fall of a meteorite is a rare occurrence, and rarer still are the cases in which the witnesses are not overawed by the brilliancy of the unexpected phenomenon, and well enough trained to be able exactly to describe the orbit on the sky, and the duration of the phenomenon, and so to make it possible for competent computers to calculate the velocity with sufficient accuracy to distinguish between an elliptic and a hyperbolic orbit. Halley has complained

---

* Present ideas of the ages of the universe and of the solar system are in a very fluid state, but there is a general consensus of opinion that they are of the order of ten thousand million years or less. As so expressed, the solar system seems to be approximately of the same age as the universe, but this may be misleading. If, for instance, the age of the universe were 9.10^9 years and that of the solar system 8.10^9 years, the former would have been in existence for a thousand million years before the solar system appeared. The uncertainty of the whole matter, however, is such that the statement in the text that "the absence of higher ages amongst the meteorites is no longer an argument against their extra-solar origin" is still true. [Ed.]

already: "It commonly so happens that these contingent Appearances escape the Eyes of those that are best qualified to give a good Account of them". (See Fig. 12.) The famous meteorite shower of Pultusk in Poland, where, on January 30, 1868, about 100,000 stones (though most of them not exceeding the size of a pea) came down,

Fig. 12. Fall of the stone meteorite near Maurkirchen at 4 p.m. on November 20, 1768 (copperplate print of 1769, slightly reduced).

was the first on which a calculation could be carried out; as luck would have it, two amateur astronomers, one at Breslau and the other at Danzig, were looking just in the right direction when the fall occurred, and the excellent data provided by them enabled J. G. Galle (one of the discoverers of the planet Neptune) to state that the Pultusk meteorites must have moved with a velocity of no less than 56 km per sec, and that, therefore, they had come in a hyperbolic curve, from outside the solar system.

How seldom circumstances were so favourable can be seen from the fact that in 1926, when C. Hoffmeister edited the painstaking life-work of G. v. Niessl, enlarged by calculations of his own, on *611 Orbits of Big Meteors*, there were not more than seven meteorites to be included; moreover, the observational data of at least two of them were so doubtful as to make the results obtained practically valueless. Omitting these two, the heliocentric velocities of meteorites as given in the Niessl–Hoffmeister catalogue are: Treysa 38 km/sec; Homestead, 40; Orgueil, 52; Pultusk, 56; Krähenberg, 57. So we see that, taking the figures at their face values, three of the five meteorites did not seem to belong to the solar system, while two did.

Considering how meagre, and by no means decisive, these figures are, one would hardly expect the uncompromising attitude of Niessl, and even more so of Hoffmeister, who, in a book published in 1937, declares the interstellar origin of the majority of meteorites to be a "well-established fact". This conviction is obviously based, not on the very few orbits of meteorites which they have been able to include, but on the statistical result of their catalogue which seemed to prove that the orbits of 79 per cent of the 611 big meteors had been hyperbolic.

This conclusion, that the greater part of meteorites must be interstellar, because this is the case with big meteors, has been accepted by many astronomers, as the statements found in some of the best-known German, English, and American books show.* There seem to be, however, two weak points in the argument: meteorites may be a special class of fireballs, and the high percentage of hyperbolic velocities found amongst fireballs by Niessl and Hoffmeister might be due to a systematic error.

Not much can be said at present about the first objection. For the sake of simplicity everybody will be inclined to assume only a quantitative difference between the smallest shooting stars and the biggest fireballs, some of which drop meteorites while others do not; but we must not forget that even amongst meteors of similar size there may be a discrimination to be made between former constituents of a comet and therefore members of the solar system, and sporadic meteors, coming from outside; and that we must not *a priori* exclude the possibility that meteorites are only related to the first group.

* More recently, however, A. C. B. Lovell writes (*Meteor Astronomy*, Clarendon Press, p. 2, 1954): "Contemporary opinion is that these bodies [meteorites], which are large enough to penetrate the atmosphere without complete evaporation, are likely to have a different origin from the meteors". [Ed.]

Still more satisfactory would it be if the sharp contrast between geological conclusions and those drawn from meteor statistics were to disappear as the consequence of a revision of the latter data. There is no doubt that astronomical observation of meteors, and, if possible, meteorites, is the most direct attack on the problem of their birth-place, and it is to be hoped that the special attention directed to this research for many years by Harvard College Observatory will bring a final answer. So far the results have been somewhat conflicting. An expedition to Arizona, led by Professor Öpik, seemed first to confirm the high percentage of hyperbolic, i.e. interstellar, meteors claimed in the Niessl–Hoffmeister catalogue; in Öpik's estimate they amounted to 70 per cent. But his final paper is not yet available, and recent photographic studies by Dr. Fred L. Whipple on nine sporadic meteors proved that at least eight, and perhaps all, of them were moving in elliptical orbits. It may be that the visual observations, on which Öpik as well as Niessl and Hoffmeister had to depend, are always subject to a systematic error which makes the velocities too high; this is the opinion of Dr. Fletcher Watson of Harvard Observatory, and of Professor C. C. Wylie of the State University of Iowa, who believes this error to be so constant that it can be eliminated, and so the real velocity found.* Perhaps the most interesting application made by him a few months ago concerns the Pultusk fall; from the 72-year old observations collected by Galle which are mentioned above the "psychological errors" of the observers are eliminated and the result is—an elliptic orbit resembling those of the nearer asteroids!†

I should not be too astonished if some astronomers were slow in accepting this new interpretation of the Pultusk orbit before more is known about Professor Wylie's procedure. But it seems to me that even if we still believe in the correctness of the hyperbolic velocity calculated by Galle, and confirmed by Niessl, we are not at all compelled to admit an extra-solar origin. Since in the case of comets it could be demonstrated that even those which now move in hyperbolic orbits have previously revolved round the Sun, the same may be true of some meteorites. Only if it could be shown by exact calculations (which would hardly be worth while, considering the

---

* "Although Öpik's results remain an enigma, the contemporary conclusions to be drawn from the surveys of the previous chapters is that only a small percentage, if any, of the sporadic meteors are moving with hyperbolic velocities; and that the few cases of small hyperbolic velocities which probably exist more likely arise from planetary perturbations than from the interstellar origin of the meteors."–Lovell, *op. cit.*, p. 247. [Ed.]

† A. V. Nielsen (*Meddel. Ole Rømer Obs.*, No. 17, 1943) confirms the hyperbolic velocity of the Pultusk shower. [Ed.]

uncertainty of the observations) that the higher velocity of these bodies is original, and not the consequence of perturbations, then, and not before, their interstellar origin would be proved beyond doubt.

We have seen that the determination of the orbits of meteorites is beset with many difficulties and uncertainties; on the other hand we can hardly expect astronomers to realize fully the great weight of the more indirect geological evidence. Geology frequently suffers from the peculiar non-mathematical character of its logical structure, which, to representatives of other sciences, makes its conclusions appear less stringent than they actually are. We are glad, therefore, to be able to draw attention to a fact that, in our opinion, leads to a very strong astronomical argument against any theory denying the relationship of meteorites and the Sun. We are referring to the statistics of the daily hours of their falls.

"It is a singular fact, that out of 72 stonefalls, whose precise hour of fall has been recorded, only 13 occurred before noon, and no less than 58 fell between noon and 9 p.m." This sentence appears in a report on luminous meteors prepared by four scientists for the 1860 meeting of the British Association. No explanation is offered. The "singular fact", however (the predominance of afternoon falls), received confirmation every time when in later years the increased material on meteorites was again arranged according to the daily hours of their falls: in 1867 by W. Haidinger, in 1888 by H. A. Newton, in 1910 by O. C. Farrington, in 1933 by Willard J. Fisher, in 1938 by Mohd. A. Khan. In the last compilation the number of morning falls has risen to 155, and of afternoon falls to 240.

The obvious conclusion to be drawn from the greater number of afternoon falls is that the majority of the meteorites move in the same direction round the Sun as our Earth. If their own movements had no relation to the solar system we should expect the Earth to encounter more meteorites with the half which is at any given moment in front during her revolution round the Sun, and with which she is, so to speak, sweeping the space. The time on this half is always between 0 and 12 noon. Meteorites striking the Earth between the hours 12 noon and midnight must follow her in her revolution, and any preponderance in the number of such falls indicates that the majority of meteorites move in such "direct" orbits. The statistics are even compatible with the assumption that there are amongst meteorites no "retrograde" orbits at all; those falling in the morning hours may have been overtaken by the faster revolving Earth.

H. A. Newton briefly discussed the possibility, already envisaged by Schiaparelli, that morning falls of meteorites might be rare, even if they are moving equally in all directions, because the higher velocity with which retrograde meteorites enter the atmosphere will increase the heat evolved and, therefore, the quantity of meteoritic mass removed by evaporation; he did not, however, accept this as a sufficient explanation, because "large velocities do not seem to be entirely fatal to the integrity of the meteorites". When, however, exactly the same argument was later advanced by Niessl, who needed it to defend his conviction that meteorites are independent of the solar system, it was almost universally accepted, as a glance through the best-known textbooks on astronomy and monographs on meteors shows. This is all the more astonishing as Niessl never seems to have bothered to prove his point by a discussion of the thermodynamic and kinetic sides of the question. Even in 1924, when C. Lönnquist published an *Essay to deduce the Frequency of Meteorites*, he fully endorsed Niessl's view, at the same time stating that the factor which Niessl considers "of utmost importance" "defies probably every calculation".

This scepticism, if justified, should of itself have discouraged simple acquiescence in Niessl's authority. Fortunately, however, the problem does not seem to be beyond the faculties of a physicist. In a well-known paper of 1922, whose essential correctness has in the meantime been proved by quite independent evidence, F. A. Lindemann* and G. M. B. Dobson derived quantitative expressions for the heating and volatilization of meteors entering the terrestrial atmosphere, and a comparison of their results with Niessl's argument shows the latter's validity to be extremely doubtful. I was very glad when, some time ago, I had an opportunity of discussing the matter personally with Professor Lindemann, who at once declared his disbelief in Niessl's idea, and was later kind enough to communicate to me a few calculations which dispose of it in a quantitative manner.

It appears from Professor Lindemann's deductions that during the few seconds of flight through the atmosphere sufficient heat cannot be imparted to a meteorite of common size to evaporate it; neither radiation nor convection can achieve that effect within this limited time. The higher relative velocity of the retrograde meteorites would, on the other hand, increase their brilliance; the total light radiated would last for a shorter time, but would be correspondingly more intense. Since the energy radiated is proportional to the square of the relative velocity we should expect that the

* Later Lord Cherwell. [Ed.]

enhanced brilliance would lead to the easier detection of retrograde than direct meteorites, just as is the case for meteors. It seems, therefore, that if there were in space equal numbers of direct and retrograde meteorites, as supposed by Niessl and his followers, probably more, and certainly not less, morning falls would be reported.

So Niessl's view is hardly tenable, and, as far as we are aware, no other attempts have been made to invalidate the obvious conclusion to be drawn from the observed hours of meteorite falls. There are other peculiarities connected with the orbits of meteorites, emphasized by H. A. Newton, which are hard to explain under the assumption that they are not connected with the solar system, e.g. their small inclinations to the ecliptic. None of them is, however, so easily established as the unsymmetrical distribution of the daily hours of meteorite falls; even quite untrained observers are not likely to make any mistakes here that would falsify the statistics, and we think, therefore, that this argument ought to receive more careful consideration in all discussions about the origin of meteorites than has so far been the case. It may well be that the stone which the builders of meteoritic theories rejected will in future become the head of the corner.

Since geological and physico-chemical evidence is today pointing more strongly than ever towards a solar origin of meteorites, and the predominance of direct orbits amongst them (after refutation of Niessl's attempt to explain it away) is doing the same—while the only argument which seemed to prove their interstellar origin, the apparently hyperbolic character of their orbits, is by some astronomers no longer considered well established—we may safely assume, I think, that *meteorites have since their formation been members of the solar system.*

This statement, of course, does not yet satisfy our curiosity; we should like to know when, and by which process, they have been formed. As these problems are part of the history of the solar system, we can hardly expect a final answer as long as there are still unsolved difficulties in every attempt to explain the origin of the planets, satellites, and comets. If we knew enough about the genesis of those children of the Sun, we could probably easily find the point at which meteorites came into existence. At present the reverse way seems more promising: we may hope to obtain some more insight into the formation of the solar system by an increasingly thorough study of these small objects which we know now to be part of it and which are the only celestial objects which we can investigate by laboratory methods. For this very reason I do not think that the study of meteorites is less significant than before, when they were believed to come from farther-distant, but unknown, stars.

Attempts to trace the history of meteorites by means of a study of their present appearance have been made so frequently that we cannot mention here more than a small selection of the results, without giving details of the methods employed.

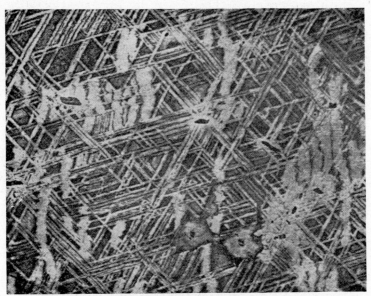

FIG. 13. Widmanstätten figures of Red River iron meteorite
(after O. C. Farrington).

The greatest success was undoubtedly achieved in the case of iron meteorites. Most of these show a peculiar crystalline structure, which becomes visible as soon as a polished plate is either heated or etched by an acid. This was accidentally discovered in 1808, and at once recognized as something of importance by A. von Widmanstätten in Vienna, after whom this structure has been named.* Although the chemical composition of meteoritic iron has been known for a long time and can easily be imitated by a synthetic alloy of iron, nickel, cobalt, and a few minor constituents, the characteristic Widmanstätten pattern refused to appear in distinct fashion in any artificial product; it still is the principal criterion of a genuine iron meteorite (see Fig. 13). With growing metallurgical

* Paneth's discovery (see p. 186) of the work of G. Thomson in this connection had not been made when this lecture was delivered. [Ed.]

knowledge, however, the approach to the Widmanstätten structure became increasingly close. I am glad to show you here the result which has recently been obtained by R. F. Mehl and G. Derge in the Department of Metallurgy of the Carnegie Institute of Technology at Pittsburgh by keeping an iron–nickel alloy with 27 per cent nickel for a week at 1,100° and then allowing it to cool down slowly to room temperature (see Fig. 14). The design on the etched plate closely

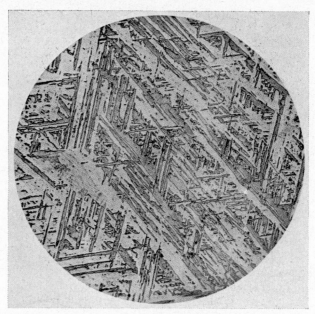

FIG. 14. Alloy of iron with 27 per cent nickel. Slowly cooled. Magnification ×42 (after R. F. Mehl and G. Derge).

resembles a meteoritic Widmanstätten pattern, the main difference being that this one is just visible with the naked eye (the picture is magnified 42 times) while the corresponding dimensions in a natural Widmanstätten structure are usually from twenty to a hundred times as big.

This, and further experiments in which the study, by X-rays, of the crystal lattices of iron meteorites was decisive, have proved that the Widmanstätten structure is not formed at the moment the molten mass solidifies, but is due to a later, slow re-orientation of the iron and nickel atoms in the crystals, an essential point being the length of time the solid iron–nickel alloy stays at the right temperature. The perfection of the natural Widmanstätten structure can apparently only be explained if we assume that after solidification an extremely slow cooling took place, at a relatively high temperature; this means that during this period the mass of which the iron meteorites are fragments must have had very considerable dimensions. You will have noted that our expressions "extremely slow", "relatively high", "very considerable", are far from precise; this is largely due to the fact that so far few experiments of metallurgists have primarily been directed to the investigation of the structure of meteorites, and there is every hope that a systematic study will be able to reveal information of a more quantitative character.

The facts already established should, however, suffice to dispose finally of theories which appear in print from time to time and would have meteorites formed directly by accretions of solid particles at low temperatures, sometimes under the influence of electric charges. We have only to look at a cross-section of an iron meteorite which contains black spheres of an iron sulphide (called "troilite") to realize that these must at one time have been liquid drops in the molten iron. How can we understand their fairly uniform distribution throughout many iron meteorites? Physical chemistry knows many cases of two liquids which are completely miscible at high temperatures but bound to separate when cooled down; molten iron and iron sulphide belong to them, and so the peculiar form and occurrence of the troilite nodules is explained by the fact that the iron sulphide was originally completely dissolved in the liquid iron, but had to separate as a new liquid phase when the temperature had fallen. The first stage of such a separation of two liquids is always a sort of emulsion, but if the one phase is definitely lighter, it will tend to rise and to form a coherent liquid layer on top. If, however, the liquids are fairly viscous (and perhaps, as V. M. Goldschmidt has added, the gravitational field weak owing to the relatively small dimensions of the celestial body in which this process occurred) no such movement will take place, the drops will not be able to unite but must solidify, dispersed throughout the other phase, as soon as the temperature has sufficiently fallen to allow crystallization.

In an exactly analogous way one can explain the uniform distribution of olivine crystals throughout the spongy mass of iron in the peculiar group of stony-iron meteorites which are called "pallasites" (after the iron described by the traveller Pallas mentioned earlier). Here also a complete mixture of the two phases, iron and stones, must have been a preliminary stage. There are many other proofs for the originally molten state of iron meteorites, for instance the regularities in the distribution of rarer chemical elements between the iron, iron sulphide, and stone phases can hardly be explained under any other assumption, but these most obvious ones may suffice.

If the final rearrangement which led to the Widmanstätten structure has taken place after the solidification, and if, as mentioned before, the necessary conditions can only have prevailed in a fairly large celestial object, it remains for us to explain in what way this object was broken up into the size of the known meteorites, without destroying this structure. To answer this question we have, unfortunately, no guidance by the analogy of laboratory experiments, but it seems to me that a well-known astronomical principle is able to give a satisfactory explanation.

The American geologist Thomas C. Chamberlin was the first to propose it in this connection, but I almost feel I ought to apologize for giving him credit for it since it appears that in later years he completely discarded this idea in favour of the well-known planetesimal theory which he worked out in collaboration with F. R. Moulton. In his last work *The Two Solar Families* (published in the year of his death, 1928) many pages are devoted to meteorites, in an attempt to show how they were formed by an agglomerative process of solid "chondrulites". (We have, I think, made it sufficiently clear why such a building process, which does not account for the melting of an enormous mass, is unable to explain the origin of iron meteorites.) In complete contrast to this is a paper Chamberlin wrote in 1901 entitled "On a Possible Function of Disruptive Approach in the Formation of Meteorites, Comets and Nebulae". It may be that some ideas expressed here have rightly not been repeated by the author in later works. But I am of the opinion that the formation of meteorites by "disruptive approach" should be very seriously taken into consideration for our problem, as it seems to offer just the kind of force we need.

When Daubrée considered meteorites as fragments of a planet, he left it open whether the catastrophe had been brought about by a collision or by an explosion. Without mentioning the many other difficulties, in either case sufficient heat would probably have been developed to melt the iron, and to destroy its Widmanstätten structure; the fragments, now only of the size of meteorites, would cool down too quickly to grow this structure again. If, however, the breaking-up is the consequence of an approach to another celestial object within the Roche limit, then we have (to use Chamberlin's own words) "small planetary bodies riven into fragments without great heat and, by reason of this, retaining the varied structure attained in the parent body". There is no indication that Chamberlin, in those days, knew about the impossibility of regenerating the Widmanstätten structure in small iron fragments, but I think that a very strong argument in favour of the mechanism of disruption proposed by him is just this "retaining" of the Widmanstätten structure, acquired during a very long period of slow cooling of the parent body.

As, quite independently of such considerations, the origin of the asteroids has been attributed to the disrupting force of Jupiter on a primeval planet, we are naturally inclined now, following E. Suess, to consider this hypothetical planet as the mass from which the meteorites sprang, although there may have been bodies of intermediate size before repeated disruption reduced the fragments to meteoritic dimensions. This linking up of meteorites with asteroids is today justifiable for other reasons too; Professor C. C. Wylie has found that not only the Pultusk meteorites but also several other bright fireballs actually moved in elliptic orbits resembling those of the small asteroids in their eccentricities, inclinations to the ecliptic, periods of revolution, and mean distances from the sun.

Age determinations, at least by the "helium method", define the time since solidification; they do not tell us, therefore, when the meteorites came into existence as independently moving small celestial bodies of present-day dimensions, but when they finally assumed the solid state; this process may have occurred much earlier, or much later.

We mentioned (p. 136) that the upper limit for the age of 30 iron meteorites has been determined; for this purpose it suffices to analyse their helium and uranium content. It is more difficult to find the actual time when solidification took place, because then the thorium content also has to be measured, and this is a harder experimental problem. Some work on these lines has been done recently, but under considerable difficulties (amongst others lack of standards for calibration), so that the absolute accuracy of the figures given in the table on the following page is doubtful, but the relative values can certainly be used as a guide.*

From this table we learn that very big differences exist between the geological ages of iron meteorites. (These differences are not reflected in their metallurgical structure, nor in their chemical

---

* The interpretation of the results of the "helium method" as applied to meteorites is, in fact, a great deal more involved than was realized when this paper was written. A considerable fraction of the helium in meteorites is now believed to originate in cosmic ray interactions with nuclei of meteoritic materials, and the variations shown in the table may well represent different degrees of screening from cosmic radiation, rather than different ages (see p. 269). [Ed.]

composition.) Some of them reached the solid state so long ago that their age is higher than that of any terrestrial rock as yet examined (fixing thereby the lower limit of the age of the solar system and the universe); others are as young as cenozoic rocks, which means, astronomically speaking, that they are of today. And we do not yet know how young, in the geological sense, a meteorite can be, as only so very few age determinations have been completed.

Name of iron meteorite	Time since solidification in millions of years
Bethany, Goamus	30
San Martin	500
Bethany, Amalia	1,000
Thunda	> 3,000

What may be the reason for these vast differences? Perhaps it is not impossible to assume that the planet or asteroid from which the "young" meteorites come preserved its molten iron core until its recent disruption. Another, probably more likely, explanation would be that the catastrophic disruption of the one (or several) parent bodies of meteorites took place at an early stage of the solar system, but that the fragments met with different fates; some keeping their crystalline state since the very dawn of things when the parent planet had solidified, while others came later near enough to the Sun to be melted and, perhaps, re-melted.

There are some iron meteorites, the so-called "ataxites", in which the Widmanstätten structure is absent, and in some specimens of this group it seems to have been destroyed by heat; these meteorites may have come within melting distance of the Sun when their size was already too small to allow afterwards of a sufficiently slow cooling for the growth of the Widmanstätten structure. Most of the iron meteorites, however, irrespective of their ages, possess this structure, which proves that at the time of their last melting and succeeding crystallization their mass must still have been fairly large; so perhaps another disruptive approach must be assumed to account for their final reduction to meteoritic size. The disintegrating body in this last case can hardly have been the Sun, whose heat would at the same time have caused melting. The known great variety of the orbits of the asteroids, and their variability owing to perturbations, may give encouragement to the supposition of very different fates to be met by meteorites in their respective life stories; but here is obviously the point where calculations are needed to test the views discussed.

Even meteorites of comparatively small dimensions may, perhaps, attain the Widmanstätten structure if, instead of the single protracted process of cooling, they were re-heated many times to suitable temperatures below the melting point. Professor A. J. Bradley of Cambridge has drawn attention to the possibility of meteorites being "heat-treated" in this fashion by frequent perihelion passages.

If we now try briefly to trace, in a similar fashion, the past history of the stone meteorites, we certainly do not expect it to be very different; for there are all possible intermediate stages between (almost) 100 per cent metal and 100 per cent stone meteorites, so that nobody could tell where to draw the dividing line. It is, therefore, very satisfactory that what geologists are able to read from the structure of stone meteorites tells a very similar tale: they must once have been parts of a much bigger body, because in some of them O. C. Farrington found slickensided surfaces which cannot have been produced in objects of their present size; as the breaking-up did not destroy these vestiges of their previous, geological history, the mechanism cannot have been too violent, or the heat evolved too great. Many stone meteorites, however, show unmistakable traces of crushing, fresh conglomeration, and new crystallization. We are referring to those of "chondritic" structure, as it is called. Without entering into the intricacies of this much discussed question, we hope to be right in stating that there is now unanimity amongst experts that this most common type of stone meteorites reveals a long, and rather wild, geological history which cannot be explained without assuming metamorphosis brought about by periodic heating and cooling. It is very tempting to see the astronomical conditions for it in the close passage to the Sun, just as in the case of the iron meteorites.

Any more detailed discussion will have to take into consideration the fact that stones and irons are not affected in the same way by radiant heat and gravitational forces. While the good conductivity of iron is likely to establish a constant temperature throughout, we have to expect more localized effects of heating on the surface of stone which may help to explain the very inhomogeneous character of some stone meteorites. As to the influence of gravitation, the formula for Roche's limit is

$$R = 2 \cdot 46 r (d_1/d_2)^{\frac{1}{3}}$$

where r denotes the radius, and d_1 the density, of the primary body,

d_2 the density of the (much smaller) body that approaches it, and R the distance within which the latter is exposed to gravitational disintegration. Since the densities of average iron–nickel and stone meteorites are 8 and 3·6 respectively, it follows that iron meteorites are safe up to a distance approximately three-quarters of that prevailing for stones. The forces of cohesion, which are much stronger in iron than in stone meteorites (some of which are so brittle that they can be pulverized between the fingers), are a further influence in favour of them; even within Roche's limit disruption naturally ceases as soon as the fragments are small enough for their cohesion to withstand the mechanical tendency to disruption. So we see that for both reasons we must expect that on the average stone meteorites will be reduced to smaller bodies than irons. It seems significant in this connection that there are reports about meteoritic showers consisting of many thousands of small stones, which apparently have already entered the terrestrial atmosphere as such, while corresponding iron showers have neither been observed nor can they be inferred from the great number of iron pieces found in some districts which are the result of subsequent scattering after one big iron meteorite hit the Earth. Such pieces are known, for example, from the neighbourhood of the famous meteorite crater in Arizona which owes its origin to the fall of a gigantic iron.

There does not seem to be any lower limit for the size of stone meteorites, except that pieces of very small dimensions are only discovered under unusually favourable circumstances (as, for instance, their black crust showing up on snow covering the ground), and that still smaller fragments are dismissed as "dust". And it is probably quite as impossible to fix an upper limit, either for irons or stones. It has sometimes been used as an argument against the hypothesis of a planetary origin that meteorites are comparatively so small. But recent aerial surveys of the Earth's surface seem to show that meteorite craters are fairly common, thus revealing the not infrequent arrival of meteorites of a bigger order of magnitude than those preserved in an unbroken state; and in October 1937 astronomers observed a celestial object about one mile in diameter, and classed as "asteroid", to come so close to our Earth that a slight disturbance of its orbit would have brought it into collision; after which event it would certainly have been called a "meteorite" by those of our fellow-men fortunate enough to observe this event—and to survive.

If, finally, we turn our attention to the third class of meteorites, the glasses, or "tektites", we quickly realize that an inquiry as to their origin can at the moment hardly get beyond the first step, the recognition of their falling from the atmosphere; the second question, whence they got there, remains still very obscure.

Since tektites have never been observed to fall, the direction of their arrival can only roughly be inferred from their geographic distribution. The time can only be stated in terms of the geological periods of the strata on which they are found. Their age cannot be determined by the method applicable to iron, and (with certain precautions) also to stone, meteorites because, unfortunately, glass is permeable by helium which, therefore, does not accumulate in tektites. Finally we must not forget that anything we know about the history of iron and stone meteorites need not pertain at all to the glasses; there are all sorts of intermediate forms between the first two classes, but none whatever between either of them and the third. This fact makes us rather doubtful whether they really are just the product of a differentiation in the same parent magma; this view has been advocated by Professor F. E. Suess in Vienna (by the way, the third of the name Suess to be mentioned in this lecture, and the genealogical link between the two others) to whom we owe the recognition of the various glasses as meteoritic, and the introduction of the general term "tektites". It is, however, not easy to understand how the chemical separation of the matter of the tektites could be effected so perfectly while the stones and irons are so mixed.

Professor Suess, however, does not assume that the tektites have entered our atmosphere as the glasses we know, but that they were melted during their flight through the air and cooled down too quickly to crystallize. Since it is well known that the heat evolved during the passage through the air of an iron or stone meteorite produces only a very thin molten crust while the material below remains cold, it is clear that this process cannot account for the melting of tektites. Suess, and another authority, the French petrologist A. Lacroix, who has enriched our knowledge of glass meteorites very considerably by the detection, and study, of the tektites of Indo-China, adopt therefore the daring hypothesis of H. Michel that on entering the atmosphere the tektites contained no oxygen but elementary silicon and light metals which, by chemical combination with the oxygen of the atmosphere, produced the heat necessary for transforming the residual siliceous mass into a perfectly molten glass. If we remember that the flight through the atmosphere lasts only a few seconds, and that the tektites arrived on the Earth as solid bodies which must have used the time of their passage through the lower atmosphere for the cooling down, we are driven to admit that the chemical process suggested must have taken place in the highly rarefied upper atmosphere. A little calculation shows that the volume of oxygen required there would be such a big multiple of the final volume of the tektite that the mechanism of such a chemical reaction during the rapid flight through a resisting medium becomes entirely incomprehensible.

Moreover, there seems to be no valid reason to separate the smaller tektites, like moldavites or australites, from the lumps of silica glass found in the Libyan desert (see Fig. 11) some of which weigh 2 kg; to assume that they also have been formed in the air, out of material of different chemical composition, would almost look like the revival of a "lithologie atmosphérique".

If, following Professor Suess, we have the courage to proclaim the extra-terrestrial origin of tektites, although nobody has witnessed their fall, we need hardly be afraid of postulating further that they arrived as glasses, being modified in the atmosphere only as regards shape and surface, just as is the case with iron and stone meteorites. The richly sculptured surface of the moldavites, and, to a lesser degree, other tektites, once considered as proof of their flight through the air, is now recognized as brought about by corrosion during the period of their lying on the ground; there was ample time for that since their fall occurred apparently in antediluvian days. For the same reason we can hardly expect to find on tektites a sort of "crust" which is so characteristic for freshly fallen irons and stones. It is most likely, however, that immediately after their fall their surface was covered by a thin layer of newly molten, and oxidized, glass; an inspection of moldavites seems here and there to reveal very small residues of it.

There is hardly any theoretical reason, either, why glass meteorites should not have been formed outside the terrestrial atmosphere. We remember that in the case of iron meteorites there was the slight difficulty in explaining how the Widmanstätten structure survived the breaking-up into small fragments; no such difficulty exists here: a body of chemical composition similar to a granitic rock, on entering the Roche's limit of the Sun, would suffer both melting and dispersion, and the swarm of glass globules leaving the perihelion at high speed would cool down too quickly to crystallize. Such swarms, in a later encounter with the Earth, may be expected to be spread over whole continents, as we know that tektites were.

I hope this survey will have made it clear that today the principal features of the origin of meteorites are emerging from the vast amount of hypothesis accumulated during a century, but that several important points are still in doubt. It is true that many details could have been added, and on various points I felt quite uncomfortable for being compelled, for brevity's sake, to omit them; but I do not think that their inclusion would dispel the darkness which still covers some of the issues. More research, experimental as well as theoretical, is needed, and considering the great number of interested workers, steady progress seems assured. In this respect at least the outlook has changed radically since the early days of meteorite study. You will remember, from the few historical remarks at the beginning of this lecture, how slow official science was to open the discussion, and it may amuse you to hear that less than a decade later some were prepared to close it again. More than once in those days the opinion was expressed that we had to be content to know that meteorites really fall down, but that the problem from where they come was insoluble. Let me quote the final verdict from the valuable book by Bigot de Morogues: "I reckon this phenomenon amongst those the first causes of which will probably always be unknown to us; since famous members of the division for physical and mathematical Sciences of the Institute, like de Laplace, de Lagrange, Haüy, and Vauquelin, have tried to explain it without obtaining a complete success, it is hardly permissible for us to hope that some day its causes will be better known to us". (Is there today any learned society whose members command such respect?)

We no longer believe, like Bigot de Morogues, that the problem of the origin of meteorites must be solved by the brilliant idea of one man, or not at all. We are aware from how many different quarters information has gradually come forth, and can be quite hopeful that such a collaboration will become ever more fruitful. There is hardly any scientist, nay any man, who is not fascinated by the great problems of astronomy, and to be able, by simple experimental work in a metallurgical, mineralogical, chemical, or physical laboratory, to contribute, however little, to the progress of this sublime science is a great privilege which only the study of meteorites can offer. This study will, I am sure, find an ever increasing number of enthusiastic supporters, and their achievements will help astronomers to tell us some day the complete story of the origin of meteorites.

15 | The Beddgelert Meteorite

I. INTRODUCTION

On September 21, 1949, about 01 45 hours (G.M.T.) a meteorite pierced the roof of a hotel in Beddgelert (53° 0½' N, 4° 6' W) in North Wales. A newspaper report of this event prompted two of us to hurry to Beddgelert in an attempt to ascertain the facts of this fall and to collect all fragments. In spite of the extensive search undertaken and the widely advertised promise of a substantial reward, no further parts of the meteorite could be traced; but the one recovered was flown to Durham and its radioactivity measured within eleven days of its fall. Subsequently, the stone was taken to the British Museum (Natural History) in South Kensington and cut in two; one half was kept there and its petrology studied, the other half was brought back to Durham for a chemical and radiochemical analysis. We present here the results obtained so far, preceded by a description of all the facts of the fall we could find out.

II. THE PHENOMENA OF THE FALL

Since the meteorite fell in the small hours of the morning in a sparsely populated district, its flight was seen by only a few people. From their description the light and sound phenomena must have been impressive. We print here the essential facts of all the reports obtained because we are of the opinion that they should be preserved as a matter of principle, although in this particular case they are too few and vague to make any calculations of the height, direction, and velocity of the flight possible.

From a letter from Mr. Edward Elwy Davies, Caernarvon, North Wales:

> "I happened to be out all night on this particular night in Caernarvon Park when about 1.30 a.m. [*sic*] I heard a terrific noise overhead, as of an approaching express or an aeroplane travelling at a terrific speed. At first I thought it might be a

shooting star, but as it approached I quickly realized it was something quite different. It came right from the direction of a Caernarvonshire village named Bont-newydd making towards another Caernarvonshire village called Waenfawr.* It illuminated the whole Park, the swans were almost scared to death, and fled in all directions as it assumed [the form of] a large ball of lightning overhead. The time would be almost a quarter of a second [*sic*] from its approach until its disappearance into space. To me who had a clear view, as it was a clear morning, it seemed like a huge rocket traversing the sky at great speed. I should estimate its length at approximately six feet. Altitude 500 ft and travelling at about 500 miles per hour. The whole process from 1 to 8 seconds. Colour would be an exceedingly bright silver.

The following morning I reiterated my experience to my friends at breakfast in what is known as the People's Cafe. I told them that as a rule I was never frightened or timid of nightfall but that in the very early hours of the morning I had seen something that had positively scared me. All sorts of visions crossed my mind at the time. At first I stood perplexed wondering if this could be the Second Advent of Our Saviour, for I had never seen anything like it, it was so spontaneous. Believe me, when I tell you I was glad to see it pass, and vanish into space once more, for I felt it might crash into the earth at any moment."

From a letter from Miss Janet Wilson, S.R.N., C.M.B., Penmaenmawr, Caernarvon, North Wales:

"I was awake on the morning of the display—my room was suddenly lit up to such an extent that I could have read headlines of a paper. I hurried to the window and saw a most beautiful sight. Flying across was a blue luminous body partially bulbous and partially elongated, but a most lovely blue colour. The whole spectacle did not occupy more than about 45 seconds. Very shortly after it had gone, I heard a slight distant explosion. I looked for a considerable time, but nothing further occurred. The clock struck 3 (a.m.) shortly afterwards, so I estimated that the display would take place approx. 2.45 a.m. [B.S.T.].†

I may state that my bungalow overlooks the Conway Estuary, almost opposite Puffin Island. I have not yet met anyone who saw it, I have enquired widely. I consider myself fortunate to have seen it, a most magnificent sight."

* Waenfawr, 53° 6½′ N, 4° 12′ W, is 3 miles E by S of Bont-newydd, 53° 7′ N, 4° 16′ W, which in turn is 1¾ miles due S of Caernarvon.
† British Summer Time: 1 hour later than Greenwich Mean Time.

From a letter from Miss Vera C. Garrood, Prestbury, Cheshire:

"I wonder whether it may be of any small interest to you to know that I saw the meteorite which fell in Wales, at what may have been only a few moments before it struck the earth. The light from it was so bright, that it shone through my bedroom curtains. On going to the window, I was surprised to see what appeared to be a disc of brilliant light about the size of a saucer, followed by a trail of sparks, drifting earthwards across the sky. I say 'drifting', because it gave the illusion of not moving faster than a plane appears to be travelling at night. I did in fact wonder at first whether it was a plane in flames and after its disappearance, waited somewhat apprehensively for any sound of a crash or explosion. As there was only complete silence, I was left guessing, until I read the news a day or so later. It fell at 2.45 a.m. [B.S.T.].

I read that you are anxious to find pieces similar to the one already found. If I am right in supposing that the 'sparks' were in fact fragments of it, then may I suggest that, by what I saw, they must have fallen many miles away from the meteorite in Wales."

From two letters from Mrs. E. Jackson, Knutsford, Cheshire:

"My mother, Mrs. Wood, who is 85 years of age, saw the meteor about 3 a.m. on Wednesday morning. She was terribly upset with it, her room was lit up and she said the sky seemed to open and a great ball of fire came towards us, with lights falling away from it and a great blue flamed nose.

We thought it was lightning she had seen, until I read in the *Daily Mirror* this morning of your experience."

"My mother states the meteorite she saw spiralled down from the sky, directly opposite her bedroom window [facing W], and fell behind the trees there. She described the light from it as going out gradually as though turning off a gas tap. It would appear that it came down between Knutsford and the west of Knutsford."

From a letter from Mr. A. C. Maines, Altrincham, Cheshire, who was a guest in the Prince Llewelyn Hotel at Beddgelert during the night of September 20/21, 1949:

"I did hear most distinctly a series of dull explosions after which there elapsed a period of complete silence for a few seconds, certainly no more than ten, but I should consider it more correct to judge some five or six—after which there was a noise which I can best describe as being like a light aeroplane, certainly not a high-pitched sound, but resembling a buzzing which grew in intensity as the missile approached. The only noise after this was the shattering of the slates on the roof top."

From enquiries made at Beddgelert* we could ascertain the following facts:

The manager of the Prince Llewelyn Hotel at Beddgelert, Mr. W. P. Tillotson, was awakened in the early hours of September 21, 1949, by the barking of his dog—in itself an unusual occurrence. He was for the moment unable to account for the dog's behaviour, but realized after a few seconds that something extraordinary was happening when he heard a series of irregularly spaced bangs which he—being an ex-naval man—says sounded like a naval broadside. The weather had shown no tendency to storminess in the last few days and the night had been clear and fine when he retired to bed, so he was almost sure that the noise was not thunder, but nothing further happened and he went to sleep again.

About midday Mrs. Tillotson entered the upstairs lounge of the hotel, a room directly under part of the roof. She found it covered in plaster dust which had obviously been released from a jagged hole in the ceiling. Lying on the floor, not directly beneath the hole but almost three feet away, was a lump of dark stone. This was undoubtedly the cause of the damage as, although covered with dust itself, there remained stuck to it a small piece of yellow plaster which corresponded to an abrasion in the wall below the ceiling. Evidently the missile had penetrated the roof, emerging at an angle to the vertical, and had hit the wall before coming to rest on the floor. The floor itself was only slightly damaged; a board was cracked across but the wood was old and not in good condition, and the manager expressed the opinion that an equal amount of damage could easily have been done by a man striking his heel hard on the spot.

Further investigations showed that the stone had indeed come through the roof, making a neat round hole in four overlapping thicknesses of slate (about 17 mm), shattering the underlying lath (about 2·5 cm × 5 cm in section), making a tiny dent in the bottom edge of an H-section iron girder, and lastly breaking through the plaster ceiling into the room below. The origin of the

---

* The Welsh name Beddgelert (pronounced Bethgelert) means "Grave of Gelert", but the widely known and touching story of Llewelyn's hound is a recent invention with no root in local tradition.[1]

stone was a mystery to Mr. Tillotson who made an attempt to cut it on an emery wheel but found it too hard; he did not connect it with the noise he had heard during the night. However, the stone was recognized that evening by an old miner in the bar of the hotel, who remembered going to a museum many years before and having seen specimens of meteorites there.

We attempted to determine the direction of flight of the stone, and alignment of the holes in separate layers of the roof indicated that it fell almost vertically, with a slight inclination to E, or ENE. No evidence was found of the stone's having rebounded from the rock, facing SSW, immediately behind the hotel; this, however, was thickly overgrown and, in places, inaccessible.

As minor pieces of information the following may be mentioned:

A shepherd had been out on the hills during the night tending a sick animal and had been going home, walking away from Beddgelert, when he became aware of a light in the sky behind him to the north-east. He turned round but the light had vanished; after three or four seconds he heard a few loud reports from the direction of the village, about a mile away, but nothing more happened.

An old man, living about 4 miles south-east of Beddgelert was awakened at the time. He saw the sky illuminated for an instant and heard the startling sounds, but he did not see the luminous body and could not give the time exactly.

Further reports about a luminous body floating through the heavens shortly before 3 a.m. in the direction of Beddgelert came from Abersoch, Knutsford, Criccieth, Caernarvon and Grange-over-Sands, without, however, giving any precise details. They all agree in describing the meteor as a brilliant white or blue-white disc. The Grange-over-Sands observer believed that the meteor broke up and a portion which became non-luminous may have fallen in Morecambe Bay.

III. THE OWNERSHIP OF THE METEORITE

The Prince Llewelyn Hotel, in which the manager's wife found the meteorite a few hours after its fall, belongs to a company. The law about the ownership of meteorites varies in different countries. In the U.S.A. there are three court decisions that a meteorite belongs to the land on which it had fallen and is, therefore, the property of the landowner.[2] These decisions have been criticized as unfair to the finders of meteorites.[3] In India they belong to the Government, in Scotland they rank as treasure-trove and as such belong to the Crown. In England the law is uncertain. It would require a court ruling on the subject of ownership, but there has been no litigation in any of the previous eight cases of meteorites which had fallen on English territory (1795 Wold Cottage, 1830 Launton, 1835 Aldsworth, 1876 Rowton, 1881 Middlesbrough, 1914 Appley Bridge, 1923 Ashdon, 1931 Pontlyfni). The matter was always settled privately.

We were anxious to acquire the meteorite, or at least part of it, for scientific investigations. Since the company who own the hotel made no claim beyond expressing the wish to obtain a plaster cast for permanent display in the hotel lounge, we had no hesitation in considering the only other possible claimant, the finder Mrs. Tillotson, as the lawful owner of the meteorite. (We wish here to express to her our gratitude for permitting us to take it immediately to Durham, before the purchase was concluded.) As the British Museum too desired to acquire a part of the meteorite it was arranged that it should be divided equally between Durham University and the British Museum, each of them paying half of its price.* The cutting was done in the Museum by Dr. M. H. Hey, using a thin, soft iron disc charged with diamond dust; it proceeded very smoothly and took not more than 1 hour and 20 minutes, only 8 g being lost in the cutting. The original weight of the meteorite was 794 g. A small slice (15·5 g) was given to the National Museum of Wales and a small polished slice (10 g) was returned to Mrs. Tillotson; 377·5 g have been incorporated in the Natural History collections of the British Museum (B.M. 1949, 259). The remainder was returned to the Londonderry Laboratory for Radiochemistry at Durham and has partly been used up for analysis.

Before the meteorite was cut, a mould and several casts from it were made at the British Museum.

IV. SEARCH FOR A β-ACTIVITY OF THE FRESHLY FALLEN METEORITE

Before entering the Earth's atmosphere a meteorite is exposed to the full force of the cosmic radiation; it is to be assumed that under its impact a certain number of atoms in the meteorite will be disintegrated, with the production of some radioactive nuclides. A

* We are indebted to the Durham Colleges Research Fund Committee for granting us the necessary sum.

rough calculation shows that any radioactivity thus produced can only be very feeble, but it did seem worth testing a meteorite shortly after its fall to find whether it displayed a measurable activity additional to that due to its uranium and thorium content.

As we had the chance of bringing the Beddgelert meteorite to Durham a few days after its fall we examined it immediately for possible β-activity, which is much more likely to be produced by cosmic rays than α-activity. The first measurements were made with a β-ray Geiger counter on October 2nd, i.e. 11 days after the fall of the meteorite, with the following results:

Background 14·2, 13·6 counts per min. (measured the previous day).

Meteorite 14·2, 13·6, 14·5 counts per min.

On October 3 we measured under the same counter a piece of magnetite of similar size and shape which gave 14·2, 14·5, 14·2, 13·8 counts per min.

On October 4th we repeated the meteorite measurements with the greatest possible precision.

Background 12·3 $\pm$ 0·5 counts per min.
Meteorite   13·7 $\pm$ 0·3 ,,   ,,   ,,
             13·7 $\pm$ 0·5 ,,   ,,   ,,
Background 13·7 $\pm$ 0·5 ,,   ,,   ,,

The figures show that 11 and 13 days after its fall we were not able to detect any measurable β-activity of the Beddgelert meteorite.

It seems unavoidable to add here a word of criticism of a paper on *The Effect of Cosmic Rays on Meteorites* which appeared a few months ago in the Contributions of the Meteoritical Society.[4] The authoress claims to have proved that some meteorites produce "stars" in photographic plates placed close to them which she considers to be due to the cosmic radiation to which the meteorites had been exposed before their fall. It is difficult to follow her reasoning but it seems that she confuses the effect of cosmic rays on meteorites with any impression the meteorites may later make on photographic plates; the radioactive isotopes of iron and sodium that she assumes to have been formed in the meteorite could never be the source of the stars she observed in the plates as these radio-elements emit only electrons and not any star-producing particle. Equally wrong is the opinion which she apparently holds that the energy of these radio-active transformations is equal to that of the cosmic rays. We should be sorry if we had erroneously attributed to the authoress such elementary mistakes but her paper does not seem to allow of any other interpretation. The stars she has seen in her plates have certainly nothing to do with the cosmic irradiation of meteorites.

V. GENERAL DESCRIPTION OF THE METEORITE
(M. H. HEY)

The only recovered mass of the Beddgelert meteorite is an irregularly shaped mass of 794·05 g original weight, measuring 9 × 7 × 6·5 cm overall. A large part of the surface shows a primary

FIGS. 15 and 16. Two aspects of the meteorite before cutting.
Reduced in size.

crust, sooty black and nearly 1 mm thick, but over considerable areas this has spalled off, probably when the stone penetrated the roof, and has exposed a fresh surface below. (See Figs. 15 and 16.) Other areas show secondary crust, also for the most part sooty black, but in one place with a brownish cast, and everywhere much thinner. Over a third of the surface shows no sign of crust; but since the meteorite is very dark-coloured, a tertiary crust or singeing could not be distinguished.

The surfaces covered with primary crust have well-rounded edges, but no flow-lines or signs of orientation can be seen; the areas covered with secondary crust and the uncrusted areas (as distinct from those where the primary crust has spalled off) are bounded by sharp, angular edges. It is clear that the mass broke up at least once quite late in its flight, and other fragments must have fallen, but the

FIG. 17.

FIG. 18.

FIGS. 17 and 18. Meteorite after cutting, with polished surface in two different illuminations. (Reproduced here actual size.) Fig. 17, metallic phase, reflecting light. Fig. 18, chondrules visible in diffuse light; compare Fig. 17.

district unfortunately is one in which dark rocks abound, and the other fragments are not likely to be found.

On a cut surface, the metallic phase is prominent under suitable lighting, while in other lights the numerous chondrules are the most noticeable features (see Figs. 17 and 18). The chondrules range in colour from a very light grey to a dark blue-grey, and in size from 0·5 mm to 3 mm. Some of the largest chondrules are compound; themselves quite clearly demarcated chondrules, they include numerous smaller chondrules, grains of nickel-iron, and groundmass. Most of the chondrules are spherical, but a few are ellipsoidal or oval. On breaking a slice, fractures run across both matrix and chondrules, and the meteorite is therefore to be classed as a black crystalline chondrite.

VI. MICROSCOPIC EXAMINATION OF THIN SECTIONS (W. CAMPBELL SMITH)

The chondrules are of many kinds (see Figs. 19–26). Chondrules of enstatite (or bronzite; no chemical analysis has yet been made) are frequent, many with the well-known eccentric radiating structure; some are broken, others embayed by or including opaque material, in part metallic in lustre and in part apparently glass. Polysomatic olivine chondrules in great variety are very common; some are nearly monosomatic, that is, composed of a single crystal, and these are bordered by a rim of small crystals. Mixed chondrules of olivine and enstatite are quite common; and one shows what appears to be a distinct chondrule of enstatite embedded within a polysomatic olivine chondrule.

Plagioclase was only identified in two chondrules. Many chondrules have opaque inclusions, some of which have a metallic lustre and seem to be nickel-iron, though some may be troilite.

This wide variety of relatively light-coloured chondrules is set in an abundant, much darker matrix, bringing the meteorite into the class of black chondrites. The matrix is composed partly of clear crystal fragments and fragments of all the above kinds of chondrules and partly of opaque material. The opaque material includes metallic nickel-iron and troilite, metal predominating, together amounting to 15 per cent of the meteorite by volume as determined by micrometric measurement of two slides. Most, perhaps all, of the metallic grains are rimmed by opaque material, slightly translucent and very deep brown in very thin layers, but quite opaque in the ordinary thin section; this is tentatively referred to as glass, and also

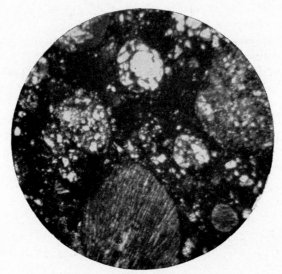

Fig. 19.

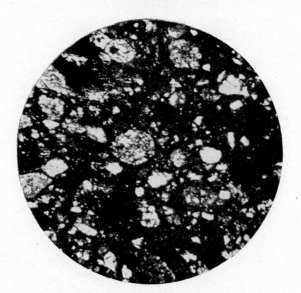

Fig. 20.

Figs. 19 and 20. Thin sections of the meteorite under the microscope in transmitted light. Fig. 19, enlargement ×17—the same as Fig. 21 at a less magnification. Fig. 20, enlargement ×30, shows many chondrules—chiefly olivine—in a dark groundmass.

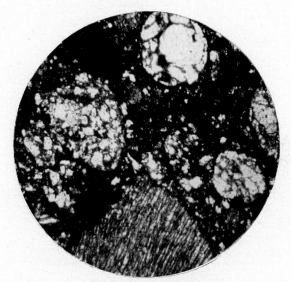

FIG. 21.

FIG. 22.

FIGS. 21 and 22. Thin sections of the meteorite under the microscope in transmitted light. Fig. 21, enlargement ×30, shows part of a radiating chondrule of enstatite and several chondrules of olivine in an opaque groundmass. Part of the latter is nickel-iron (not distinguishable in the figure). Fig. 22, enlargement ×35, shows a large chondrule composed of intercrossing bars of olivine with dark glass in between the bars; part of a circular rim of clear olivine is shown in the north-east quadrant; the black patches just outside the chondrule in the south-west quadrant are nickel-iron.

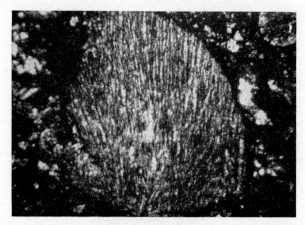

FIG. 23. Radiating enstatite chondrule in transmitted light.
Enlargement × 32.

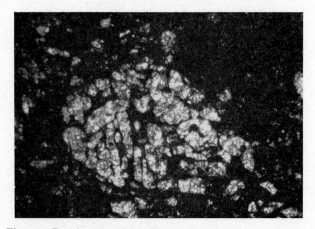

Fig. 24. Porphyritic olivine chondrule in transmitted light.
Enlargement × 32.

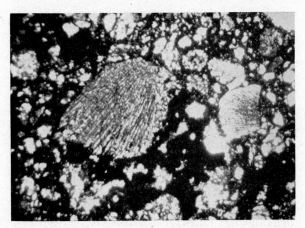

FIG. 25. Enlargement × 32. Portion of thin section in transmitted light showing two radiating enstatite chondrules, one broken, and smaller olivine chondrules, in an opaque groundmass.

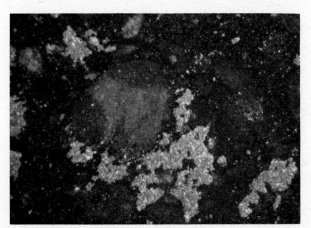

FIG. 26. Enlargement × 32. The same field as in Fig. 25 in oblique, reflected light to show the distribution of nickel-iron (pale-grey).

forms the medium in which the fragments of chondrules and crystals are embedded.

The density of the meteorite was determined as 3.64. The micrometric data are not yet sufficient to compare this with a computed value.

The chondrules in Beddgelert resemble very closely those in Suwahib,[5] and the two meteorites are very much alike except that in Suwahib the chondrules are packed more closely together and their matrix is mostly opaque glassy material without the great abundance of comminuted chondrules seen in Beddgelert. Cronstad is also rather similar, but does not show such a rich development of well-defined spherical chondrules, nor the deep black glass.

VII. CHEMICAL COMPOSITION OF THE METEORITE

As mentioned in Section V the metallic phase is so abundant that under suitable lighting it can be made very obvious (see Fig. 17). The meteorite is also strongly attracted by a magnet. We have separated the metallic and stony phases by two different chemical methods:

(a) By fusing the pulverized meteorite with KOH, leaching with water, and centrifuging.

(b) By vigorously stirring the pulverized meteorite with iodine solution for six hours. The solution was made up in the following proportions: 30 g iodine, 25 g potassium iodide, 120 ml of water. This method was used by Taylor-Austin in work on non-metallic inclusions in steel ingots.[6] After the treatment the iodine-soluble portion was taken to be the metallic phase; the iodine-insoluble portion which was centrifuged off and washed with potassium iodide solution till iodine-free was taken to be the silicate phase.

According to method (a) the Beddgelert stone contains 18 per cent of free metal; almost the same figure (17·5 per cent) was found by a mechanical and magnetic separation method.

We have not yet attempted a complete chemical analysis of the meteorite but conclusions as to its composition can be drawn from an investigation with a *Hilger* Large Automatic Quartz Spectrograph (*Littrow Type*).* For the range of 2,800–4,600 Å an *Ilford* Zenith plate was used under the following conditions: slit width 0·015 mm;

* We have to thank the Consett Iron Company (Consett, County Durham) for permission to use their spectrographic equipment.

Hartmann diaphragm; copper and graphite electrodes; air gap 3 mm; current 4 amp; exposure time 30 sec. For the range 2,200–2,800 Å a *Kodak* B 10 plate was used and the current increased to 7 amp, the other conditions remaining the same.

The analyses were carried out separately on a fragment from the interior of the meteorite, without any preliminary treatment, and on metallic nodules separated from the same fragment by KOH fusion, leaching, etc. The results are given in Table I.

TABLE I

	Fragment (untreated)	Metallic nodules
Major constituents	Fe, Si, Mg	Fe, Ni
Minor constituents	Ca, Al, Ni, Cr, Mn, Na	Si
Heavy traces	Cu	Cu, Mg, Ca
Traces	Ti, V, Co	Cr, Co, Mn, Al, Na
Slight traces	Ba	

It will be noted that Ti, V and Ba are present only in the untreated fragment. Elements sought but not detected were:

As, Ag, Au, B, Be, Bi, Cd, Ga, Ge, Hf, Hg, In, Ir, Mo, Nb, Os, Pb, Pd, Pt, Re, Rh, Ru, Sb, Sr, Ta, Th,* Tl, U,* W, Zn, Zr.

No characteristic rare-earth absorption bands could be seen on examining Beddgelert solutions with a spectroscope.

Table II gives a rough quantitative estimate of some of the constituents of the untreated fragment, based on comparison with Fe reference lines.

TABLE II

Elements	Semi-quantitative estimate (%)
Si and Mg	15 each
Ca, Al and Ni	1·0–1·5 each
Cr and Mn	0·5 each
Ti	0·07
V	0·015
Co	≯ 0·05

* U and Th were detected by radioactive methods (see Section VIII).

VIII. RADIOCHEMICAL COMPOSITION OF THE METEORITE

In a number of publications between 1928 and 1942 attempts have been described to find the geological age of iron meteorites by a determination of their uranium, thorium and helium content.[7] Iron meteorites were chosen because in them the helium is safely occluded, while from most stone meteorites it tends to escape, the easier the higher the temperature. Even stone meteorites, however, are likely to retain practically the whole helium produced by the radioactive decay of uranium and thorium if they are of a dense and hard structure and their temperature has always been low. These conditions are fulfilled in the Beddgelert stone which is very hard—it cuts glass easily—and of which we know definitely that after its fall its temperature was never raised; as is well known, the heating of a meteorite during its flight through the terrestrial atmosphere is confined to the crust. We decided, therefore, to apply our methods for radioactive age determination to this stone meteorite; it promised to be specially illuminating as its high iron content provides the possibility of dealing with the metal and stone phases separately.

Before describing our procedure and results it may not be superfluous to state that we do not share the views expressed by C. A. Bauer[8] about the helium content of meteorites. It is now known that α-particles are found amongst the products of atomic disruption caused by cosmic rays, and as meteorites have during some time been exposed to cosmic radiation in space, it is certainly necessary in radioactive age determinations of meteorites to make allowance for this addition to their helium content. So far we agree completely with Bauer, but his attempts to calculate this fraction seem to us based on untenable assumptions. We hope to discuss this question thoroughly in a paper which is in preparation; for the present it may suffice to say that we believe that Bauer's grouping of meteorites according to their present museum size is of questionable value in such deliberations; that we see no reason for his belief that small and big meteorites during their flight through the atmosphere lose the same percentage of their mass and that we doubt whether the mass-helium content diagrams drawn by him have much physical significance; we are sure that the small difference in the helium content we found between two points of an iron meteorite (Bethany) could only be used for his far-reaching conclusions if it had been proved that the uranium and thorium content is absolutely uniform in every piece of an iron meteorite—which it is not—and according to our experiments there is no indication at all of the enrichment of helium near the crust, which he expects. For these reasons Bauer's conclusion that the main helium content of meteorites is due to cosmic radiation is, in our opinion, unlikely; we still believe that our figures are indicative of the geological age of meteorites.[9]

The principle of our method of helium determination is already well known; some of the latest technical improvements have been described in a recent paper,[10] where references to earlier publications are given.

In the present work the helium has been extracted from the stone phase by fusion with KOH in vacuum, and—after crushing, sieving and magnetic separation—from the iron phase by solution in sulphuric acid. The further treatment hardly differs from that used for the helium determination in stratosphere samples.[10] As to the uranium and thorium analyses, the techniques last described briefly[7] have been considerably modified by the introduction of electronic counting methods in place of photographic recording; but as we intend to describe our apparatus in detail in the paper in preparation, we will here only quote our results.

Table III gives the uranium, thorium and helium values for both of the phases separately.

TABLE III

	He $\times$ 10^6 cm^3/g	U $\times$ 10^8 g/g	Th $\times$ 10^8 g/g
Metal phase	2·8	9·1 $\pm$ 1	8·5 $\pm$ 4·9
Silicate phase	30	10·8 $\pm$ 2·7	39 $\pm$ 8

The values given in Table III are the weighted means of several determinations. For the uranium and thorium analyses, quantities of the order of 20 g of meteorite were used, but for most of the helium analyses less than tenths of a gram; it is not surprising, therefore, that variations found in the helium analyses averaged out in the uranium and thorium figures.

For an age calculation it will be necessary to determine helium, uranium and thorium in one and the same sample; only as preliminary figures we can state that the silicate phase seems to have solidified more than 1,000 million years ago, the iron phase about 200 million years ago.

13

REFERENCES

1. Carr, H. R. C., and Lister, G. A., *The Mountains of Snowdonia*, London, p. 18, 1948.
2. Carpenter, R. R., *Pop. Astron.*, **53**, 186, 238 (1945).
3. Nininger, H. H., *Pop. Astron.*, **58**, 267 (1950).
4. Stücklin, H., *Pop. Astron.*, **58**, 186 (1950).
5. Campbell Smith, W., *Min. Mag.*, **23**, 43 (1932).
6. Taylor-Austin, W., *8th Report of the Committee on the Heterogeneity of Steel Ingots*, Iron and Steel Institute, 1938.
7. Arrol, W. J., Jacobi, R. B., and Paneth, F. A., *Nature*, **149**, 235 (1942).
8. Bauer, C. A., *Phys. Rev.*, **72**, 354 (1947); **74**, 225, 501 (1948).
9. Paneth, F. A., *Nature*, **165**, 454 (1950).
10. Chackett, K. F., Paneth. F. A., and Wilson, E. J., *J. Atmosph. Terr. Phys.*, **1**, 49 (1950).

16 | The Akaba Meteorite

The *Londonderry Laboratory for Radiochemistry of the University of Durham* wishes to put on record the following facts about a recently acquired meteorite.

On September 22 of last year a Bedouin travelling towards Akaba was camping in Saudi Arabia not far from the border of the Hashemite Kingdom of Jordan when, two or three hours after sunset, he saw a flaming object falling from the sky towards him. Whilst still high it appeared to divide into three pieces; one dropping near his camp he picked up; it was a stone of deep black colour. He could not find either of the other two pieces. He broke off about a third from the recovered stone, and seeing in the interior specks of white metal he thought it might be of value; so after his arrival at Akaba he reported his experience to Mr. L. K. Williams, a mining engineer, who bought the main mass.

After reading about the Beddgelert meteorite and our interest in buying more fragments of it Mr. Williams thought that the Arabian meteorite might be one of these. (Actually its fall took place some 40 hours later, if the date given by the Bedouin is correct.) He sent us a few grams of the stone, which convinced us of the genuineness of the Bedouin's story although the two meteorites were obviously quite different. We purchased the meteorite from Mr. Williams.

Since Akaba (29° 32' N, 35° 0' E) is the place name nearest to the fall, the meteorite should be given this name. The mass received by us weighed 779 g. It was completely covered with a velvet black, very thin crust, except where parts of the stone had been broken off; here it showed a very light grey colour. Little metallic spherules were easily discernible. We have cut the meteorite and made a few thin sections; it appears to be a white chondrite, but the systematic investigation has only just started.

It may be mentioned that as a result of our advertisement of a reward of £50 for any further fragment of the Beddgelert meteorite we received about 250 parcels (and still more letters) from Wales and

England, most of them containing nodules of pyrites which are popularly known as "thunderbolts" and therefore supposed to be identical with meteorites. The Akaba meteorite is the only reward for a rather trying correspondence and much trouble in reversing the overwhelming flood of parcels.

17 | The Breitscheid Meteorite

I. THE FALL OBSERVED

On August 11, 1956, between 15 30 and 15 45 hours, a stone meteorite fell on a meadow dotted with fruit trees in the village of Breitscheid in the district of Dill (50° 51′ N, 8° 12′ E). The fall of the meteorite was seen and heard by several persons. Mrs. Josefine Reich was engaged in hanging up laundry outside her house; she heard a crescendo of sound like the hissing of an engine releasing steam. When she looked in the direction of the sound, she saw in the air a dark body approaching in a spiral path from the west; at a distance of about 40 metres it disappeared with a dull thud in the earth; she also noticed the cracking of a breaking branch. Mr. Joseph Klier, who was sawing wood a few yards away from Mrs. Reich, heard the same sound as she did but did not see the fall of the meteorite as he stood with his back to the spot where it hit the ground. Two more inhabitants of the village, Mr. Rudolf Zenziger and Miss Vorck, stood next to each other at about 600 metres distance from this spot but on lower ground so that they could not see the landing of the meteorite on the Earth; from their position, they did, however, notice in the southwestern sky a glowing red body that rushed towards the Earth along a course running from right to left at an inclination of about 40 degrees to the ground.

About two minutes earlier a jet aeroplane had passed the village. The falling object and the accompanying noise reminded Mrs. Reich of bombs dropped by aeroplanes; she therefore assumed that the aeroplane had accidentally released such a bomb, and avoided approaching the spot where it had hit the ground. However, Mr. Karl Reich, her husband, who had been working in the house and who had also heard the noise, immediately went straight up to the spot and found, next to an apple tree, a few freshly broken branches and a hole in the ground in which a black stone had got stuck which felt noticeably warm but not hot. As he could not remove it with his hands, he fetched a pick-axe and dug it out. He noticed that the stone had been broken into four unequal pieces and that there was a block of basalt which it had obviously hit and thereby been broken. Mr. Reich found it easy to put the pieces together again in his garden. He and some neighbours who had joined him were struck by the appearance of the stone, with its grey interior and black surface, but they were all of the opinion that it had fallen from the aeroplane and was probably a piece of cement, in any case without value. The four pieces were further broken up, and everybody who felt so inclined took some with him. One fragment was put into the kiln of the nearby clay works of Westerwald in order to test whether it would melt.

It was only a few days later that a chemist, Mr. Günther Thielmann, who is employed in the laboratories of the Burg Iron Works, saw one of the stones and at once suspected it might be a meteorite. After making a preliminary analysis, he sent a short article on this and other meteorite falls to the local newspaper, the *Dill-Post*, which printed it on September 1.

The *Dill-Zeitung* published on September 20 an article by another author, which, however, did not add anything essential to that of Mr. Thielmann. (The date of the fall was there erroneously given as August 4.) Since both papers have only a very restricted circulation, and perhaps also because both essays diverged into general considerations of meteorites and meteors instead of directing attention mainly to the actual fall of a meteorite in Breitscheid, the news did not reach wider circles, and the rare event might easily have been soon forgotten if the *Frankfurter Rundschau* had not inserted 10 lines about it in its edition of September 25. This short notice was seen by Miss Ilsemarie Schüler, a chemical technician, working in the Max-Planck Institute for Chemistry, who brought it to the Institute. On the following morning one of the scientific assistants, Dr. Klaus Ebert, went to Breitscheid and returned with two pieces of the stone, an inspection of which precluded any doubt of the genuineness of the meteorite.

Our first task was obviously to save as much of the scientifically valuable material as was possible at that stage. As Dr. Ebert had found that the pieces had already been distributed amongst many different owners, we inserted an advertisement in the newspapers of Dill and in the *Wiesbadener Kourier und Tagblatt*, asking the owners of pieces of the Breitscheid meteorite to communicate with the Max-Planck Institute. This invitation had no direct result, but it caused a student of the University of Marburg, Mr. Horst F. Hauschild, of Herborn, to offer us his services for the discovery of the whereabouts of the pieces. Mr. Hauschild has visited the village of Breitscheid, situated 8 km to the west of Herborn, on a number of occasions and has carefully followed up every clue. He has also made independent inquiries about the circumstances of the fall. The facts given above are based on the evidence of witnesses, collected by him and Dr. Ebert, and are independent of the reports in the newspapers. Both gentlemen also investigated the hole made by the meteorite; from its inclination and from the broken branches of the tree they could confirm the observation of the witnesses, that the meteorite had hit the earth from the west at an angle of 35 to 40 degrees with the horizontal. Owing to the scantiness of the data available from the eye-witnesses, it is of course not possible to calculate its course or speed; compared with those characterizing the falls of other meteorites, the light and sound phenomena were so little impressive that no news of observations from a greater distance could be hoped for.

In conclusion we would like to emphasize the fact that a meteorite which hit the ground in day-time and in an inhabited part of Germany, whose fall was observed by several people, and which was found without difficulty, might almost have been lost to modern meteorite research, for which such material is of great interest. We would therefore appeal to anyone who in future hears of a meteorite fall in Germany, not to confine himself to a communication to a local paper, but immediately to inform the Max-Planck Institute for Chemistry in Mainz, which is in a position to purchase meteorites from the lucky finders.

II. THE PIECES OF THE METEORITE

By persistent efforts we have succeeded in acquiring eight pieces of the broken meteorite of Breitscheid for the Max-Planck Institute. Six of these were still in the hands of inhabitants of Breitscheid; although some of those owners, having originally under-estimated the value of the meteorite, now erred in the opposite direction, we were nevertheless able to buy all these pieces. The seventh piece was most obligingly put at our disposal by a collector, in exchange for a meteorite which had fallen earlier and which could be regarded as of equal value from a collector's point of view, though not for our investigations. The eighth piece was given to us as a present by a young girl who had been on holiday in Breitscheid at the time of the fall, and who had taken this considerable piece home with her. As a result of friendly discussions, she accepted a splinter of the stone set as a pendant and wearable as a talisman. The piece which, as mentioned above, had been heated in the kiln for 12 hours up to a temperature of 1,300°C had to be regarded as useless for our purposes; it can now be seen in the local museum in Herborn.

The weight of the eight pieces of the Breitscheid meteorite that reached the Max-Planck Institute totalled 796 g. Mr. Karl Reich gave 3 to 3½ German pounds* as the weight of the four pieces dug out by him. It may be worth while to compare these estimates with calculations of the maximum weight based on the dimensions of the hole made by the meteorite. When this hole was investigated by Herr Hauschild and Dr. Ebert, it had already been enlarged by the digging out of the stone; its extension in depth was, however, limited by the basalt rock, and since the meteorite did not protrude from the hole, its dimensions in this direction cannot have amounted to more than 15 cm. From the description of the first observers, and guesses based on the pieces of crust in our possession, it seems to have had more or less the form of a brick whose longest edge had the length just mentioned. The two dimensions at right angles to it should not have amounted to more than 8 and 5 cm respectively, according to the presumed size of the original hole. From this there follows, on the basis of a density of 3·3,† a maximum weight for the whole stone of about 2 kg, which can be regarded as confirming the weight of at least 1·5 kg estimated by Mr. Reich.

The difference between the combined weight of the eight pieces acquired by us and the initial weight is accounted for by the absence of the piece now in the Herborn museum (82 g), by the using up of material for the analytical work of Mr. Thielmann (estimated at 10 g) and by the weight of a number of small and very small pieces which remained in Breitscheid and elsewhere in various hands, whose total weight, according to the investigations of Mr. Hauschild, should not exceed 80 g. In addition a not inconsiderable mass of material must have been scattered in small pieces or dust when the stone was broken up, and so lost. The severity of the breaking-up process is indicated by the fact that of our eight pieces only three, having a weight of 365 g, could be fitted together into a block; the other pieces had been altered too much by abrasion and loss to permit a trustworthy reconstruction of the original form of the meteorite.

Thus, while the combined weight of all the pieces of which we have knowledge amounts only to about 970 g, we would be inclined to assume that the original weight was approximately 1,500 g.

---

* i.e. 1500 to 1750 g. [Ed.]

† From Professor Hentschel's petrographic examination (see footnote on p. 179). [Ed.]

III. THE COURSE OF THE SCIENTIFIC INVESTIGATIONS

It is generally recognized that all meteorites are very valuable material from a scientific point of view. On their chemical analyses are based estimates of the cosmic abundance of the elements, their petrographic examination throws light on the circumstances of their formation, the application of methods of radioactive age determination reveals the epoch of their solidification, and a study of their isotopic composition gives insight into the effect of cosmic radiation on matter. As this effect consists, *inter alia*, of the production of short-lived nuclides, which have now disappeared from meteorites which fell in earlier times, freshly fallen meteorites, like that of Breitscheid, are of particular interest for the study of cosmic radiation. We therefore endeavoured to subject this stone to as many methods of investigation as possible, both by the classical and by the modern radiochemical procedures.

The equipment of the Max-Planck Institute for Chemistry, and the training of its scientific workers, allowed us to carry out the majority of the investigations within this Institute; amongst these were the complete chemical analysis of the meteorite, the age determination based on the helium–uranium and on the argon–potassium methods, and the identification of various nuclides produced by cosmic radiation. As the apparatus for the detection of the tritium produced by the exposure to cosmic radiation was not then available to us, we were very grateful to Messrs. K. Goebel and P. Schmidlin, in CERN Institute of Professor Gentner in Geneva, for carrying out investigations which from their very nature could not be delayed indefinitely. We hope to be able to continue the tritium measurements in the near future in the Max-Planck Institute. For the investigation of the isotopic composition of the rare gases, helium and neon, isolated from the meteorite, we could, as in former years, enlist the help of Dr. K. I. Mayne in Oxford. The study of the petrographic composition of the meteorite lay well outside the scope of the work of our institute; Professor Dr. Hans Hentschel, of the Institute for Mineralogy and Petrography of the University of Mainz, undertook this.

As the results of these separate investigations were naturally closely inter-related, we have thought it expedient to give a combined account of them in a single publication.*

---

* There followed three papers containing detailed accounts of the chemical, petro-graphical and radiochemical investigations by some of Paneth's collaborators (*Geochim. et Cosmochim. Acta*, **17**, 320, 323, 339 (1959). [Ed.]

Meteorites: The Number of
18 Pultusk Stones and the Spelling
of "Widmanstätten Figures"

PART I

(1) In *Nature* of July 17, Dr. Stenz[1] expresses the opinion that not more than 3,000 stones fell near Pultusk in the famous meteorite shower of January 30, 1868, and that only a curious misreading of a chemical analysis led to the usually quoted number of 100,000 stones.

The Pultusk fall is of special interest, being one of the very few—six or seven—cases in which the orbit of a meteorite could be calculated; according to the astronomer Galle,[2] for the Pultusk stones a hyperbolic velocity, hence an extra-solar origin, is proved. Furthermore, from the acoustic and optical phenomena of the fall he concluded that the stones were not fragments produced by an "explosion" in the atmosphere, but had already entered the solar system as a shower. The question as to their approximate number is, therefore, of some importance, and it may be permissible to quote a few statements from the literature which seem clearly to contradict Dr. Stenz's drastic reduction of the figure.

The well-known Bonn mineral dealer, Dr. A. Krantz, procured 34 kg of the stones.[3] He ascertained that 1 kg contained some 210 stones with a perfect crust,[4] this being proof that all the stones he counted had fallen as separate units, although some did not weigh more than a gram. It follows that this one dealer possessed more than 7,000 stones, that is more than twice the number Dr. Stenz ascribes to the whole fall. Altogether 200 kg were secured,[3] representing—on the basis of Dr. Krantz's statistics—some 42,000 stones. In the shower the smaller stones were obviously more numerous than one would infer from some collections, for which the bigger ones were preferred; but, for example, Dr. Melion's description of the 125 Pultusk stones in his possession,[5] of a total weight of 1,150 g, shows still the marked preponderance of the small type (86 stones of less than 7 g).

Now, considering that in the shower of stones the majority only weighed a few grams—the so-called "Pultusk peas"—and that the fall covered an area[6] of 17 km × 6 km of rough and partially flooded land,[7] the assumption that the total number was two or three times the number of stones recovered is very conservative. Vom Rath[4] even thinks it possible that several hundred thousand stones fell. There is certainly no reason to change the usually quoted round figure of a hundred thousand for the 3,000 of Dr. Stenz.

One gram was apparently the smallest mass anyone in the Pultusk area called a "stone" and thought worth picking up, but Galle[2] may be right in assuming in the original shower the presence of "innumerable" smaller particles.

(2) For more than a century the well-known etching-patterns on iron meteorites have been called "Widmanstätten figures", after their discoverer, Alois von Widmanstätten (1754–1849). He, however, personally published nothing on the subject, but left this duty to his friends. Four years ago, Dr. Spencer,[8] in a very thorough survey of meteorite literature, showed that the spelling of the name Widmanstätten was not consistent, the "tt" sometimes being replaced by "dt", the "ä" by "e", and so on, and stated that all the various forms hitherto used are wrong, the correct spelling of the family name being Widmanstetter. Following Dr. Spencer, writers on meteorites in Great Britain and abroad[9] begin to speak of "Widmanstetter figures".

It is certainly no use trying to decide whether "tt" or "dt", "ä" or "e" is the more correct spelling of an Austrian name of a hundred years ago; as these differences are not audible in pronounciation, both ways of writing were then considered as equivalent. The "r" instead of "n" at the end of the name is a somewhat more serious difference. A study of the history of this particular family shows that for decades both forms occurred; but Cohen, who was already aware of this discrepancy, on the authority of Wurzbach's dictionary,[10] declares[11] that the discoverer of the etching-figures himself usually wrote "Widmanstätten" and therefore this form ought to be chosen. In view of Dr. Spencer's publication, I asked friends in Vienna and Graz to inquire anew about the form of the name personally used by the scientist. They went rather fully into the question and completely confirmed Wurzbach's and Cohen's statement. Official documents are still preserved which mention Alois von Widmanstätten as the owner of a house in Graz, as the inventor of a balance, etc.

Keepers of meteorite collections may be glad to learn that there is, therefore, no reason to alter the hundreds of labels bearing the name Widmanstätten.

REFERENCES

1. Stenz, E., *Nature*, **140**, 113 (1937).
2. Galle, J. G., *Abhandl. d. Schlesischen Gesell. vaterländ. Cultur.*, Breslau, p. 79, 1868.
3. Wülfing, E. A., *Die Meteoriten in Sammlungen*, Tübingen, p. 287, 1897.
4. vom Rath, G., *Ueber die Meteoriten von Pultusk im Königreich Polen*, Festschrift Gesell. für Naturkunde, Bonn, p. 135, 1868.
5. *Die Meteoriten des Dr. Jos. Melion*, Brünn, p. 7, 1889.
6. Brezina, A., *Die Meteoriten vor und nach ihrer Ankunft auf die Erde*, Wien, p. 22, 1893.
7. *Notice sur la météorite tombée le 30 Janvier 1868 aux environs de la ville de Pultusk, publiée par la Haute École de Varsovie*, 1868; Meunier, St., *Météorites*, Paris, p. 491, 1884.
8. Spencer, L. J., *Miner. Mag.*, **23**, 329 (1933).
9. For example, Heide, F., *Kleine Meteoritenkunde*, *passim* Berlin, 1934.
10. von Wurzbach, C., *Biograph. Lexikon d. Kaiserthums Österreich*, Wien, p. 258, 1887.
11. Cohen, E., *Meteoritenkunde*, I., Stuttgart, p. 40, 1894.

PART II

(1) Since writing my first note[1] I have come across a passage in the meteorite literature which, I think, definitely establishes the view that the high figure usually quoted for the number of Pultusk stones was based on a reasonable estimate and was not due to a misreading of a Warsaw publication, as suggested by Dr. Stenz.[2] Daubrée[3] mentions this very publication, and refutes energetically the low figures therein given as being "bien loin de la réalité". He knows already (August 1868) of more than 3,000 stones actually found, and emphasizes the exceptionally unfavourable circumstances for their collection. So, evidently, it was not ignorance of the statement made by the Haute École de Varsovie, but opposition to it, based on more extended knowledge, which induced French, Austrian and German authorities to adopt the high value for the total number of the stones.

Dr. L. J. Spencer's contribution[4] to the question contains interesting details about the transfer of Pultusk stones from the Krantz collection to that of the British Museum. He is right in saying that I over-estimated the proportion of small stones originally present in the former. While the expression used by vom Rath is ambiguous, fortunately it happens that in a paper by Buchner[5] definite figures are given concerning the unsorted material which had been collected for Dr. Krantz. The average weight of Krantz's 2,012 stones was 61·2 g. His collectors seem to have paid somewhat more attention to the small stones than did those of Daubrée—who had 942 stones of an average weight of 67·5 g—but even in Krantz's material the small stones were certainly not represented in the same proportion as in the original shower, because of the difficulty, or impossibility, of finding them. For other reasons (as Dr. Spencer puts it, because "the best museums strive to acquire the best specimens") there is a further shift towards the big stones in most of the museum collections. In the British Museum the average weight of the Pultusk stones is as high as 252 g.

A characteristic feature of the Pultusk shower was the high proportion of small stones. None were collected of less than 1 g but the reports mention black "dust", and we know that in meteorite showers of this type the stones between 0·1 g and 1 g may outnumber all those between 1 g and 10 kg. Statements as to the supposed total number of stones should be accompanied by an indication as to the supposed average weight; to speak of 100,000 Pultusk stones may be misleading if the reader, or visitor, visualizes the average composition of certain museum collections. The weight of the total shower was perhaps only a small multiple of the 200 kg recovered, while 100,000 stones of the British Museum quality would make a total weight of more than 25,000 kg.

(2) As to the spelling of "Widmanstätten figures", the issue now simply is whether we want to adopt the form of the name used by other members of the family, or the one chosen by the man himself. Dr. Spencer prefers the former alternative: those who share his opinion should speak of Beckh-Widmanstetter figures, or simply Beckh figures, for Beckh is the real family name. The discoverer of the etching figures, however, had dropped the Beckh entirely, called himself Widmanstätten, and was officially and privately known under this name.

Since Dr. Spencer does not appear to dispute this fact, I do not think it necessary to quote more of the historic material from the Austrian archives than was given in my first note; but I should like here to express my thanks for all the trouble they have taken in making, or answering, inquiries, to Dr. H. A. Beckh-Widmanstetter, and Professor H. Benndorf, A. Lecher, S. Meyer and P. Puntschart. I am especially indebted to Professor S. Meyer for collecting and forwarding the material to me.

REFERENCES

1. *Nature*, **140,** 504 (1937); (p. 180 of this volume).
2. Stenz, E., *Nature*, **140,** 113 (1937).
3. Daubrée, A., *Compt. rend.*, **67,** 369 (1868).
4. Spencer, L. J., *Nature*, **140,** 589 (1937).
5. Buchner, O., *Poggendorff's Ann.*, **136,** 589 (1869).

19 The Discovery and Earliest Reproductions of the Widmanstätten Figures

The significance of the Widmanstätten structure for meteorite research, and beyond it, for metallography in general, is nowadays so widely recognized that nothing need be said about it here. About the history of this important discovery, however, surprisingly little can be found in the relevant literature; notwithstanding its considerable age of more than 150 years, the science of "meteoritics" does not yet possess anything that might be called a "handbook", a book of reference which would treat in detail all the problems connected with the study of meteorites, including its historical development. One attempt to provide such a book has been undertaken, namely by Emil Cohen, Professor of Mineralogy at the University of Greifswald; the first instalment appeared in 1894, the second in 1903, but in 1905, before completing the third, Cohen died and the book remained unfinished. It gives the early history of the Widmanstätten figures in greater detail than other works, but it suffers from one serious defect: there are no illustrations. Their absence serves to remind us how comparatively recent are the modern methods of reproduction, which would nowadays, as a matter of course, make an essential contribution to such a book as this; even detailed descriptions cannot give the impression which a good reproduction of the Widmanstätten figures immediately conveys to the reader. Both discoverers of this remarkable and important phenomenon realized that it demanded visual reproduction, and in what follows their attempts to meet this need will be described.

Two discoverers have been mentioned. One was of course Alois von Widmanstätten, the director of the Imperial "Fabrik-Produkten-Cabinett" in Vienna, who not only discovered this novel phenomenon in 1808 but also gave many years to its study, so that its connection with his name is fully justified. It seems to be little known, however, and to have escaped the notice of even such a conscientious historian as Cohen, that quite independently of Widmanstätten and, so far as can be ascertained, almost exactly simultaneously, another scientist observed the peculiar structure of meteoritic iron: an Englishman living in Naples, called G. Thomson. So far as publication in a journal is concerned, Thomson undoubtedly even has priority. His observations appeared in 1808 in the *Atti dell' Accademia delle Scienze di Siena*, **9**, 37–57, under the title: "Saggio de G. Thomson, sul ferro malleabile trovato da Pallas in Siberia".

Widmanstätten's publication of his discovery does not merely not antecede this; it does not exist at all: he left the publication to his friend Carl von Schreibers, the director of the "Hof-Naturalien-Cabinette" in Vienna, from whom he had received the material for his investigations. All we know about the history of this fundamental work of Widmanstätten (except for some biographical notes which Haidinger[1] provided later) is found in a pamphlet published by Schreibers in the year 1820: *Beyträge zur Geschichte und Kenntnis meteoritischer Stein- und Metall-Massen*.

This pamphlet is called an "appendix" to Chladni's book *Über Feuermeteore und über die mit denselben herabgefallenen Massen* (Vienna, 1819); it appeared, however, a year later and really constitutes a completely independent publication. In his own very bad style, characterized by sentences of monstrous length, Schreibers presents his personal views, which sometimes are opposed to those of Chladni's book; the format of the pamphlet also is so different—foolscap instead of the handy octavo of Chladni's book—that the two treatises are rarely found together in antiquarians' sales. The most valuable parts are no doubt the nine plates with numerous reproductions of meteorites, of which five are devoted to the Widmanstätten figures. Before we deal with these more thoroughly, we shall discuss Thomson's publication, which chronologically preceded them.

We have been able to discover little about the personality of G. Thomson. In the *Dictionary of National Biography* his name is not mentioned and we owe it to pure chance that Schreibers mentions him, as the publication which interests us here was unknown to him as well as to Chladni, who was extraordinarily well read; as it happened, the sample of a stone meteorite from Siena, preserved in the collections in Vienna, had passed through the hands of a Thomson, to whom it had been sent in Naples by the Italian Father Soldani from Siena; Schreibers reports in this context that the meteorite shower of Siena (June 16, 1794) was heard of abroad mainly owing to the fact that "several respected and learned Englishmen, Thomson, Hamilton and Lord Bristol" took an interest in it. This Thomson must be identical with the author of our article, who mentions Soldani as his friend. The interest of the other two Englishmen in the stone-shower of Siena is documented in the early meteorite literature. Hamilton is no other than the British ambassador to the Kingdom of Naples, Sir William Hamilton, who, during his long stay there, rendered, as an archaeologist, signal service in connection with the excavations at Herculaneum and Pompeii. He also described a new eruption of Vesuvius, and Lord Bristol, who resided in Siena at the time of the stone-shower, supposed the two events to be connected and corresponded about them with Hamilton, to whom he also sent samples of the stones. Hamilton returned to London in 1800, but Thomson must have stayed on in Naples, for Soldani[2] mentions in a later work a written scientific communication which he received in 1803 from Thomson in Naples.

Thomson's own publications showed that he belonged to that class of amateurs, which was particularly numerous in England, whose thorough scientific education and extensive knowledge of the literature entitled them to be put on a level with the professional scientists on the continent. The care with which he tried to investigate the properties of the meteorites experimentally was especially creditable at a time when many scientists were satisfied with putting forward more or less daring theories about the origin of these celestial bodies. Thomson's radically different attitude can be recognized in the motto—taken from Torbern Bergmann's works—which he puts at the head of his treatise and which is most fitting for the difficult science of "meteoritics" even today: "Compositio experimentis idoneis nudari potest, raro genesis".

Soldani was a general in the Camaldulensian order; he contributed to palaeontology by his works on foraminifera and assisted research on meteorites by collecting information about the shower at Siena[3] and about some other falls of meteorites.[2] Thomson considered his contributions so important that he suggested that the stones that had fallen from the skies should not be called brontolites, aerolites, meteorites or meteoritic stones, but "soldanites", and always kept to this designation in his own publications.

Thomson discovered the Widmanstätten figures in the course of his experiments on the malleability of meteoritic iron. He first published observations on the iron from the Siena stones. Then he experimented to see whether the metallic component of Pallas iron was malleable also. Pallas iron—the prototype of the so-called pallasites—was the then current name for the Siberian "Krasnojarsk" iron, containing olivine, whose meteoritic nature Chladni had recognized and from which he had developed his revolutionary theory in 1794.[4] In the course of his investigations, it occurred to

14

Thomson to treat his polished sample with acid. As the original voluminous publication is not easily available, we quote, in translation, the passages mainly concerned with the malleability of the meteoritic iron, as the ones most important for our purpose. The Italian text on which we have to rely is the translation of an English manuscript, to which fact awkwardnesses in style may be due; unfortunately one can hardly hope to find the original text of this remarkable treatise.[5]

If therefore one cannot describe the mass (of the Pallas iron) as porous or cellular, just as one cannot describe thus a granitic rock from which the superficial grains have fallen, still less is one entitled to describe the iron itself as porous, though it was thus characterized by its discoverer. It is as hard as common wrought iron, whilst the perfect polish of which it is susceptible, together with its specific gravity (9·000), show that it is not inferior to the latter even in compactness. Nevertheless, from what follows it will be seen that this iron is a mixture of three components, of which some parts are considerably denser than others, though even the least dense of them cannot justly be called porous. Although, as I believe, the polish imparted to one of my samples has contributed much to preserving it from rust, which readily attacked the other samples, nevertheless, after I had had it for seven years, the iron of the polished fragment (which I was keeping in order to demonstrate the simultaneous occurrence and genesis of iron and olivine) began to show several spots of rust and I was obliged to polish it anew. Not succeeding straight away in removing from it the dirt left by the lapidary, I employed for this purpose for a period of several seconds some diluted nitric acid, which brought out clearly the structure of the fragment, though removing the polish, which can be restored at will. Here chance had operated for me in a manner which I myself have often employed to discover the structure of composite stones by dissolving one of their ingredients. In destroying the polish, which was a purely artificial product, the nitric acid revealed to me the laminar and crystalline texture of the Siberian iron. At a suitable moment, I arrested the solution of this metal in the diluted nitric acid and made it possible to distinguish, both by their different degrees of solubility and by their differing grades of polish, the three varieties of which it is composed; and this suggested to me the idea of trying on this sample the effect of a stepwise dissolution.

I observed that its lamellae intersect each other at given angles, leaving between these angles rhomboidal and triangular spaces which differ in colour from the lamellae; and as a result the surface of the metal, which had formerly possessed a uniform polish, assumed a spotted aspect, similar to a chessboard (Fig. 27). One of these spaces (the largest to be found in the iron of $1\frac{1}{2}$ French lines*) has alternate angles measuring 76 and 104 degrees, as far as I have been able approximately to ascertain (cf. Fig. 27). The smallness of the object, and the altogether too uniform reflection from this opaque and shining flat surface, made the finding of

Fig. 27. Portion of Krasnojarsk (Pallas) iron showing Widmann-
stätten structure. Reproduced from Thomson, 1808.

these dimensions extremely difficult, as well as most painful to the eyes.

These lamellae all end as they begin in the surface of the iron and retain all its properties. The surface is everywhere in contact with a thick layer of olivine, which, in consequence, forms a continuous phase with regard to the iron in question. The structure of the iron is sketched in Fig. 27, which, although circular, will serve to represent any section chosen at random of this iron.

If these lamellae, instead of being enclosed in the crystalline matrix of olivine, had encountered a cavity, they would probably have appeared in some regular crystalline form; and from some instances which deviate from the generally curved surface of the contact between the two substances (i.e. iron and olivine), I hazard the guess that if the olivine could be dissolved whilst leaving intact the iron, one would find these lamellae much freer and more prominently crystallized. While these lamellae appear to shine brightly, the spaces are in contrast to the lamellae, and are matt, as if they were in shadow, and vice versa; and even where,

* The Paris line was 2·256 mm, hence $1\frac{1}{2}$ lines equal about 3·4 mm.

as a result of some suitable circumstance, the light reflected by both is almost the same (so that the mass appears momentarily homogeneous) there is a persistent shade of difference in their colours, the one being of a bluish hue (turchinette) the other yellowish (giallognole). But this is not their only difference! The nitric acid dissolves most easily the surface and its related lamellae, then the iron in the spaces between the lamellae, and finally, with more difficulty, a small, thin and brilliant lamella or border of flexible iron, which forms the boundary between the lamellae and the spaces which they enclose.

From this description there can be no doubt that Thomson not only observed the distinctive pattern of the Widmanstätten figures, but also noticed the constancy of the angles and even distinguished according to their different solubility the three components which were first differentiated by Partsch and later named kamazite, plessite and taenite by Freiherr von Reichenbach. Thomson must have been an excellent observer, considering how small the iron surfaces on a section of Krasnojarsk pallasite are; we readily believe him, when he says that the investigation was a great strain for his eyes. What is most admirable is that, as evidenced by the last sentence of the passage quoted, Thomson recognized the presence and low solubility of the taenite lamellae with such certainty in such an unfavourable object. His reproduction shows up very clearly these taenite lamellae occurring with the kamazite stripes. Thomson remarks that this drawing was made "to sufficient scale" to allow the details of the complicated structure of the iron, as described by him, to be clearly recognized. (It seems to be enlarged about five times.) This illustration is the first visual reproduction of the Widmanstätten pattern. In order to show how indistinct and small the Widman-stätten figures appear in the Krasnojarsk, we give a photographic reproduction of a newly etched Krasnojarsk surface in two-thirds natural size (Fig. 28) and also, five times enlarged, a portion of this photograph, in which the phenomena described by Thomson are visible without difficulty (Fig. 29).

Compared with Thomson, who did not have an iron meteorite but only a pallasite on which to make his observations, Widman-stätten made his discovery under rather favourable conditions. Schreibers tells us that in 1808 he gave him a piece of the Hraschina meteorite to study the structure of the iron. This meteorite is a perfectly crystallized octahedrite of medium coarseness. At first Widmanstätten observed that the meteorite structure showed up in

FIG. 28. Newly etched surface of Krasnojarsk pallasite. Reduced to two-thirds actual size.

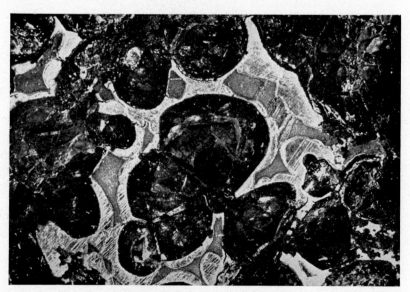

FIG. 29. Section of Fig. 28 enlarged to ten-thirds actual size.

a pattern of surface colouring, if a small polished plane section was heated—the original sample can still be seen in the Vienna collection. He soon found, however, that etching the surface with acids was even simpler and more effective, i.e. the same process that Thomson had employed.

It is especially interesting to note that Widmanstätten and his friends tried immediately after the first observations to make the phenomena known to their colleagues by reproductions. He made use of a technique which was later (1852) applied in a similar way

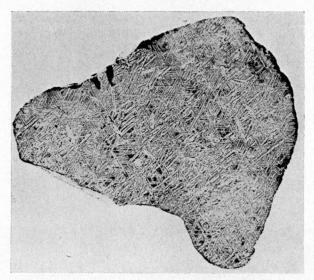

Fig. 30. Reproduction of a 'nature-print' of the Elbogen
meteorite. Reduced to about half actual size.

especially to plants, as the so-called "Naturselbstdruck" (nature-auto-printing), by the director of the Vienna Imperial printing works, Alois Ritter Auer von Welsbach, the father of the famous chemist. Essentially the object itself was used to make the printing block. We learn from communications by Schreibers that Widmanstätten's nature prints became known to many of his colleagues in the years following his discovery.* They were first published officially in 1820 in the above-mentioned work by Schreibers, on to whose pages reproductions then still extant were stuck; the illustration in Plate IX in that publication renders most clearly the structure of the

---

* References to the Widmanstätten figures appeared in various places before the publication by Schreibers (cf. Cohen, *Meteoritenkunde*, Stuttgart, Vol. 1, p. 41, 1894).

iron meteorite of Elbogen, which, having been etched suitably
deeply, was rubbed with printer's ink and used as printing block.
For the reproduction of the other illustrations Schreibers made use
of the admittedly still simpler lithographic technique, with drawings
executed apparently by very skilled experts. By a fortunate coincidence we also find in Schreibers's Plate VIII a reproduction of the
Pallas iron investigated by Thomson. This is the only one executed
in colours. We notice that the polished surface had been etched only
on one (the left) side, where one can, with some effort, discern the
phenomenon described by Thomson. The description which
Schreibers gives here of the Widmanstätten figures in this meteorite
is based on another sample as well, and is of its kind no less excellent
than that of Thomson.

As Fig. 30 we give a reproduction of the "nature-print" of the
Elbogen meteorite by Widmanstätten and Schreibers. It must be
emphasized that unfortunately the technique of this modern reproduction does not allow us to discern the subtleties of the original, as
even in a slight enlargement the screen employed becomes annoy-
ingly evident, while in the original reproduction a magnifying glass
shows additional details of the structure. In contrast to the drawing
by Thomson, this second oldest reproduction of the Widmanstätten
pattern is of documentary accuracy.

When Partsch,[6] the then custodian of the Vienna "Hof-Mineralien-
Kabinett", published a description of its meteorites, he also wanted
to include an illustration showing clearly the characteristic Widmanstätten structure of the iron meteorites. He followed the procedure
of Widmanstätten and Schreibers with a slight alteration and
improvement: the etched surface of a piece of the Lenarto meteorite
was not used directly as a printing block, but a plaster cast was made
and filled with a lead–tin–antimony alloy which was then used to
print on paper (see Fig. 31).

The later Vienna researchers on meteorites, Haidinger and
Brezina, have repeatedly made use of the technique of the "nature-
print" and others have followed them. It is sufficient to mention,
for example, the reproductions of the iron meteorites, Fort Pierre,[7]
Sarepta and Magura,[8] Tucson,[9] Staunton, Trenton, Juncal and
Ruff's Mountain,[10] Russell Gulch,[11] Oscuro Mountain,[12] and
Bethany,[13] and the stone meteorites Anderson, Brenham Township
and Estherville.[14] The similar reproduction of the Neumann lines
of hexahedrites is also feasible in this way, as is shown by a very
beautiful reproduction of Coahuila.[11]

After photography and photographic processes of reproduction had been invented, it became possible to use instead of nature printing the so-called "photo-prints". These could render the details at least as faithfully and offered the further advantage that the object could be reproduced as desired on a larger or smaller scale. The process was expensive but "thanks to the generosity of the Vienna Imperial Printing Works" Brezina could carry out extensive tests of the reproduction of meteorites in photo-print. He applied this

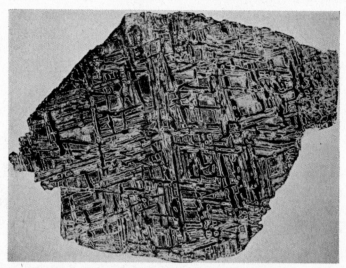

Fig. 31. Reproduction of Widmanstätten structure of Lenarto meteorite as shown by Partsch (1843) using a modification of the 'nature-print' technique. Reduced to two-thirds actual size.

technique with particular success to etched iron-meteorite plates (cf. for instance the reproductions of the Butler iron in two- and four-fold magnifications).[15]

One must not, however, overlook the fact that an arbitrary alteration in the size falsifies the qualitative impression of the Widmanstätten structure; the characteristic distinction between "fine" and "coarse" octahedrites may be completely obliterated by it. The most trustworthy of the photo-prints are therefore those which render the objects in natural size but so faithfully that the details can be investigated with a magnifying glass just as well as they could be in the original or in a nature-print. This was achieved, for instance, in the reproductions of the Widmanstätten structure in the octahedrites Rowton and Juncal and of the Neumann lines of the hexahedrite Hex River Mountain.[15] The last named reproduction especially represents an astonishing technical achievement in view of the fineness of the Neumann lines.

The results of the modern processes of reproduction, especially of the screen techniques, the "auto-typing" generally used since the end of the 1880s, although fully satisfactory to the naked eye, have yet led to a considerable deterioration in meteorite illustrations; as we have said, they do not admit of enlargement without obtrusion of the interfering screen, and the fascinating detection of substructures in the meteorite surface is impossible in these pictures. We would therefore like to conclude with the suggestion that, when one day the hitherto lacking handbook of the science of "meteoritics" will appear, if a revival of the older photo-printing technique without screens is not feasible, at least some selected reproductions should be included which show the Widmanstätten structure and the Neumann lines in nature-auto-prints by the technique developed by Widmanstätten, Schreibers and Partsch.

REFERENCES

1. Haidinger, W., *Sitzber. Akad. Wiss. Wien*, **35**, 361 (1859).
2. Soldani, A., Storia di quelle Bolidi, che hanno da se scagliato Pietre alla Terra, compilata dal Padre D. Ambrogio Soldani, *Atti accad. fisicocrit. Siena*, **9**, 1–29 (1808).
3. Soldani, A., *Sopra una piogetta di Sassi*, Siena, 1794.
4. Chladni, E. F. F., *Über den Ursprung der von Pallas gefundenen und anderer ähnlicher Eisenmassen und über einige damit in Verbindung stehende Naturerscheinungen*, Hartknoch, Riga, 1794.
5. Thomson, G., Saggio sul ferro malleabile trovato da Pallas in Siberia, *Atti accad. fisicocrit. Siena*, **9**, 42–47 (1808).
6. Partsch, P., *Die Meteoriten oder vom Himmel gefallene Steine und Eisenmassen im k.k. Hof-Mineralien-Kabinette zu Wien*, Wien, 1843.
7. Haidinger, W., *Sitzber. Akad. Wiss. Wien*, **42** (1860).
8. Haidinger, W., *Sitzber. Akad. Wiss. Wien*, **46**, 286 (1862).
9. Haidinger, W., *Sitzber. Akad. Wiss. Wien*, **48**, 301 (1863).
10. Brezina, A., *Denkschr. Akad. Wiss. Wien*, **43** (1880).
11. Huntington, O. W., *Catalogue of the Harvard Collection*, Cambridge, Mass., 1887.
12. Hills, R. C., *Proc. Colo. Sci. Soc.*, **6**, 30 (1897).
13. Foote Mineral Co. Catalogue, Philadelphia, 1912.
14. Huntington, O. W., *Proc. Amer. Acad. Arts Sci.*, **26**, 1 (1891).
15. Brezina, A., *Meteoritensammlung des Mineralogischen Hof-Kabinettes*, Wien (1885).

20

The Frequency of Meteorite Falls throughout the Ages

I. THE PROBLEM

"We can only presume that a gentle rain of meteorites has fallen regularly and impartially upon the Earth since the morning stars first sang together."

When O. C. Farrington, the late Curator of Geology in the Chicago Natural History Museum and well-known authority on meteorites, wrote these lines, he was evidently unaware of a highly significant fact which, decades earlier, the astronomer Olbers had noticed: that there are no "fossil" meteorites known, from any period older than the middle of the Quaternary. The quantity of coal mined during the last century amounted to many billions of tons, and with it about a thousand meteorites should have been dug out, if during the time the coal deposits were formed the meteorite frequency had been the same as it is today.[1] Equally complete is the absence of meteorites in any other geologically old material that has been excavated in the course of technical operations. It is impossible to assume that all the miners would have failed to report such an unusual find. For anyone interested in stones, it is not difficult to recognize the peculiar character of meteorites; this has recently been proved by the magnificent results of H. H. Nininger's campaign for meteorites in the middle west of the U.S.A.[2] After he had instructed the farmers that stones obstructing their ploughing might be meteoritic, he succeeded in collecting meteorites from nearly 300 different places in the states of Colorado, Kansas, Nebraska, Wyoming, New Mexico, and Texas. If it is so easy for farmers to unearth them from the top layer of agricultural soil, whilst none have ever been found by miners, one might conclude that they are absent from the deeper layers.

If during some periods no meteorites—or at least far fewer meteorites than today—were falling on our Earth, we may well ask if there have ever been times when the frequency of meteorite falls was greater than it is now. Seven years ago, in a Friday evening lecture delivered to the Royal Institution,[3] I discussed facts which seemed to me to prove that in antiquity the fall of iron meteorites must have been a much commoner phenomenon than in recent times. Since then I have realized that this opinion had been expressed before, by G. F. Zimmer in the course of his long and very valuable paper "The Use of Meteoric Iron by Primitive Man";[4] while some of the arguments Zimmer, and I, have used seem to me today no longer tenable, others I have since studied appear to strengthen our conclusion. A brief restatement of the question is, therefore, indicated.

II. LINGUISTIC CONSIDERATIONS

It has often been stated[5] that the similarity of the Greek word for iron (sideros) and the Latin for stars (sidera) implied the belief that the metal iron had come down to Earth in the form of shooting stars. From Professor J. B. Skemp and Mr. N. E. Collinge, of the Department of Classics of the University of Durham, I learned that a relationship between these two words is probable, or at least possible, but that the most likely semantic connection is

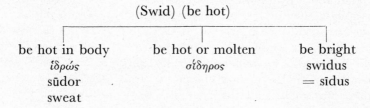

No knowledge of the celestial origin of iron can be inferred from the similarity of the two words.

There are, however, other languages in which the name for iron does indicate a connection with the sky. In the later Egyptian language, and in Coptic, the word for iron (Benipe) means "metal from the sky", for which information I am indebted to the late Professor W. Wreszinski of the University of Königsberg; the fact that the attribute "from the sky" came into use only about 1500 B.C., at a time when the Hittites are known to have obtained iron from ore, suggests the interpretation, in my opinion, that it became advisable by then to emphasize the source of real meteoritic iron which, owing to its nickel content, had superior qualities. This knowledge, possessed by the Egyptians, of the celestial origin of iron seems to indicate that in ancient times falls of iron from the sky were not so extremely rarely observed as they are today. At present, on the average, less than one fall per year is reported from all parts of our globe and not a single record exists of a fall of an iron meteorite on Egyptian soil in historical times.

This argument can be further strengthened by a consideration of the literal meaning of the Sumeric word AN.BAR for iron. According to Professor V. Christian, a member of the Austrian Academy of Sciences, to whom I am very grateful for this information, this word means "separated from the sky", i.e. a meteorite.[6] The lecturer in Assyriology of the University of Durham, J. W. Kinnier Wilson, pointed out to me that both the Akkadian word anāku and its Sumerian equivalent AN.NA indicated a connection with the sky, but that it did not stand for iron, but probably for tin.[7] This would seem to invalidate any conclusion as to an origin from the sky; however, Professor A. Falkenstein of the University of Heidelberg kindly provided the further information that also in the Sumerian language the metal in question must sometimes mean iron and not tin, for it is mentioned that oaths are delivered on daggers made of AN.NA, and that the metal of these daggers cannot have been tin, but was most probably meteoritic iron. This supports Professor Christian's interpretation.

Although, therefore, the etymological considerations based on the Sumerian word for iron are not so clear, or universally accepted, as those of the Egyptian word, it seems that most of the experts are quite satisfied that also in that language the name of iron has a definite connection with the sky. Zimmer certainly exaggerated when he claimed that nearly all the ancient folk of culture "used in their appellation for iron such words which translate into metal or something hard from heaven"; but the two cases quoted appear to be well enough established to be used as arguments in favour of our conviction that in ancient times the celestial origin of iron was common knowledge. This cannot be understood if we assume that observed falls of iron were as rare then as they are now.

III. HISTORICAL CONSIDERATIONS

Several scattered remarks in historical works lead to the same conclusion that many of the primitive peoples, who obtained their first iron implements by chipping pieces from blocks of iron meteorites, knew whence these blocks had come. When, after the conquest of Mexico, the Aztecs were asked by the Spaniards about the origin of the little iron they possessed, they pointed to the sky.[8] A Finnish saga relates that the milk shed from the breasts of aerial fairies upon the Earth turned to iron, which later a smith found and took to his smithy.[9] An inventory of a temple of the Hittite Empire which gives the geographical place of origin of their gold, silver, bronze, and copper, describes iron only as "from the sky".[10]

IV. STATISTICAL CONSIDERATIONS

These and many similar instances seem to confirm a general knowledge of the fall of meteorites in antiquity; but for statistical purposes we need to know the exact dates of the falls. Our catalogues of falls[11] go back to several centuries before Christ, but the material extracted from the writings of Livy, Pliny the Elder, Plutarch, and other chroniclers is much too scanty and ambiguous to allow of any decision as to whether falls have been more frequent in earlier days than they are today.[12] Fairly reliable statistics are available only for the last 150 years, after Chladni had made the study of meteorites respectable. From column 3 of Table I it appears that the number of meteorites falling within a decade has grown slightly between 1800 and 1939. This increase has, as far as I know, never been considered as actually proving any higher frequency of falls, but has been attributed to the increase in population, improvement of education, or better means of communication.

In the paper mentioned, I made the point that this reasoning is not only valid, but that according to the much more widespread interest in scientific phenomena and the efficient news service of our daily papers, one should expect the number of reported meteorite falls to have risen much more steeply between 1800 and 1939. It is extremely difficult to make a reasonable allowance for these educational and technical factors. I attempted to obtain an indication of the increase to be expected, by a comparison with the number of asteroids discovered during the same period[13] (see column 2 of Table I). This comparison is obviously open to serious objections because of the introduction into astronomy from 1891 on of photographic methods of detection. Recently I have tried to evaluate the human factors in the statistics of meteorite falls in a different and, I hope, better founded way, by comparison with observations on ball lightning.

The two phenomena of meteorites and ball lightning have in their appearance much in common; so much, in fact, that in some of the older reports it is difficult to distinguish between them. In either case the element of surprise, often also of shock and danger, is

Chemistry and Beyond

present, and both occurrences are so rare that the observers are hardly ever trained scientists, so that we have to rely on the narratives of common folk.

I am well aware that the reality of the whole phenomenon of ball lightning is doubted by some scientists. For this sceptical attitude the authority of Humphreys as a meteorologist is largely responsible; but anyone who takes the trouble to read the frequently quoted

TABLE I

Years	Number of asteroids discovered	Number of meteorites observed	Number of ball lightning observations
1800–09	4	17	1
1810–19	0	21	0
1820–29	0	23	3
1830–39	0	22	3
1840–49	6	32	4
1850–59	47	33	7
1860–69	53	53	13
1870–79	105	49	8
1880–89	80	40	47
1890–99	264	46	50
1900–09	776	52	36
1910–19	788	55	30
1920–29	1262	68	–
1930–39	2799	72	–

paper[14] in which to his own satisfaction he succeeded in explaining away all the reports of ball lightning will hardly be impressed. If only one person has seen the phenomenon, he usually dismisses it as an optical illusion due to persistence of vision; if that simple interpretation does not seem to be applicable, he invents, without any support by the facts, stories like an owl flying at some distance, an owl which had spent the day in a decaying hollow tree and had thereby become luminous; or he fancies a piece of red-hot iron having been melted by the impact of lightning, etc. The method used by Humphreys of freely re-editing from his desk the reports of eye-witnesses of a phenomenon he is determined not to believe is ominously reminiscent of the arguments used by many eighteenth-century scientists, including Lavoisier[15] who discounted all reports on meteorite falls; and the reason given by Chladni why such a procedure is wholly unjustifiable holds good here too: Chladni pointed out how extremely improbable it was that the reports of people in different parts of the world and in different times, who knew nothing of each other, should in all essentials be so similar. Amongst the stories dismissed by Humphreys with very ill-placed irony is one of a coachman, who saw the fiery ball rolling against his buggy and was stunned by the explosion when the ball touched a wheel. Recently a very similar account appeared in the *Daily Express* (November 25, 1952) concerning a driver who, after having encountered such a dangerous ball, had, partly paralysed, been delivered to a northern hospital.

Of course, some sifting of the reports is in this case as necessary as it was when Chladni collected every piece of information concerning meteorite falls. Such a critical survey has been made by Dr. W. Brand, who from some 600 accounts considered about 200 as trustworthy. I have made use of his book[16] to compile statistics of reports on ball lightning between 1800 and 1919; if several balls were observed during one thunderstorm, they have been counted as one, since we are not interested here in the number of balls appearing, but in that of reports about them. The figures obtained are to be seen in column 4 of Table I. If it is assumed that the number of such balls occurring per decade has been essentially constant, then the big increase in the number of trustworthy reports must be ascribed to just those human factors which ought to affect the observations and reports on meteorites. If meteorite falls too had remained constant during the same period, one would expect a similar increase in the number of reports. It can be seen from a comparison of columns 3 and 4 that this increase is far less marked in the case of meteorites, and from this fact I should like to draw the conclusion that the number of meteorite falls has become definitely rarer since 1800.

It may even be possible to get a first very rough estimate of the actual decrease in their numbers. Between 1800 and 1879 the average number of reported cases of ball lightning per decade is 4·9; between 1880 and 1919 it is 41, an increase by a factor of 8·36. The average number of reported meteorite falls increased over the same interval only by a factor of 1·55. So it looks as though the frequency of meteorite falls since 1880 was only about a fifth of what it used to be in the beginning and middle of the nineteenth century.

V. ASTRONOMICAL CONSIDERATIONS

I do not expect that any astronomer, whatever his views about the origin of meteorites, will consider secular changes in the frequency of meteorite falls as in any way astonishing; we have only to remember how much the brilliance of periodic meteor showers varies. And if some meteoriticists—to use this American expression—should still cling to Farrington's view, let them be reminded of the case of the "tektites" which we must consider as genuine meteorites.[17] No fall of any glass meteorite has ever been observed in historical times, but millions of them were scattered over whole continents in the late Tertiary, or early Quaternary, i.e. at a period which preceded the fall of iron meteorites.[18,19] Apparently since then the Earth has completely ceased to intersect the orbit described by glass meteorites, and there is, as far as I can see, no astronomical reason which would conflict with the assumption that the probability of an encounter of the Earth with iron and stone meteorites is also very variable in time. Moreover, recent experimental results make it appear quite possible that during the early history of the Earth there were no meteorites in existence.[20]

The result of our discussion is that glass meteorites fell on our Earth only during the late Tertiary and early Quaternary; that iron and stone meteorites did not fall before the late Quaternary; that centuries ago the fall of iron meteorites was a much more common phenomenon than today; and that even since 1800 meteorite falls seem to have become noticeably rarer.

REFERENCES

1. Schwinner, R., *Gerlands Beiträge z. Geophysik*, **16**, 195 (1927).
2. Nininger, H. H., and Nininger, A. D., *The Nininger Collection of Meteorites*, Winslow, Arizona, 1950.
3. Paneth, F. A., *Proc. Roy. Inst.*, **34**, 375 (1949).
4. Zimmer, G. F., *J. Iron and Steel Inst.*, **94**, 306, 342 (1916).
5. See, for example, Reyer, E., *Mitt. Anthropologische Gesellschaft Wien*, **13**, 132 (1883); Zimmer, G. F., *loc. cit.*, p. 320.
6. Christian C. V., *Babyloniaca*, t. XIII, p. 128, Paris, 1933. [This author says: "Das Ideogram AN.BAR 'Eisen' wird man auf Grund der Tatsache, dass das älteste im Orient verwendete Eisen von Meteoren stammt (s. Wainwright) wohl als 'Himmel-abgetrenntes Meteoreisen' fassen dürfen."—(Wainwright, G. A., *J. Egyptian Archaeology*, "Iron in Egypt", vol. XVIII, pp. 3–15, London, 1932, with full bibliography.)]
7. After Prezworski, S. *Orientalica*, **12**, 149 (1943).
8. Hensoldt, H., *Amer. Geologist*, **4**, 28, 37 (1889). [Hensoldt does not give the origin of his information. Iron ores were available to the Aztecs but they did not know how to extract the metal; pyrites was used as decorative stone, for instance, for the eyes of the famous Tezcatlipoca mask. (No. 586 of the recent Tate Gallery Exhibition in London).]
9. Zimmer, G. F., *loc. cit.*, p. 345.
10. Wainwright, G. A. *Antiquity*, **10**, 5 (1936).
11. The most informative is still the one compiled by E. F. F. Chladni in his book *Über Feuermeteore und über die mit denselben herabgefallenen Massen*, Wien, 1819.

12. Petrie, W. M. Flinders (*J. Iron and Steel Inst.*, **94,** 352, 1916) erroneously believes that Livy describes twenty-one meteorite falls within fifty-one years, which would indicate a very high frequency; but many of Livy's stories refer obviously to hailstones or volcanic eruptions. True meteorite showers are possibly reported in Book I, Chapter 31, and Book XXII, Chapter 1.

13. Paneth, F. A. *Proc. Roy. Inst.*, **34,** 375 (1949).

14. Humphreys, W. J., *Proc. Amer. Phil. Soc.*, **76,** 613 (1930).

15. See Paneth, F. A., *Durham Univ. J.*, **10,** 45 (1949). [See also p. 127 of this book–Ed.]

16. Brand, W., *Der Kugelblitz*, Hamburg, 1923.

17. Paneth, F. A., *The Origin of Meteorites*, Oxford, 1942. [p. 127 of this book–Ed.]

18. Paneth, F. A., *Proc. Roy. Inst.*, **34,** 375 (1949).

19. A very interesting attempt has been made to date the fall of the Libyan glass pieces from their use as implements by Late Palaeolithic, but not Early Palaeolithic man. See Oakley, K. P., *Nature*, **170,** 447 (1952).

20. Mayne, K. I., Paneth, F. A., and Reasbeck, P., *Geochim. et Cosmochim. Acta*, **2,** 300 (1952); see also further papers from this laboratory: *Geochim. et Cosmochim. Acta*, **3,** 257–309 (1953); *Nature*, **172,** 1168 (1953); and *Naturwissenschaften*, **41,** 99 (1954).

21

A Seventeenth-century Report on Copper Meteorites

A few years ago H. H. Nininger published a paper on a small coppery nugget which, according to the story of its owner, had fallen from the sky.[1] With all due caution he considered it as a well-authenticated copper meteorite; in support of this conclusion he pointed out that small inclusions of metallic copper had been observed before in some meteorites of the well-known type, and that there was one other report of the fall in recent times of a copper meteorite which, however, had not been preserved.

Considering our ignorance about the origin of meteorites and the mechanism of their formation we must certainly keep an open mind as to what may or may not fall from the sky, and approve of Mr Nininger's attitude in accepting the story of the fall of the copper meteorite because the witness appeared perfectly trustworthy. The fact that so far not more than one sample of a copper meteorite is known is no reason to deny their existence; we must not forget that for instance in the case of tektites the assumption of an extra-terrestrial origin seems unavoidable although not a single glass meteorite has been observed to fall. Their occurrence was apparently restricted to an earlier period when iron meteorites had not yet started to hit the Earth.[2]

Since the arguments in favour of the existence of copper meteorites as presented by Mr. Nininger are so few, it might be of some interest to draw attention to an old report which points in the same direction but has escaped notice. It is to be found in E. F. F. Chladni's rather rare book on "Fiery Meteors". Chladni, with infinite industry and supreme judgement, collected from every accessible journal stories which had a bearing on meteorites. In his book[3] he gives the summary of a Latin treatise of 1677 which, in view of the present interest in copper meteorites, it may be worth while making more accessible by an English translation. Chladni writes:

> Stones which seem to have been very different from the others fell in the evening of May 28, 1677 at Ermendorf, not far from

Grossenhain in Saxony. Chr. Ad. Balduin, together with the Mayor of Grossenhain, investigated the facts right on the spot, and later chemically analysed the stones as well as could be expected according to the knowledge of the times. He published a report in the Miscell. Nat. Curios. anno 1677, append. p. 247 in a treatise: *Venus aurea in forma chrysocollae fossilis cum fulmine coelitus delapsa, etc.* (Golden copper, in form of the mineral chrysocolla, fallen with a lightning stroke from the sky, etc.). If, as it seems likely, the facts described are true, the phenomenon is extremely strange, because the stones, containing copper, must have been of quite a different composition from the other meteorite stones. From the title of the paper as well as from the words: "coelo internitente crebris ignibus effudit tempestas lapidum vim" (While the sky was illuminated by frequent lightning the storm released the shower of stones), it is obvious that at the time a fiery meteor was seen which was mistaken for lightning. The stones were green intermixed with blue, somewhat like copper green and copper blue, and produced bluish streaks on the walls of the houses against which they fell. Some of them were of the size of walnuts, others like eggs. The taste was vitriolic. They were heavy, easily pulverized, and contained small golden-yellow metal grains (which seem to have been similar to copper pyrites). On the touchstone they left a streak like crown gold or brass. If held in a burning light their colour changed into blue. When heated in a crucible the major part of the substance went off in smoke and only white ashes remained (perhaps some silica). Pulverized, mixed with three times the quantity of saltpetre, and heated in a crucible it did not catch fire but developed smoke and assumed a burning taste. After having been exposed to a stronger fire it deliquesced in air as green oil, with a white precipitate at the bottom. Dissolved in alcohol with a few drops of nitric acid it produced on an immersed paper a fine green colour. A solution in vinegar was blue, and a knife dipped into it was tainted with the colour of copper. When iron was added, copper was precipitated. If the solution was concentrated by evaporation it could be used for writing in green. Mixed with an equal quantity of borax it gave a green and yellow glass. In nitric acid it dissolved under effervescence, and became blue. Distilled in a retort it gave a sublimate of a white and yellow salt, leaving behind a black earthen substance with a taste like vitriol. The sublimated salt, dissolved in water, gave a white earthen precipitate. Molten with Venetian glass it gave a flux like aquamarine and, after more of it was taken, like sapphire.

I think everybody will agree with Chladni that the story sounds convincing, and also that the chemical proofs for the presence of copper as one of the essential constituents are beyond doubt; especially the precipitation of copper on iron carries conviction. Different from the specimen described by Mr. Nininger these copper meteorites of old were not metallic nuggets but stones containing a high proportion of a copper compound. It is unfortunately not possible to deduce from the report what kind of copper mineral, and what other elements, these strange meteorites contained.

REFERENCES

1. Nininger, H. H., *Pop. Astron.*, **51**, 273 (1943).
2. Paneth, F. A., *Proc. Roy. Inst.*, **34**, 375 (1949).
3. Chladni, E. F. F., *Über Feuer-Meteore und über die mit denselben herabgefallenen Massen*, Wien, p. 237, 1819.

22 | Did Chladni ever see the Pallas iron in St. Petersburg?

As is generally known, scientific meteorite research began with the work *On the origin of the iron found by Pallas and similar iron masses, and on some related phenomena*, which E. F. F. Chladni published in Riga in 1794. It is also known that during that same year Chladni visited St. Petersburg, where the main body of this iron meteorite described by Pallas was kept, and it is therefore not surprising that the study of this block of iron in St. Petersburg has been held to be responsible for Chladni's writing his book. The well-known Russian investigator of meteorites, Professor E. L. Krinov, says that Chladni undertook the journey to St. Petersburg with the intention of looking at this strange piece of iron, and that it was on the basis of his observations there that he wrote the book. The fact that Riga, where it was published, is situated in the Baltic Provinces, which were then part of Russia, leads him to make the further statement that the science of meteoritics was inaugurated in Russia.[1]

As it seemed to me that the assumption that Chladni had studied the Pallas iron in St. Petersburg could not be reconciled with his own publications, I asked Prof. Krinov to give me the source of his statement. He was kind enough to tell me that his authority was the Academician V. I. Vernadsky who had written as follows:[2]

"On a visit to the Academy of Sciences in 1794 E. F. F. Chladni, an original thinker, musician and scientist, who gave with a great success a concert at a ceremonial sitting of the Academy, demonstrating (in the presence of Catharina II) a musical instrument—euphon—invented by him, studied our specimen of Pallasite and in the same year, 1794 (after a study of old literature) Chladni published in Riga a special paper on the Pallas iron; in the paper he undertook to prove that this iron was distinctly different from all the terrestrial bodies, that the possibility of its having been formed on our planet was ruled out, and that its origin must have been cosmic."

It is worth noting that Vernadsky does not state that Chladni undertook the journey to St. Petersburg because of the Pallas iron, but mentions, in the first place, the demonstration of the euphon. This agrees very well with Chladni's autobiographical communications, from which it can be seen that in 1794 he undertook extensive travels, in order to demonstrate the euphon, which he had invented, in a number of towns, and so arrived in St. Petersburg.[3] Unfortunately Vernadsky does not say on what data he bases his further statement that Chladni studied the Petersburg iron on this occasion, and we are tempted to assume that this is no more than a supposition—albeit a natural one—of Vernadsky who was not sufficiently acquainted with Chladni's writings.

The words chosen by Vernadsky lead the reader to assume, in agreement with Krinov's statement, that it was his study of the Pallas iron in St. Petersburg which caused Chladni to write the treatise. Careful reading of the treatise, however, makes it clear that on his long journey Chladni could not possibly have found time and opportunity to study intensively numerous rather rare works of old literature, and to publish the book in the same year. Indeed, we know, again from Chladni himself, that as early as 1792 he was engaged in studying the relevant literature. Nor can we assume that he inserted the passages referring to the Pallas iron into an essentially complete text after having studied it in St. Petersburg, since the whole argument of the book is based on the existence of this strange lump of iron. Further, Chladni's biographer, Bernhardt,[4] states explicitly that it was on a journey *to* Russia that he published this book in Riga.

But above all we must be guided by what Chladni himself tells us in his publications about the Pallas iron. He confined himself strictly to facts which it was possible for him to have gleaned from the fundamental work of Pallas before his journey to St. Petersburg. His description follows closely the well-known description by Pallas; indeed, he often even uses the same words, and nowhere does he indicate that he himself had confirmed these observations. He continually refers to observations made in the past, at the time of Pallas; the lump "weighed", it "showed", not the lump "weighs", it "shows", as would be natural if he had seen it in St. Petersburg before writing his treatise and were speaking from his own experience.

While it is thus clear that Chladni completed the manuscript before inspecting the Pallas iron, it might yet be that he had taken the opportunity while in St. Petersburg to see with his own eyes a specimen which was so important for his book. It seems, however, that he omitted to do so, for even in his main work on meteorites, published in 1819,[5] whatever he says about the main body of the iron in St. Petersburg is based again exclusively on statements made by Pallas, which he repeats for the second time, and again in the same words. He does, however, add on this occasion a personal observation about an olivine crystal, but this observation was made on a small piece of the Pallas iron which at that time he owned himself. Anyone who is acquainted with Chladni's publications knows how carefully he distinguishes between statements which he has taken over from other authors and facts which he could test himself. In the case of the Pallas iron he always says "according to the description" when he does not speak of his own specimen or of two small pieces of sulphur iron which von Schreibers had extracted and of which Chladni never omits to state that he "saw them in his collection".

Even in the separate papers on meteorites which Chladni published after his main work, there is nowhere any mention of a personal observation of the main body of the Pallas iron. We must thus assume that Chladni failed to take the opportunity offered to him in 1794 to inspect this highly interesting large iron-stone meteorite. However, this is by no means so astonishing as it may seem at first sight. He could not hope that an inspection of the iron would add anything essential to the argument of his book. He was himself at that time still quite inexperienced in the mineralogical investigation of meteorites. On the other hand, the specimen had been excellently described by so famous an expert as Pallas, and no one had ever in any respect questioned his description. The theme of Chladni's book was that an iron with the properties described by Pallas and found in the place ascertained by Pallas had fallen from heaven, and this bold assertion would not have become more convincing if Chladni had inspected the iron himself. He was inclined to believe the legend of the Tartars, reported by Pallas, that the fall had been observed, but far more convincing was a document preserved in Vienna, which, on the authority of the Bishop's Consistory in Agram, confirmed that a piece of iron in the Imperial collections there had fallen from heaven. This document, available in print, had much greater significance for Chladni's immediate purpose than a possible personal inspection of the Pallas iron. The importance of a chemical and mineralogical investigation of meteorites was only established after the appearance of Chladni's first book, when analyses executed by Howard and Graf Bournon had shown that meteorites have certain properties which distinguish them from terrestrial stones.

The following passage in Chladni's second book[6] takes up this point. "When I published my writings in 1794 I could not say anything about the chemical and mineralogical properties of meteoritic masses because I had not at that time seen anything of such things. I saw the first meteoritic stones in 1798 in Vienna." To complement the negative evidence mentioned so far, this gives us an explicit confirmation of the fact that Chladni did not see the Pallas iron in 1794.

In later years Chladni would presumably not have missed so rare an opportunity. We know that before completing his main work he endeavoured to see for himself as many meteorites as possible. For this purpose he undertook many journeys, and did not shrink from considerable detours if there was any hope of enriching his experience. Whenever he was successful in this, he mentioned it, even when his observations possibly only confirmed those of earlier investigators.

From all this it seems that there can be no doubt that on the visit to St. Petersburg the very delicate glass musical instrument and the concerts which he intended to give with it occupied the whole of Chladni's attention. His views about the origin of the Pallas iron were destined to cause violent disputes amongst experts, but only after his book became known.

Perhaps it would be appropriate to add a word about the choice of Riga as the place for the printing of the book. The fact that this town was at the time a part of the Tsar's Empire had nothing to do with the matter. Hartknoch in Riga was towards the end of the eighteenth century a well-known German publisher, who printed, amongst others, the books of Kant, Haman and Herder. To infer the existence of significant relations with Russia for Chladni's epoch-making book of 1794 would be as legitimate as to regard Kant's *Critique of Practical Reason* as a Russian publication, because it was printed in 1788 by Hartknoch in Riga.

If the question of which country was most important for the development of the new science of meteoritics in its early days is to be discussed, then Austria must be considered. The Imperial collections in Vienna contained, as well as the iron mentioned above and the unique document relating to it, the then most extensive collection of stone and iron meteorites. Hence, when Chladni wrote his book on Fire Meteors, he took up residence in Vienna for a prolonged period.

Since then political and economic conditions have changed so radically that today the Vienna collections are surpassed by several others, and Vienna is even further outdistanced with respect to scientific research on meteorites. At the present time the U.S.S.R. leads in this field. Several years ago the Russian Academy of Sciences appointed a Meteorite Committee consisting of experts, and in a specialized journal *Meteoritica* fundamental research on meteoritics is regularly published. Considerable resources are placed by the State at the disposal of expeditions for the careful investigation of new meteorite falls. Only the United States of America can at present compare with Russia in quality and quantity of research on meteorites. It is much to be hoped that in future meteorite research will receive the same support in Western Europe as it enjoyed in Vienna during the first half of the nineteenth century, and as is now accorded to it in the U.S.S.R. on so generous a scale.

REFERENCES

1. Krinov, E. L. *Himmelssteine*, Leipzig/Jena, p. 11, 1954.
2. Vernadsky, V. I., *Meteoritica*, **1**, 13 (1914).
3. Chladni, E. F. F., *Akustik*, Leipzig, p. XXI, 1802.
4. Bernhardt, W., *Dr. Ernst Chladni der Akustiker*, Wittenberg, p. 57, 1856.
5. Chladni, E. F. F., *Über Feuermeteore und über die mit denselben herabgefallenen Massen*, Wien, 1819.
6. Chladni, E. F. F., *ibid.*, p. 11.

Miscellaneous

FOREWORD

In this section are collected a few articles of general interest which do not belong to well-defined categories. The first of them—on the *De Alchimia* of Albertus Magnus —could indeed have been included in Section I, dealing with the history of chemistry, but the peculiar circumstances associated with it, which are explained in the text, seem to give it a character of its own. The Codex, as the text states, has now been acquired by the Library for the History of Science and Medicine of Yale University, where it is hoped that it will receive the attention that Paneth desired.

The article in Chapter 27, "How Old is the Universe?", was published posthumously. It is a good example of Paneth's interest in the subject which he liked to call *Cosmochemistry.* It seems fitting in this connection to quote his reply to a questioner after a lecture on this subject,* who inquired whether the belief in the eternity of matter was still held in any form by scientists, and whether isotope research had yielded any scientific result that contradicted the philosophical-theological assumption that the world was created at a definite time in the past.

"In my opinion," said Paneth, "all we can assert as scientists is that if we pursue the physical laws of nature backwards in time, we reach a point beyond which the state of our world is incomprehensible. For the formation of the double stars and star clusters cannot have taken place more than ten milliard years ago, or they

---

* See "Die Bedeutung der Isotopenforschung für geochemische und kosmochemische Probleme", Vortrag gehalten für Arbeitsgemeinschaft für Forschung des Landes Nordrhein-Westfalen, Heft 67, Westdeutscher Verlag, Köln und Opladen, 1957.

would no longer be observable in the skies. And it is the same with radioactive elements: these all disintegrate. If we assume that they were formed an infinite time ago, then none would be here today. Therefore their existence must be assumed to be finite in duration.

"To me personally it seems that, in the present state of scientific knowledge, we should not try to decide between a creation—be it unique or continuous—and a change of natural laws. We can state definitely that the known laws of nature cannot have operated for an infinite time. We are free to choose between a change in the laws of nature and a creation of the world: we do not know."

(Interjection) "Ignoramus et ignoramibus!"

"We shall not know until we obtain some information about the laws of nature at earlier times. We cannot today accept the simple standpoint of some philosophers of last century, based on the perpetuity of the world and of its present natural laws. This no longer makes sense because, for the reasons stated, the time-coordinate in our formulae cannot be given an infinite value.

"We had better agree not to use the expression, 'infinite time', as a scientific term. Like Kant, we have, I believe, to say that neither of the two possible answers completely satisfies us: if we assume an existence of the world throughout an infinite past, then we run into certain philosophical difficulties, and if we assume a limitation in time, then we encounter other difficulties, which were pointed out by others, especially Leibniz, even before Kant."

23 | A Genuine Copy of the *De Alchimia* of Albertus Magnus

In the older histories of chemistry a special place was usually reserved for Albert von Bollstatt,* usually called Albertus Magnus, who died in 1280 and was canonized by the Roman Catholic Church in 1931. His zealous devotion to chemistry was recorded and much knowledge of experimental chemistry, remarkable for his time, is attributed to him. These judgements did not stand up to later investigation, for they were based mainly on writings which appeared under the name of Albertus but were not genuine. In the Middle Ages, it was a widespread practice to gain a greater prestige for publications by attributing them to recognized authorities. Albertus, for his part, was not only famous as a theologian, but was also very interested in the natural sciences, and he knew the writings of Aristotle on these subjects as well as was possible in his time and with his ignorance of Greek and Arabic. Further, in his famous commentaries on Aristotle, he was concerned with all the natural sciences. It is, therefore, easily understandable that his name should have provided an especially popular pretext for later falsifications.

Several of the writings commonly passing under his name are such that it is clear at first glance that he cannot have been their originator. In the particular fields of chemistry and alchemy it is mainly owing to two monumental but unreliable collections of his works, which appeared in France, that this claim to his authorship has been obstinately maintained. The first complete collection of the works of Albertus was printed in 1651 in Lyons by Jammy in 21 volumes, and in spite of the uncritical compilation, the faulty text and the numerous misprints, this was reprinted in 1890 in Paris by Borgnet "unintelligently, frivolously and without any scientific understanding", as has been said by the editor of a model new edition of his scientific writings.[1]

Surprisingly enough, these two collections both contain a treatise

* More correctly "von Lauingen", cf. Scheeben, H. C., *Albertus Magnus*, Cologne, p. 24, 1955.

attributed to Albertus called *De Alchimia*—also called *Semita Recta*—although all connoisseurs of the work of Albertus, beginning with his earliest biographer, Petrus de Prussia, right down to the scholars of this century[2] have declared unanimously and without the slightest doubt that he cannot have been the author of this treatise, an opinion which everyone who is at all familiar with the genuine scientific writings of Albertus will endorse. Petrus de Prussia was a Dominican—born in Danzig and thus called de Prussia[3]—who wrote on Albertus 200 years after his death and who was specially concerned to protect him against the bad reputation which he might acquire amongst believers because of his alchemical views and experiments. He therefore took great trouble to prove, on the basis of his genuine writings, that Albertus had quite different views on alchemy from those which the book *De Alchimia* fostered upon him. He quotes verbatim Albertus' condemnation of alchemical claims, which appears in his work *De Mineralibus*, and he makes his intention clear with this remark in his powerful monk's Latin:*

"Ut quorundam fatuorum ora claudantur per ista qui forte libros de alchimia conscriptos habent quorum auctores dum ignorant Alberto mendaciter ascribere non formidant."

(Thereby to close the mouths of some fools who happen to have books about alchemy and, in ignorance of their authors, have the effrontery mendaciously to ascribe them to Albertus.)

Even at the present time, however, his objective of silencing the calumniators of Albertus has not been completely achieved. If the treatise *De Alchimia* is not genuine, then all conclusions drawn from its contents as to the experimental activity of Albertus in the realm of chemistry become invalid. Modern authors who still wish to regard him as an experimental chemist therefore understandably base their case on this treatise which, owing to an unfounded confidence in the editions of Jammy and Borgnet, they regard as genuine, or at least as possibly genuine. This applies, for instance, to name only two of the best known historians of chemistry, to Thorndike and Holmyard. In the chapter on Albertus in his many-volumed

---

* The quotation is from Chapter 16 of the anonymous incunabulum 913 of the Prussian State Library, which—according to a handwritten note inside—was printed about 1480 by Johannes Guldenschaiff in Cologne. (This early printed copy seems to be very little known; reference is usually made to an Antwerp print of 1621.) Copinger erroneously attributes this incunabulum, as number 4443, to Rudolphus de Novimagio, in spite of the fact that his *Legenda Alberti Magni* was only published a few years later by another Cologne printer and also is quite different in content. (Cf. the 2nd edition published by H. C. Scheeben, Cologne, 1928.)

work,[4] Thorndike devotes to the spurious *De Alchimia* such an extensive commentary that at least some of his readers, unlike Thorndike himself, must have realized that such pious alchemical phrases are just as unlikely to have originated from Albertus as the laboratory experience. Albertus was no experimenter!

Thorndike's mistaken idea of him as a practising chemist is also shown by his mistaken translation of the passage from *De Mineralibus*: "Experiri feci, quod aurum alchimicum, quod ad me devenit, postquam sex vel septem ignes substinuit, statim amplius ignitum consumitur et deperditur, et ad faecem quasi revertitur". This does not mean, as Thorndike thinks, "Albertus has subjected gold to fire"; the wording "experiri feci" (instead of "expertus sum") indicates clearly that Albertus did not himself undertake even the simple experiment of testing the genuineness of the gold by heating it, but that he had had the experiment carried out for him.*

Holmyard[5] states, as a reason for holding the book to be genuine, that it had been attributed to Albertus before the year 1350. He must have been thinking of the so-called *Catalogue of Stams*, a list of writings by Dominicans which is kept in the Cistercian Abbey of Stams in the Tyrol. It was compiled before the middle of the fourteenth century but probably goes back to an even older original[6] and is generally regarded as very reliable. When this Catalogue was compiled, the flood of spurious Albertus treatises did not exist, although falsifications under his name occur as early as the thirteenth century[7] and even the very careful compiler of this list included a most suspect title (*Secretum Secretorum Alberti*).† However the work *De Alchimia*, which he mentions, cannot have been the spurious treatise *Semita Recta*, as Holmyard and Thorndike believed, for the simple reason that the contents of this book clearly indicate a later time of writing.[8]

The fact that a treatise *De Alchimia* is mentioned in the *Catalogue of Stams* makes it very probable that Albertus was, indeed, the author of a treatise with this title. Since it cannot be the book *Semita Recta*, and still less one of the completely worthless alchemical writings which later passed under his name, we are forced to the conclusion that a genuine treatise by Albertus with this title did indeed exist at one time but is now lost. It is possible, however, that "lost" here means only that it has lost its independent existence. Numerous

---

* See a former correction of this mistake in translation (Nature, **129**, 612 1932), which has been committed not only by Thorndike.

† Pangerl (*loc. cit.* p. 529) has such confidence in the unknown author of the Stams catalogue that he regards this treatise too as genuine and supposes it to be Albertus' version of a pseudo-Aristotelian treatise.

scholars investigating the work of Albertus have devoted much trouble and ingenuity to establishing the chronological and contextual sequence of his writings. Many of them believe that he revised several of the works a number of times, and that on these occasions he embodied short treatises in the wider context of his later writings.[9] This might explain the considerable confusion which exists in his writings from chronological references which cannot be reconciled with one another. This supposition of different versions edited by Albertus himself has, however, also been disputed,[10] and the view has gradually gained ground that only the finding of new manuscript texts could bring clarity.[11]

It would now appear that in the case of Albertus' *De Alchimia* such a find has been made, which would solve the mystery surrounding this treatise. In a mediaeval codex a short treatise on alchemy was discovered, which seems to be the work by Albertus mentioned in the *Catalogue of Stams*.

The codex in question is a collection of manuscripts, comprising $3 + 689$ large parchments leaves ($23 \cdot 5 \times 33 \cdot 7$ cm, pages $1-1,378$). Forty-two treatises, mostly on medical subjects, have been entered in two columns in beautiful, careful writing (see Fig. 32). To judge from the type of writing, the work was done in Upper Italy, possibly in Bologna, shortly after 1300 A.D. It contains many initials, decorated with miniatures on a gold background, which refer to the text (see Figs. 33 and 34). It is especially remarkable that many of these miniatures were apparently executed not in Italy but in Bohemia, since they show the influence of the distinguished Prague school of illuminators of the fourteenth century.

That the codex was indeed domiciled in Bohemia shortly after its compilation is attested by a Latin-Czech glossary of the names of flowers that has been entered on one of the empty pages, and by an obituary notice of the year 1326. This codex has recently been mentioned in the daily press on the occasion of its acquisition by the Library for the History of Science and Medicine of Yale University; it had previously been in the possession of the family of the author for some eighty years. During the 1920s the well-known historian of medicine, Professor Karl Sudhoff, kept it in his Institute for the History of Medicine in Leipzig for some time for closer investigation, and he has published on authoritative illustrated description.[12]

So far as the various medical contents are concerned, Sudhoff's description mentions that the text begins with six articles from the *Ars Medicinae* "which had in the middle of the twelfth century become the first textbook for instruction in Salerno and by the

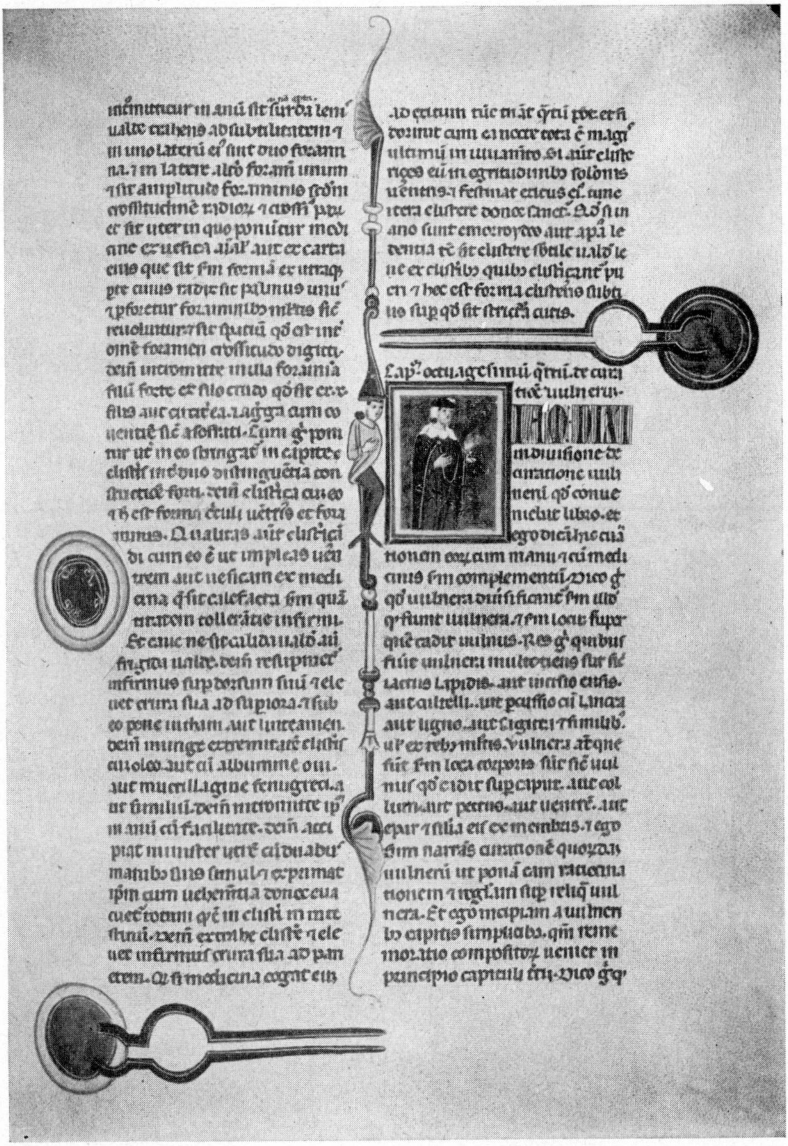

FIG. 32. Opening of the 84th chapter of the *Surgery* of Abû 'L Qâsim, on the treatment of wounds.

FIG. 33. Opening of the *Liber Urinarum* of Theophilus.

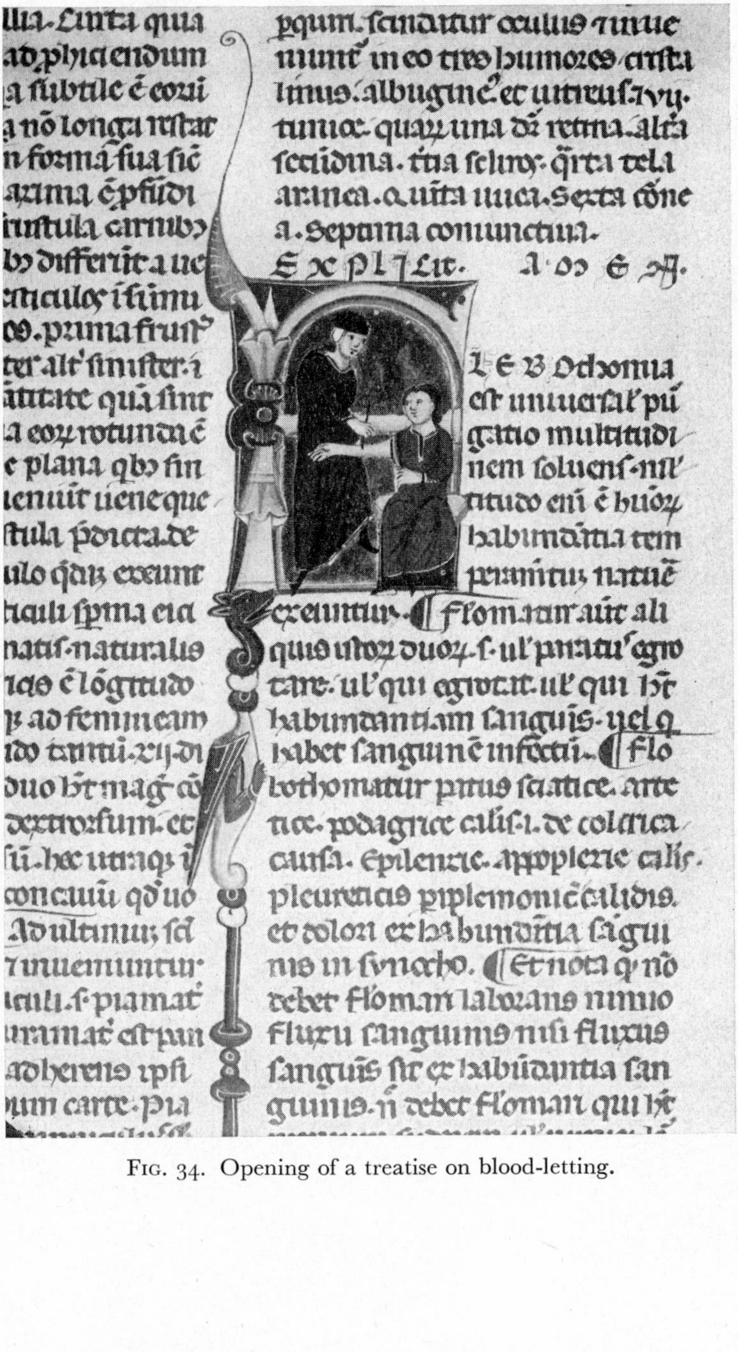

Fig. 34. Opening of a treatise on blood-letting.

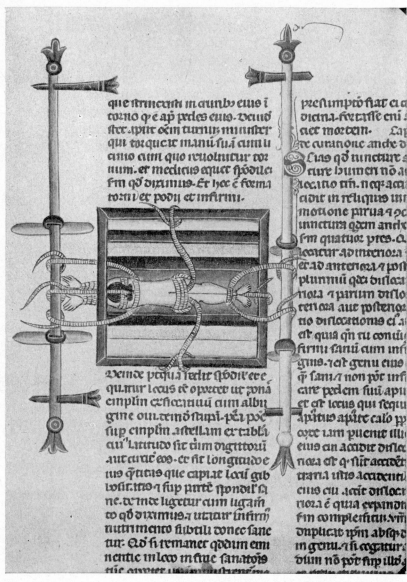

Fig. 35. Apparatus for stretching the spine, from the *Surgery* of
Abû 'L Qâsim.

beginning of the thirteenth century had also been introduced, for instance, in Paris; it later made its way through all the universities". This is supplemented by "elementary didactic material of the early days of Western European academic activity", as is shown by two short texts on anatomy from Paris and Salerno. There follow articles about venesection, urine examination, and taking the pulse, various collections of medical aphorisms, writings of Hippocrates and pseudo-Hippocratic treatises. The surgical treatise of Abu' L Qâsim is especially voluminous—comprising 150 of the parchment pages—and richly illustrated with pictures of instruments (Fig. 32); amongst them is a particularly striking representation of the stretching of the spine (Fig. 35). The major part of the originally Arabic work consists of a translation of the Ar-Râzî into Latin, but noteworthy also are the health tables of Abu 'L Hasan al Muchtar, which are made clear by the masterly lay-out of the text.

In conclusion, it may be stated that the manuscript combines Salernian and French medical textbooks with ancient traditions. Two books on vegetable pharmacology and one on the remedial properties of jewels are somewhat exceptional. The concluding treatises deal with veterinary care and remedies, i.e. with falcon breeding, and equine medicine.

The contents of the codex show little connection with Upper Italy, where it was written down; most of the material comes from the southernmost part of Italy and from southern and central France. "It seems to me that the pattern of the codex Paneth belongs to that interesting group of manuscripts which combine Salernian and French material. The conjunction of the items in this large sumptuous volume contributes almost more to its interest than do the individual contents, which naturally provide what was mainly common knowledge. With regard to that, only a detailed study of the wording of the individual texts can show whether the manuscript before us might be of value for a new edition, a study which at the moment I do not propose to undertake."

The codex clearly aims at an encyclopaedic presentation of the sum-total of the medical knowledge of its time, and the fact that it was brought to Bohemia from Upper Italy, even before its complement of miniatures was completed, makes it probable that it was written in response to an order received from Bohemia. A short description issued by Yale University makes the suggestion that the manuscript might have been written for the medical faculty planned at the University of Prague. After prolonged preparation, this university was founded in 1348 at the instigation of the German king, and later Emperor, Charles IV, and with the permission of the Pope; it was the first University of the German nation within the territory of the Holy Roman Empire. It is, of course, possible that, even before the founding of the University, there were some in Prague who were seeking for texts for the intended instruction in medicine, and it is known that at that time there were close scientific contacts between Prague and Bologna.

From the type of medical writings included, Sudhoff draws the conclusion that the selection must have taken place considerably earlier than the inscribing of the text in Upper Italy: "If such a comprehensive manuscript of applied, didactic and general knowledge in medicine had been compiled in Bologna or in Padua round about 1320, the contents would have shown quite a different character". This statement with regard to chronology is important for our further considerations.

Sudhoff refers briefly to the fact that in the middle of the codex some non-medical writings are found, which he calls an "alchemical–magic interlude". The magic writings derive from Arabic ones and are connected with pseudo-Platonic writings on magic.* Their inclusion within the framework of a medical encyclopaedia is, however, not quite so incongruous as the expression "interlude" would lead one to suppose; several of the medical treatises belong to the same group, as, for instance, the article on the prognostication of death, wrongly ascribed to Hippocrates, in which for example, from the patient's wish for certain foods, the conclusion is drawn that he will die on the forty-fifth day thereafter. The superstitious prognoses and recipes of the pseudo-Hippocratic books form a bridge to the pseudo-Platonic books on magic; the book about the miraculous properties of the precious stones belongs to the same school of magic.

What we are interested in is mainly the alchemical treatise of four pages (see Figs. 36–39) which Sudhoff mentions only *en passant* and which presents some characteristic features which set it apart from all the others. It is anonymous, begins without the customary "Incipit" and concludes as abruptly without an "Explicit". The handwriting, too, is not quite the same as in the main body of the book; it is somewhat less careful, and more concise abbreviations are used, so that the treatise is occasionally difficult to decipher. It soon became obvious, however, that we were here concerned with

* Cf., e.g., H. Ritter, *Vorträge der Bibliothek Warburg*, p. 115, 1921/22. "These magic recipes are designated by the Persian word 'nirendsh' or the Greek word 'nawamis', i.e. nomoi. The latter name seems to come from the title of a pseudo-Platonic book of the Laws, which has been preserved in Arabic, Hebrew and Latin; the latter, e.g., in the codex Paneth." (Here it is called *Liber institutionum activarum Platonis*.)

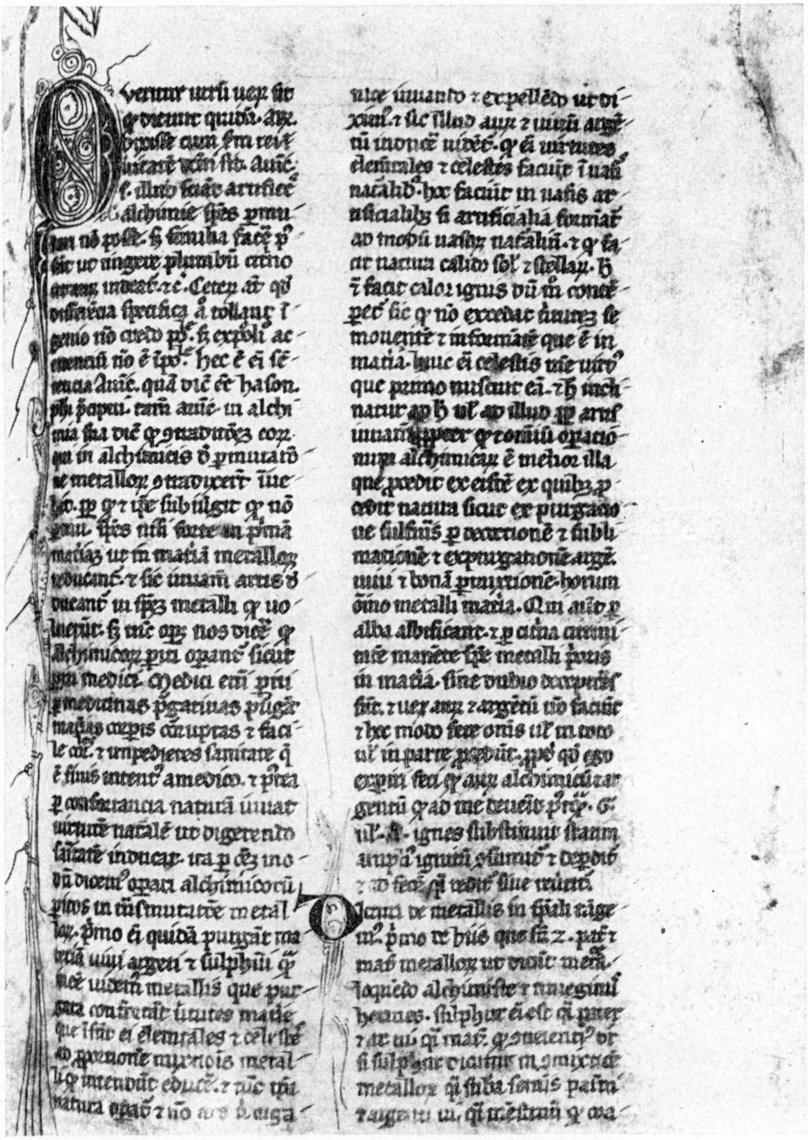

Fig. 36. Opening of the alchemical treatise.

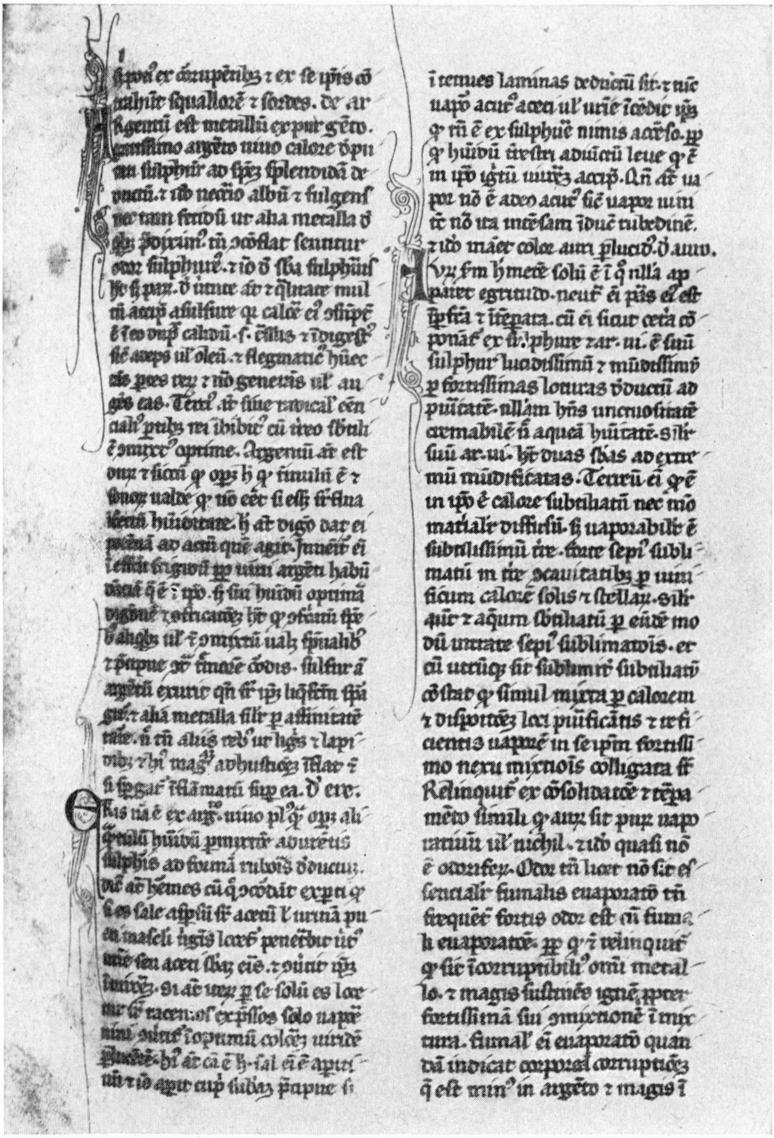

FIG. 37. Second page of the alchemical treatise.

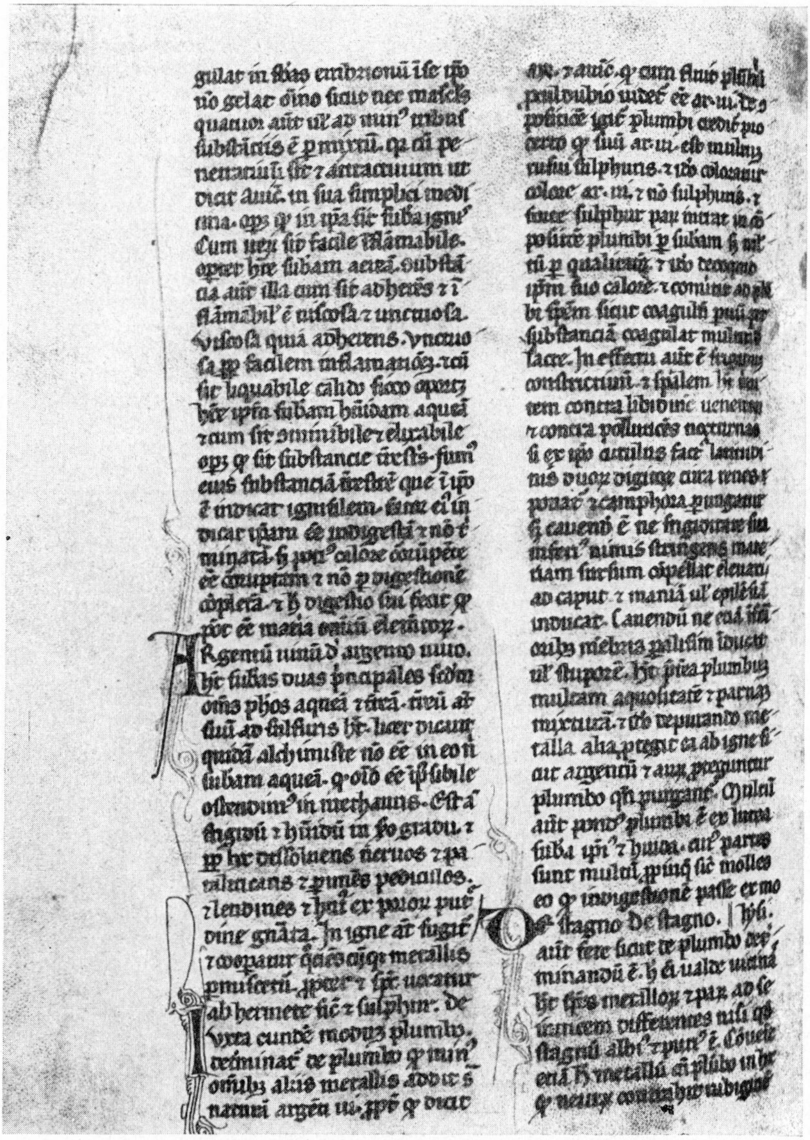

Fig. 38. Third page of the alchemical treatise.

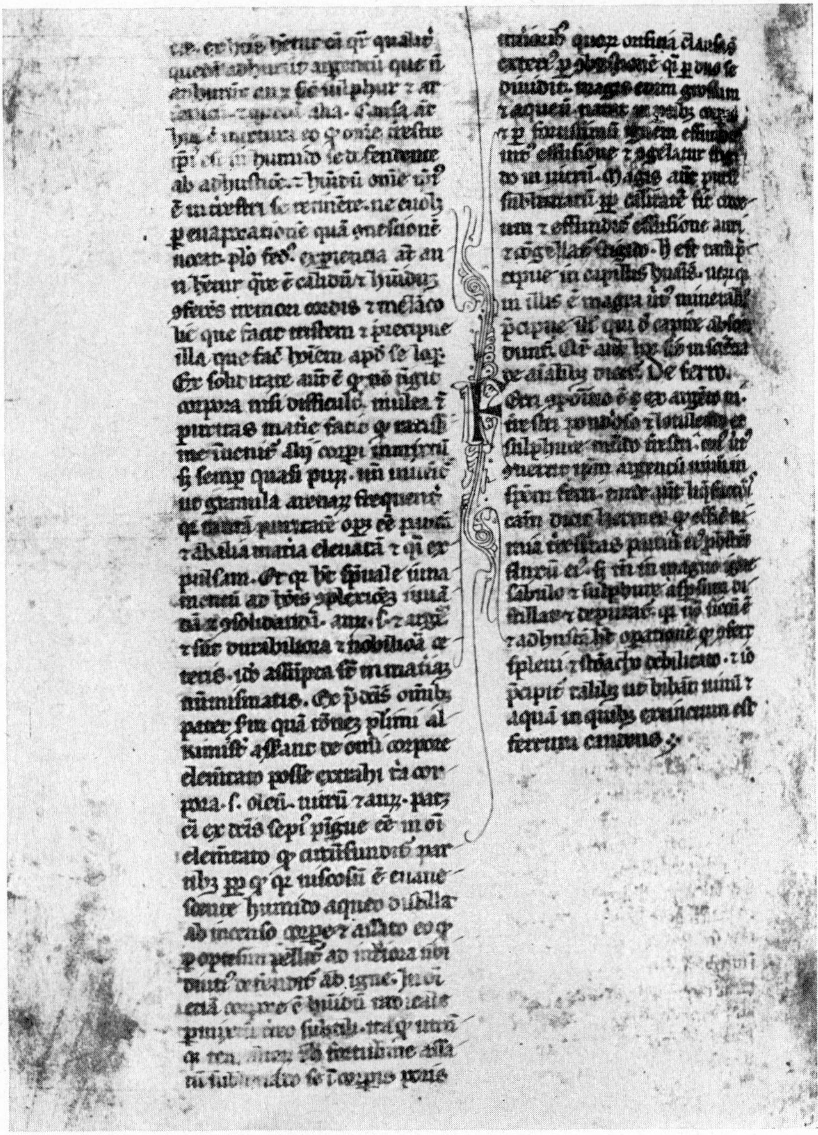

FIG. 39. End of the alchemical treatise.

a philosophical treatise on the composition and possible transmutation of the elements, and the wording occasionally seemed to coincide with well-known quotations from the writings of Albertus Magnus. The pursuit of this clue revealed the fact that everything in this short treatise occurs scattered, but in very similar form, in Albertus' much more comprehensive treatise, *De Mineralibus*, more specifically in Liber III, Tractatus I, Caput IX and in Liber IV, Tractatus Unicus, Caput I to VIII.*

The question that now arose was that of the relation of the text in *De Mineralibus* to this much shorter treatise. Was the latter perhaps an extract from *De Mineralibus* or, on the other hand, a much earlier version? A thorough investigation revealed that only the second interpretation is possible.

Albertus' treatise *De Mineralibus* has been printed many times. In addition to the complete works edited by Jammy and Borgnet, already mentioned, six earlier printed editions of this separate treatise were available to me, viz. Cologne 1491, Venice 1495, Oppenheim 1518, Venice 1518, Augsburg 1519 and Cologne 1569.

Also, I was able to look at two good early manuscripts, the codex lat. number 353 of the Munich State Library, dating from the thirteenth century, and the manuscript MS 5 (Wall) quarto of the Wallenroth Library in Königsberg in East Prussia. There is so much accordance in essentials between the manuscripts and prints that, for our present purposes, we can disregard such discrepancies as there are. The reasons for believing that the anonymous manuscript is an earlier version are briefly the following.

If the manuscript were an extract from *De Mineralibus* one would have to assume that the work was done with quite extraordinary expertise. For the manuscript presents a transparently clear, well

---

* In "Über eine alchemistische Handschrift des 14. Jahrhunderts, und ihr Verhältnis zu Albertus Magnus' Buch *De Mineralibus*" (Archiv für Geschichte der Mathematik, der Naturwissenschaften und der Technik, 1, Leipzig, 1929, p. 408), which refers to this same document, F. A. Paneth had stated: "We shall refer to the printed text of *De Mineralibus* simply as 'D'. The text of the manuscript we are investigating here shall be called 'H'. Their mutual relationship is as follows: The total text of H is contained in the much more comprehensive D. The first part of H, which discusses the possibility of a transmutation of metals in general, is found with only a minor amplification in Liber III, Tractatus I, Caput IX of D; the second part of H, which treats of the seven metals separately, is found in Liber IV, Tractatus Unicus, Caput I to VI of D. In this second part D is roughly three times as voluminous as H; the sequence of the substances discussed is the same (a rather significant one, since it is unusual: sulphur, mercury, lead, tin, silver, copper, gold, iron); within the sections, however, the sentences of H are not only embedded in a more comprehensive new text, but their order is frequently changed as well. In spite of this, the verbatim agreements are so close that there can be no doubt that a very close connection exists between H and D." [Ed.]

laid out treatise on the possibility of a transmutation of elements and on the properties of all the metals, on the assumption of their synthesis from sulphur and mercury; the treatise is closely related to the teachings of Geber and Avicenna. In *De Mineralibus* the internal coherence of the argument is obscured by a superfluity of far-ranging discussions as well as by much new factual material, so that the resulting treatise is far removed in content from the teachings of the Arabic chemists, and is so confused in its presentation that it would be extremely difficult to produce a short extract as homogeneous as our manuscript.*

All the passages of the manuscript can be found in *De Mineralibus*, mostly, moreover, verbatim. It is significant for our argument, however, that in several places the text of the other manuscripts and prints mentioned is obviously corrupt, while the anonymous manuscript presents the correct version. Two instances must suffice: In the "silver" passage, *De Mineralibus* says: "Sulphur autem exurit argentum quando spargitur super argentum liquefactum". It is chemically a nonsensical experiment to strew sulphur on molten silver.† The anonymous manuscript says: "Sulfur autem argentum exurit, quando super ipsum liquefactum spargitur". This version also indeed admits the interpretation that the "liquefactum" applies to "ipsum" (i.e. silver); but it is more likely that "liquefactum"

---

* In the article quoted in the previous footnote, F. A. Paneth also says: "Further, the form of the transitions to the text of H in D leads us to assume that H has been incorporated with other material, with the intention of producing a new treatise having a homogeneous appearance. E.g., H begins briefly: 'Quaeritur utrum verum sit . . .'. D says: 'Ex omnibus his inductis possumus considerare, utrum verum sit . . .'. After this cumbersome introduction, however, there follows nothing more significant in matter of fact than after the 'Quaeritur' in H; other passages of H are introduced into D with equally fulsome transitions." [Ed.]

† F. A. Paneth, (loc. cit.): "I have considered it desirable to convince myself by a few laboratory experiments that the correct text must mean the melting of the sulphur and not of the silver. If one scatters sulphur on molten silver, only some of the sulphur is burnt without causing any effect, and there is formed a layer of silver sulphide floating in the silver, but its dark colour becomes visible only after it has cooled down and one has scratched the regulus with a file, since the surface all the time remains white because of its contact with air. The 'burning' of silver in any case cannot be called a striking phenomenon if the experiment is arranged this way. If, on the other hand, molten sulphur is poured on solid silver—an experiment which in any case is much easier to carry out, owing to the much lower temperature needed for the melting of the sulphur—the surface of the silver immediately becomes deep black in colour; a silver sheet reacts all through its thickness, so that the blackened part becomes brittle and breaks out if even lightly touched. This specific 'burning' effect of molten sulphur on silver (in contrast to its effect on wood, stone, or, as mentioned later in the text, on gold) is so impressive that there can be no doubt that this is the intended experiment. (N.B. for possible repetitions: the sulphur must be heated beyond the viscous state nearly to its boiling point; the liquid sulphur first produced by gentle heating—which was probably passed over unnoticed by the coarser methods of earlier centuries—hardly attacks the silver at all.)" [Ed.]

goes with "sulfur", especially if one takes into account the fact that in the next sentence, which deals with the effect of sulphur on other metals, we find the closely analogous and not at all ambiguous construction: "si (sulfur) spargatur inflammatum super ea". In this passage, then, the text of the anonymous manuscript admittedly does not exclude the possibility of a misunderstanding, but is still correct, while the text of *De Mineralibus* has unambiguously come down on the side of the misunderstanding. Another fact carries even greater conviction. In all the texts of *De Mineralibus* accessible to me, in the passage about mercury, we find, after the mention of its volatility: "Propter quod ab Hermete vocatur sicut et sulphur"—a completely unintelligible sentence, which, however, finds a fully satisfactory explanation in the surely correct amplification: "Propter (quod) et spiritus vocatur ab Hermete sicut et sulphur".

The version preserved in the medical codex thus proves to be in some passages obviously better, and for this reason probably earlier, than the known manuscripts and prints of *De Mineralibus*. If we take this as proven, the further question arises: which version was written by Albertus? To begin with, it can be regarded as established that the text of *De Mineralibus* handed down to us is by him. This seems to apply *a fortiori* to the part with which we are concerned, since the section on copper contains the passage (missing from our manuscript) which runs: "in nostris partibus, Parisiis videlicet et Coloniae et in aliis locis in quibus fui et vidi experiri": this has always, and surely justifiably, been regarded as a rendering of personal experience. The first conjecture to which this leads us is that our manuscript might have been one of the known sources which Albertus used and incorporated almost verbatim in his more comprehensive works, often without quoting the authors. This interpretation, however, does not seem possible, since no text is known of those authors who are the most likely to be involved that bears even a remote resemblance to it so far as I have been able to ascertain by consulting the encyclopaedias of Arnoldus Saxo,* Thomas de Cantimpré,† and Bartholomaeus Anglicus.‡

The only further possibility, as a source for Albertus, would be a hitherto unknown author,[13] but this also is ruled out by the consideration that in our manuscript, as well as in *De Mineralibus*, the writer speaks of himself in the first person, and does this in such an

---

* Printed by E. Stange in the *Beilagen zum Jahresbericht des Gymnasiums zu Erfurt*, 1904–05, 1905–06, 1906–07.

† There is no printed copy; the municipal library of Breslau permitted the use of its famous illustrated manuscript.

‡ The early copy printed by A. Koberger (Nürnberg, 1483) was used.

important passage as the one quoted previously (p. 217) which shows, amongst other things, that he did not carry out experiments himself. The reasons for believing that this passage was written by Albertus are no less cogent: while he has often been reproached[14] for not mentioning the writers who collected scientific data before him, he has never been explicitly accused of going further and presenting as his own experience what did not originate from him; and since the passage just quoted is found without any alteration in *De Mineralibus*, we must consider that it was written by him.

Apparently Albertus wrote first a short treatise on the theoretical aspects of the composition of the metals and their mutual transmutations, which he then incorporated in this more comprehensive work, *De Mineralibus*—a process which did not enhance its lucidity.

If we wished to give a title to the anonymous manuscript, it would be difficult to find one more fitting than that given to it by a later user of the codex in a handwritten table of contents on one of the blank pages; this reader apparently did not guess who the author of the treatise was, but he characterized the contents aptly by the title: *De mettallis et Alcimia*. This immediately reminds us of the entry in the *Catalogue of Stams*, which mentions amongst Albertus' writings an independent treatise entitled *De Alchimia*!

We therefore suggest the explanation that in early days there existed a separate treatise by Albertus, called *De Alchimia*, and that it was apparently being copied up to the time of its incorporation in his larger work. One of the copies seems to have been preserved in Italy or France and, like the book on magic, to have been inserted somewhat thoughtlessly when the medical codex was compiled. Sudhoff's proof that this compilation took place after 1250, and in any case considerably earlier than the calligraphic transcription, agrees well with our assumption that the treatise of Albertus lost its independence during his lifetime, but yet existed for some time during the thirteenth century as a separate work.

The sporadic occurrence and the anonymity of the treatise need not surprise us, as there are definite records that Albertus, who often visited Italy and France, liked to present the monasteries in which he stayed on his travels with some treatise he had written, as a parting gift;[15] one would naturally not expect such documents to contain the author's name or the usual "Incipit" or "Explicit".

Pangerl[16] discussed some time ago the possibility that the title "De Alchimia" in the *Catalogue of Stams* referred to a part of the book *De Mineralibus*. He based his argument on Petrus de Prussia, who, as mentioned above, attempted to infer Albertus' attitude to alchemy from this work. Petrus correctly realized the importance and relative independence of the section about alchemy in the more comprehensive work,* but apparently he did not then know the independent short treatise, *De Alchimia*; otherwise he would surely have mentioned it, as it happens to contain the particularly important passage quoted by him, in which Albertus expresses the conviction that the alchemists are cheats and cannot make genuine gold. We completely agree with Petrus de Prussia and Pangerl insofar as we assume that the most essential pronouncements by Albertus about alchemy are to be found in *De Mineralibus*. The fact that, in all the prints and manuscripts of this work so far examined, passages of the text, which are correct in our manuscript, appear in a corrupt form, inclines one to believe that these mistakes were slips, perpetrated by Albertus himself when he inserted the short *De Alchimia* into the text of *De Mineralibus*. While it is usual to accord the highest praise to Albertus for the immense extent of his activity as a writer, Stadler[17] has shown, by a large number of entertaining examples, that, just because of the rapidity of his production, he was often astonishingly careless in his treatment of the texts before him—an attitude which contrasts strangely with his reliable description of his own observations.

The reasons here given, and some additional ones, were published some years ago, together with a copy of the treatise, in two articles.†

---

* Petrus's uncommonly sound judgement has often been emphasized, e.g. by C. H. Scheeben (*Revue Thomiste*, **14,** 260 1931): "Pierre de Prusse attaque les sources avec un sens critique vraiment extraordinaire pour son époque".

† Paneth, F. A., *Archiv für Geschichte der Mathematik, der Naturwissenschaften und der Technik*, **12,** 33 and 408 (1929). The following somewhat condensed passages are relevant in this connection:

(1) In addition to this general impression a number of individual passages contribute to favour the supposition that D (see footnote on p. 229) was written later than H, e.g. in H it is stated of sulphur and mercury "quae sunt et pater et mater metallorum" while D says "quae quasi universalia metallorum sunt, sicut pater et mater". Similarly, H says almost immediately afterwards, with reference to sulphur, "materia omnium elementorum", while D has "materia universalis omnium elementorum". H adds to the deductive proof that gold must always be rare, only that it indeed always occurs in small grains; D adds the modification "tamen jam inventus est granum centum marcharum simul".

(2) H too is a part of a more voluminous work following a similar plan to D, for in both there are found in exactly corresponding places—in the sections about mercury and gold—the references "ostendimus in metheoris" and "in scientia de animalibus dicetur".

(3) If, finally, a more general argument is to be adduced, one may well say that not only D but also H shows everywhere "le cachet de cette latinité barbare" which M. Bormans (*Bull. Acad. royale, Bruxelles*, 1852) had already emphasized as characteristic of Albertus.

(4) H is then, as it were, a general introduction which differs little from the Arabic models, but its text was amplified later for an independent textbook D.

The conclusion then reached, that we have before us a short genuine treatise by Albertus which was later incorporated in *De Mineralibus* in an enlarged version, has, so far as we know, not been disputed. Even so, it might not be superfluous to adduce one further argument for this view, which only came to mind later, namely, the known fact that Albertus worked into several of his longer writings certain so-called *Quaestiones*, which he had written down earlier. It seems that Pelster[18] was the first to notice that in some parts of Albertus' *De Unitate Intellectus contra Averroistas* the style is not of the "simple explanatory type, as manifested in the commentaries", but "the structure of a Quaestio disputata shows through", and that even later, when he wrote the *Summa Theologiae*, Albertus included the same *quaestio*, "though probably here too with slight alterations", in the new work.

Similarly, Planzer[19] has pointed out, on the basis of his study of the titles of mediaeval Albertus manuscripts in library catalogues, that in Albertus' writings on logic and also in his expositions of physics, different forms seem to occur, *commenta* and *quaestiones*. The point in which we are interested is clarified even more by a discovery which Wingate[20] has made in a manuscript of the fourteenth century. There we find: "Quaestiones super de animalibus quas disputavit frater Albertus, repetendo librum animalium fratribus colenie". These are notes concerning lectures which Albertus delivered in 1258 in Cologne on the book *De Animalibus* by Michael Scot. His own book, *De Animalibus*, was not written before the sixties; we can therefore, as Wingate says, "regard these questions . . . as a sort of preliminary study for the longer work". The questions mentioned begin always by "Queritur utrum"; our alchemical text begins with the identical phrase! In the later, more extensive, chapter of *De Mineralibus*, however, the character of this "quaestio" is obscured by

---

(5) This theory does not seem unlikely in view of the fact that the writing down of Albertus' commentaries on Aristotle took a long time (according to Pelster, from 1250 to 1270—*Stimmen der Zeit*, 2nd series, No. 4. Herder, Freiburg i. Br., 1920); cf. also the statements by H. Stadler about the "Archetypus der Tiergeschichte" (*Sitzber. Bayer. Akad. der Wiss.*, No. 1. p. 5, 1912); some scholars even assume as a first step the gathering together of a collection of appropriate material by Albertus (cf. J. A. Endres, Hertling–Festschrift, Freiburg i. Br., p. 96, 1913), which would agree closely with our assumption of two versions; further, it has been proved that Albertus worked on some treatises at different periods of his life (e.g. on the *Liber de principiis motus processivi;* cf. Stadler, H., *Programm des Maximilians-Gymnasiums*, München, 1909) and cases are known of parts of his treatises becoming publicly known and copied before the finished work was published by him. (This is proved for Albertus' treatise on falcons, which was incorporated in the encyclopaedia of Vincence of Beauvais before the publication of his *De Animalibus* (see Pelster, F., *loc. cit.* p. 101).) [Ed.]

the fulsome introduction: "Ex omnibus autem his inductis possumus considerare, utrum . . .". Our supposition that Albertus at a later date revised his earlier treatise, *De Alchimia*, which had been linked to a "Queritur utrum", thus receives unexpected new support from the knowledge that he applied an analogous procedure in another scientific work.

We have occasionally had to venture into the realm of hypothesis. The following points, however, can be regarded as safely established:

1. Amongst the writings of Albertus Magnus, we find mentioned, at a time when few falsifications were to be expected, one entitled *De Alchimia*.
2. The treatise *De Alchimia* (or *Semita Recta*) which has been included in a number of his collected works is spurious.
3. In a medical collection dating from the beginning of the fourteenth century—which, however, comprises considerably older treatises—an anonymous manuscript on alchemy is found.
4. The opinion concerning alchemy, which an earlier biographer attributes to Albertus, is expressed in a concise form in this manuscript, and, mixed with other subject matter, in the treatise *De Mineralibus*.
5. This manuscript and *De Mineralibus* have Albertus as their author.
6. The introductory words of the newly found manuscript ("Quaeritur utrum") are those usual at the beginning of short disputations.
7. In several passages, only the newly found manuscript has the correct text.

From these considerations we venture to draw the conclusion that a treatise by Albertus Magnus entitled *De Alchimia* was later incorporated by himself in *De Mineralibus*, but that a copy of the original text was inserted during the thirteenth century into the material collected for a medical codex and has thus been preserved. As this is obviously the treatise *De Alchimia* mentioned in the *Catalogue of Stams*, we hope that its identification will finally remove all grounds for supposing that this was an alternative title for the spurious treatise *Semita Recta*, and that Petrus de Prussia's ardent desire to erase this blot on Albertus' memory will at last be realized.

The conclusion that the anonymous treatise is often more correct than other available manuscripts and prints of *De Mineralibus* must not be taken to imply that it is itself free from textual errors. In many places other texts are preferable. It would, indeed, be worth while to compare these texts in order to eliminate from the treatise

17 (20 pp.)

the easily recognizable mistakes in copying, and so to attempt to recover the correct text of Albertus' genuine treatise *De Alchimia*. As the codex has now found a home in a library devoted to the history of medicine, it will presumably be used mainly for research in this field, and it was very pleasant to hear from the Librarian that such studies have already been initiated. We would, however, like to express the hope that the short, inconspicuous treatise on alchemy, unadorned by any miniatures, will also be given the attention it deserves by biographers of Albertus.

REFERENCES

1. Stadler, H., *Albertus Magnus, De Animalibus libri XXVI*, p. XI, Cologne, 1916.
2. Cf., e.g., de Loë, B. P., *Analecta Bollandiana*, **21**, 361 (1902).
3. Sighart, J., *Albertus Magnus, sein Leben und seine Wissenschaft*, Regensburg, p. XI, 1857.
4. Thorndike, Lynn, *A History of Magic and Experimental Science*, New York, Vol. II, p. 571 ff, 1923.
5. Holmyard, E. J., *Makers of Chemistry*, Oxford, p. 91, 1931.
6. Denifle H., and Ehrle, F., *Archiv für Literatur– und Kirchengeschichte des Mittelalters*, Vol. II, No. 2, 1886.
7. Pangerl, F., *Zeitschrift für katholische Theologie*, **36**, 304, 512 and 784 (1912). p. 517.
8. Kopp, H., *Beiträge zur Geschichte der Chemie*, III, Braunschweig, p. 76, 1875.
9. Pangerl, F., *loc. cit.*, p. 516.
10. Pelster, F., *Ergänzungshefte zu den Stimmen der Zeit*, 2nd series, No. 4, 1920.
11. Grabmann, M., *Beiträge zur Geschichte der Philosophie des Mittelalters*, **17**, Nos. 5–6 (1916).
12. Sudhoff, K., *Archiv für Geschichte der Mathematik, der Naturwissenschaften und der Technik*, **12**, 1 (1929). [Sudhoff had previously mentioned a miniature from the codex that is of great significance for the history of medicine (*ibid.*, **10**, 152 1927).]
13. Cf. Stadler, H., *Natur und Kultur*, **4**, 86 (1906).
14. Especially convincingly by Bormans, M., *Bull. Acad. royale Bruxelles*, p. 132, 1852, and by V. Rose, *Zeitschr. f. deutsch. Altertum*, **XVIII**, 321 (1875).
15. Petrus de Prussia, *loc. cit.*, Chapter 27: "Inde in pluribus locis ubi missus fuerat eius libri de manu propria reperiuntur".
16. Pangerl, F., *loc. cit.*, p. 529.
17. Stadler, H., *Sitzsber. Bayrische Akad. Wiss., Philosophisch—Philologische Klasse*, 1st treatise 1912; *Archiv für Geschichte der Naturwissenschaften und der Technik*, **6**, 387 (1913); Blätter für das Gymnasial-Schulwesen, München, p. 274, 1916.
18. Pelster, F., *loc. cit.*, p. 141.
19. Planzer, D., *Divus Thomas* (3), **10**, 246, 275 (1932).
20. Wingate, D., *The Mediaeval Latin Versions of the Aristotelian Scientific Corpus, with Special Reference to the Biological Works*, The Courier Press, London, p. 83, 1931.

24 | Goethe's Scientific Background

It has been said that whereas we know next to nothing about Shakespeare's life, almost too much is known about Goethe's. His autobiography, diaries, correspondence, carefully recorded talks, and innumerable scattered notes which were never meant for publication, provide such an inexhaustible wealth of material that any exegete intent on emphasizing a special tendency in Goethe's mind could produce some evidence for his thesis if he were willing to spend enough time on the perusal of every available source.

A recent book by Dr. Ronald D. Gray, *Goethe the Alchemist*,* sets out to show "that Goethe was profoundly influenced throughout his life by the religious and philosophical beliefs he derived from his early study of Alchemy". It is a very learned book, so rich in not easily accessible material that admirers of Goethe will study it with pleasure and profit, even though they may be unable to agree with the author's opinion.

Goethe's interest in alchemy is well known to every reader of *Faust*; it may even be correct to say that all that the average educated German knows about alchemical imagery is contained in the few very colourful and impressive lines in which Faust describes the laboratory experiments of his deceased father. From the second part of *Faust* many will remember also the alchemical origin of Homunculus. It is certainly a merit of the author to have searched with enormous industry for further alchemical ideas and symbols not only in Goethe's lesser-known poetical works but also in his scientific writings, and much of what he has to say about alchemical reminiscences in Goethe's *Farbenlehre*, his *Metamorphose der Pflanzen*, and his anatomical, geological and meteorological papers, will strike the reader as worth pondering about; but it is usually far from convincing.

* *Goethe the Alchemist: A Study of Alchemical Symbolism in Goethe's Literary and Scientific Works*, by Ronald D. Gray, Pp. x + 312 + 3 plates. (Cambridge: At the University Press, 1952.) 35s. net.

A great deal has been written about Goethe's strange theory of the origin of coloured light and his stubborn refusal to listen to any German defender of Newton's explanation. To Goethe, his theory of colours was much more than the solution of an isolated problem in physics; it was, as has been shown by many writers, intimately connected with his personal way of searching for explanations of natural phenomena; but whether we can see in his colour-theory as close a connection with alchemy as Dr. Gray suggests is quite a different question. He wants to make us believe that the empirical appearance of Goethe's colour-theory is only "superficial" and that, first of all, it had to conform with alchemical doctrines, with the colour changes described by alchemists as essential for their "Great Work". Considering the small number of the six or seven rainbow colours mentioned in alchemical writings, occasional similarities with Goethe's statements will not surprise us—all the less, since the alchemists, like Goethe, were starting from actual observations, and many of them were by no means so completely lost in symbolism as readers of some recent books (for example, those by C. G. Jung) may believe. The influence on Dr. Gray of Jung's re-interpretation of alchemy is very obvious, and he goes even further in the same direction in his attempt to show that in Goethe's theory of colours, too, not the experimental content but the symbolism is essential; but it is almost inconceivable that anyone could get such an impression who studies Goethe's work without a preconceived idea. With infinite patience experiment after experiment was described by Goethe, and the reader exhorted to repeat and check them; this has been done by many who have realized with admiration that Goethe, whose colour sense must have been of a very high order, was not only extremely accurate in his descriptions but was also sometimes even the first to notice some delicate phenomenon. To the countless experiments and historical studies connected with his theory of colours, Goethe devoted probably more effort than to any other single work.

Goethe himself was very careful to draw a clear line between the scientific part of his theory, which he was confident could by experiments be demonstrated to be superior to Newton's, and the entirely different concluding section on "the sensorial and moral effect of colour" ("Sinnlich-sittliche Wirkung der Farbe"). This subject is naturally quite different; here Goethe the artist is speaking, and it is very unfortunate that without warning to his readers Dr. Gray mixes the quotations from both parts. Right at the end of this last section, one or two pages are devoted to the "Allegorical, symbolical and mystical use of colours". Here Goethe declares that he did not want to be suspected of mysticism ("Schwärmerei") and predicts that, according to the fashion of his days, there would anyhow be no lack of allegorical, symbolical and mystical applications of this theory. This remark is no encouragement for such attempts, and Goethe did not foresee that he might have to fear even an alchemical interpretation, such as is presented now in Dr. Gray's book. As "final evidence" for his thesis, Dr. Gray quotes a passage in which an old anonymous writer says that his remarks about colours "can be combined with the secret philosophy and experience of the chemists", a passage republished by Goethe in one of his occasional minor writings; we are told that this is "the frankest declaration on Goethe's part of the fact that his Colour-Theory was only to be fully understood in terms of alchemical symbolism". If that is the frankest, our doubts are scarcely dispelled as to whether the author is on the right track, or whether he is perhaps deluding himself when he believes he notices everywhere in Goethe's theory of colours the smell of alchemy.

Discussing the meteorological images in Goethe's poetry, Dr. Gray quotes a passage from the final scene of Part II of *Faust* where clouds change into a host of blessed spirits. "The immediate source of this image can be traced back to a moment of Goethe's life some fifty years before those lines were written"—so we are told, and a remark is quoted from a letter written in the far-distant days when alchemy was still near to Goethe's heart. Now for the modern author, who has all Goethe's works simultaneously available, this source may appear "immediate"; but for Goethe himself a letter written to a friend fifty years earlier can scarcely have been an immediate source, nor is it likely that just one, not at all unusual, observation of so long ago was still present in his memory.

It is not to be expected either that the alchemical explanation of the *Urpflanze*, to which Dr. Gray devotes much space, will convey conviction to many. We are informed that the stages of this hypothetical plant correspond to Boehme's *Seven Qualities of God*, and in some of the stages no doubt resemblances can be found; but it is only "by ignoring Goethe's definite statement that there are six stages in the life of the plant, and including what he omitted, the original seed" that it was possible for the author to establish "a very close parallel with mystical doctrines". Here again we meet the usual trouble: Goethe was careful "to publish only the barest hints. The passages which most reveal his thoughts are found almost entirely in his private notes or in later publications,"

It must be conceded to Dr. Gray that, although it was his professed task to go so far as possible in an attempt to follow up in Goethe's works alchemical influences, he nevertheless sometimes shows restraint, when we are already fearing the worst. We are certainly grateful to him that, after drawing *Iphigenie* into a chapter on Amazons, hermaphrodites and the symbolism of the "male and female" in alchemical writings, he assures us that in spite of "the union of opposites, sun and moon, brother and sister", which provides a happy conclusion of the play, "it would be absurd to claim Iphigenie as an example of Goethe's use of alchemical symbolism". Mignon is not so fortunate; she is plainly called a hermaphrodite, although Dr. Gray admits that she is not quite so perfect a being as this—in alchemical parlance—very laudatory expression indicates. On the other hand, one feels again relieved when the sentence "it would make for a neat interpretative pattern if one could agree with C. G. Jung that the whole of *Faust* II is a poetic representation of the alchemical work", is followed by a "but"; one would wish, however, that here the author's objection was not confined to the lack of alchemical symbolism in the third act of *Faust* II, but that he would say in so many words how pointless the whole *Faust* II would appear to most of us if Goethe's ambition had really been what Jung supposes; we should be inclined to say, in Mephisto's words, "ein grosser Aufwand, schmählich, ist vertan".

Dr. Gray is so convinced that the expressions Goethe uses in the description of natural phenomena must come from the writings of the alchemists, that he assumes such a parallel even if he has no proof at all to offer. Goethe believed that the crystallization of rocks was accompanied by a tremor; the author admits that here the parallels with alchemical literature "are not as close as one could wish", but he "feels" that some of the alchemists "also must have used such expressions" for their process, although he has "not chanced to come across any such passages". Why should we look for such a distant and purely hypothetical source of Goethe's views if (in a paragraph quoted in the present book) he refers to the simple observation that "water in a vessel, on the point of freezing, is transformed by the slightest shock into solid ice"? Let us not forget that if Goethe was anything in science, he was a brilliant observer. For a similar reason, there can be no necessity at all for assuming that, when Goethe likened little clouds to white doves, these birds must have been reminiscences of alchemical symbols he had come across in his youth, and that only "later he came to feel that Nature herself offered such symbols in plenty". After all, he was a poet too.

It is to be hoped that no reader of this book will forget that its aim is to bring out certain aspects of Goethe's *Weltanschauung* by sharply illuminating them from a certain angle, and that by this process other features are necessarily obscured. The study of *Goethe the Alchemist* should be followed by the reading of books with titles like *Goethe the Classicist*, *Goethe the Spinozist* and, most necessarily, *Goethe the Scientist*. The author himself is helpful here in providing a list of "Books and Articles Consulted", which comprises, in the section entitled "Goethe's Science", some fifty authors. Three very valuable contributions to the subject are, however, missing: Helmholtz's and Tyndall's well-known studies on Goethe's scientific work and—less astonishing, but still more regrettable—C. G. Carus's little book *Goethe* (Leipzig, 1843). For anyone who has ploughed his way through the complicated symbolism attributed to Goethe in Dr. Gray's book, it will be most refreshing and clarifying to read Carus's chapter on "Goethe's Relation to Nature and Science". Discussing his various contributions to science, Carus gives pride of place to the idea of the *Urpflanze* which had been "of the highest and most enlivening effect on the whole field of botany". (Similar praise is bestowed on his anatomical ideas.) Is it likely that a revival of Boehme's and other alchemists' and mystics' abstruse ideas, "a cunning and intricate pattern of metaphor and simile, elaborated down to the smallest detail"—as Dr. Gray calls Goethe's botanical theory—could have had such a beneficial influence on the progress of modern science? I believe it to be very significant that neither in this chapter, nor in the one which attempts to explain Goethe's works "from an understanding of his personality", are alchemical interests mentioned by Carus even once. He must be considered as one of the most competent judges, as he knew Goethe personally, enjoyed his affection and respect as shown in their correspondence and had many scientific and artistic interests in common with Goethe, being himself eminent in such various fields as anatomy, psychology, philosophy and painting. If Carus, in his explanation of Goethe's scientific background, could leave out alchemy completely, one's suspicion is strengthened that Dr. Gray's point of view is only the purely literary and utterly non-scientific attitude of a late interpreter, and that it is the arbitrary emphasis which he lays on a few of the remotest of Goethe's utterances that makes the alchemical influence appear of such over-riding importance.

We are nevertheless indebted to Dr. Gray for having spent so great an effort on the pursuit of this single line of research, and for having collected the scattered material in a very original book.

25 | Science and Miracle

Goethe's *Faust* may be right in proclaiming miracle to be "des Glaubens liebstes Kind"; but this "dearest child of faith" is certainly less loved by science. At times their relationship was strained to breaking point. This happened especially during periods when science was no less certain than religion of the solidity of its foundations and of the finality of its answers. It may suffice to give here one example, the attitude taken in the sixties of the last century by the well-known physicist, John Tyndall, in several polemical articles in which he discussed the possibility of miracles from the point of view of the scientist. He calculated, for instance, that the mechanical energy necessary for stopping the sun in order to enable Joshua to complete his victory was infinitely greater than that actually demanded for a crushing victory over a handful of Amorites; but as the old Israelites were not able to estimate the horsepower involved, this tremendous energy would have been completely wasted, whether, in Tyndall's words, "we consider the miracle as purely evidential, or as a practical means of vengeance".[1] Correct as Tyndall's mathematical physics was, it is not likely that his line of argument impressed other than scientists; but most of these were surely convinced that the fundamental laws of nature were as general, as simple, and as well known to us as Tyndall assumed.

Much has happened in science since to shake this belief; but during the same period there were changes too in the Church's attitude to the question of miracles. In Tyndall's days his opponent, the Oxford professor of divinity, Dr. Mozley, considered them as the very foundation of the Christian faith, which was therefore more "rational" than other religions which, lacking the evidence of miracles, were "unfit for the acceptance of an enlightened age and people".[2] Today an authoritative report recognizes that some churchmen advocate the rejection of miracles not simply as a concession to science but even as a "religious gain", although others still attribute

242

to them a special value as a "striking demonstration of the subordination of the natural order to spiritual ends".[3] Widely divergent convictions have been quite recently expressed by representatives of the Church of England.*

In view of this complex situation it seems worth while to examine again the place of miracles in the world of the scientist.

Let us first of all be clear about the sense in which we are going to use the expression "miracle". Sometimes everyday occurrences which we cannot explain fully are called miraculous; if this is the accepted meaning, then everything in the world is a miracle, not only the complicated reactions of living beings but even the behaviour of inorganic matter, because our explanations must always stop at a certain point. An older generation of physicists tried to explain electric phenomena by mechanical models; the modern one assumes that the mechanical properties of matter can be explained in terms of its electrical structure; the "nature of matter" had to remain unexplained in the first period, the "nature of electricity" in the second. We prefer, however, to speak here of a "mysterious" background, not of a "miraculous" one; likewise we would not call it a "miracle" if a homing pigeon comes back, as this happens every day, although it is still a "mystery" to us which sense the bird is using. The word "miracle" we are going to reserve for occurrences which are not to be expected from the course of our usual experiences; or, if we want to use the somewhat more precise language of the scientist, a miracle is an event which it is in principle impossible to foresee even if the present physical state of the system under observation is completely known to us.

The opinion of many eighteenth and nineteenth century scientists was that miracles in this sense could not happen because the future of a given system was completely determined by its present geometric and kinematic conditions; the law of causality did not allow of any exceptions. However, this conviction was of a comparatively recent date, so recent indeed that the steps by which it had been reached can be accurately traced. It was the outcome of a develop-

---

* Adherents of a "biblical principle of historical interpretation" turn down some miracles reported in the Old Testament because of their unimportance for the Christian faith (see Alan Richardson, *Christian Apologetics*, S.C.M. Press, Ltd., London, p. 175, 1947); others discuss the possibility of drawing the line between "healing miracles" and "nature miracles" (see, e.g., C. J. Wright, *Miracle in History and in Modern Thought*, Constable and Company Ltd., London, p. 307, 1930). Many nuances are possible between the outright negation of miracles (E. W. Barnes, *The Rise of Christianity*, Longmans, Green and Co., London, 1947) and their wholesale acceptance (C. S. Lewis, *Miracles*, Geoffrey Bles, London, 1947).

ment which started with Galileo and which with inexorable consequence had driven the scientists into this position.

There have been times when science and the belief in miracles were
not in the least opposed to each other. The official representatives of
religion were often the only scientists in their community; witness
the priests in Babylon and in Egypt. There were regularities in the
physical world, especially in the sky, about which they knew a good
deal, but the whole world was dependent on the will of gods who
could be induced by men to influence it in a miraculous way. Even
after much progress had been made, it was not yet felt that there
was any contradiction between science and religion; the two were
still in perfect concord when the great west-European encyclopaedias of the thirteenth century were written. Let us take, for
instance, Bartholomew Anglicus's *De Proprietatibus Rerum*.[4] In 29
books he deals successively with physiology, anatomy, sociology,
medicine, astronomy and meteorology, with birds, rivers, mountains,
countries, minerals, plants, animals, colours, smells, mathematics,
musical instruments, and other subjects in a very interesting and
frequently scientifically valuable way; but the first book is devoted
to a theological treatise on the characteristics of God, and the second
discusses the properties of seraphim, cherubim, archangels, and
angels. Man and his world find their places most naturally after
them; there is no gap between biblical and worldly wisdom. One
can hardly read these encyclopaedias without some nostalgic longing
for the days when all the scattered fragments of which our knowledge
nowadays consists were still parts of one harmonious world.

Even nearer to the time when modern science was born there was
still no antagonism between miracles and science. The fifteenth and
sixteenth centuries saw astrology at its greatest height; the deeper
meaning of innumerable scientific and literary treatises, poems, and
works of art produced in those days cannot be understood by anyone
ignorant of their astrological background. Astrology is not extinct;
but whoever buys today at a news-stand one of the astrological
periodicals will hardly understand from their miserable content that
once astrology fascinated the best and most educated minds, that
learned scholars, free-thinkers amongst the princes, protestant
theologians and the Popes in Rome, likewise believed in it. (There
was a Chair of astrology in the papal University.) Before its decline
set in, it was a most elaborate system of relations supposed to exist
between all the physical and psychical events in the world; such
relations were not assumed on the basis of experience but deduced
from general principles. The planet Saturn, most remote of all,

with its pale light and slow motion, was obviously in correspondence with the heavy, dull metal lead, with old age, with the melancholic temperament, with brooding scientists, with exile and silence, with all the professions which dig into the dark earth, and so on.[5] Much sagacity can be found in some of the leading astrological writers who tried to satisfy intellectual as well as emotional demands; it has been aptly said that astrology with all its miracles was both a science and a religion.[6] Far above the silly superstitions which today are comprised under that name, it was a grandiose attempt to arrive at a unified idea of the Universe.

Some idealistic philosophers have succeeded so well in explaining the hidden sense in astrology and in assuring us that the form of reasoning in such a mythical system is of the same dignity as the totally different one in modern science, since "the world has for us the appearance which the mind gives to it",[7] that the reader may ask himself, a little puzzled, why has science after all dethroned astrology? The answer, I think, is very simple. The aim of both, astrology and science, is to prophesy, and science can do it infinitely better. Kepler was certainly one of the most competent astrologers of his time; and he read from the horoscope of Wallenstein—the treacherous leader of the Hapsburg armies who was murdered at the age of fifty by loyal officers—that he would die of fever at seventy! But when Halley, using Kepler's laws of planetary motion and Newton's mathematical methods, predicted the return of a comet, after a lapse of $75\frac{1}{2}$ years, for the end of 1758 or the beginning of 1759, and in the fullness of time astronomers all over the world were waiting, the comet was actually seen again for the first time on the night of Christmas Day, 1758.*

This contrast throws a sharp light on the fundamental change which had occurred in man's conception of nature. Mythical thinking had been replaced by mathematics. We have already mentioned that this development started with Galileo; his mathematical formulae for the laws of motion introduced the new era. Great as is the number of his scientific discoveries, they are surpassed by far in importance by the new metaphysics of nature underlying all his work. It is the idea that nature works like a purely mechanical system whose motions can be subjected to mathematical treatment.

The history of modern science is to a large extent an account of the

---

* It might perhaps be remarked that Kepler was reluctantly compelled to undertake astrological predictions for financial reasons. Tycho Brahe, on the other hand, who was under no such obligation, gave a reasoned defence of astrology as a young man, though in later years, while he still cast horoscopes, his belief in their value became somewhat qualified. [Ed.]

spreading of this new idea. To some of its first exponents it came with the force of a revelation. Descartes has described how one night at the age of twenty-three the Angel of Truth appeared to him and assured him that mathematics can unlock the secrets of nature; he himself considered that vision as the turning point in his life. It is too well known to need repeating how deeply the scientific outlook of Newton's generation was changed when he proved that the celestial bodies obeyed the formula of his law of gravitation. The recognition that nature can be understood, and frequently mastered, by the application of mathematics, was the fundamental discovery of modern science.

It is true, of course, that the beginnings of this idea can be traced to the Pythagorean philosophy. Very many concepts used in modern science made their first appearance in old Greece. Two of them, atomism and Pythagoreanism, have surpassed in importance all the others; they may be said to be the two leading ideas of present-day physics. But there were many centuries during which neither of them was a force in the development of science. Atomism was under a cloud because of its open anti-religious tendency, and the opinion has been expressed that it was state interference which hindered its development.[8] Pythagoreanism remained sterile for other reasons; its experimental foundation in classical days was very small and it succumbed to the temptation of wild speculations; but when Galileo based it on well-planned experiments, its triumphant conquest of science began and it became as dangerous to some cherished ideas as the decried atomism.

This unavoidable consequence was not foreseen for quite a while. Many of the founders of modern science were deeply religious. It was in the eighteenth, and not in the seventeenth, century that science became separated from the religious background, and only then it became really mechanical.[9] It is interesting to note that Newton believed that gravitational forces would cause all the fixed stars to fall upon one another, if divine interference did not keep them apart, and that even the Solar System wanted from time to time some supernatural reformation.[10] The idea that the laws of nature needed supervision was also Boyle's conviction; so the necessity of miraculous acts could still be used to prove God's existence. But more and more the view gained ground that the world, once created, could continue by itself, and that its beautiful order was a better argument than interference for God and Providence. This had been most clearly stated by Spinoza;[11] Newton's great rival Leibniz considered it already an insult to the Deity to insinuate that he was under the necessity of tinkering with the creation from time to time in order to keep it in running condition.[10] Finally Laplace succeeded in showing by strict mathematics that the Solar System is in a much more stable state than Newton had dared to assume; when Napoleon asked him why in his *Mécanique Céleste* no mention was made of God, he gave the well-known reply: "Je n'avais pas besoin de cette hypothèse-là". It is tempting to consider the limitations modern science is inclined to impose on the duration of the Solar System and on Laplace's confidence, but this is outside our present purpose.

This new attitude necessarily brought science into opposition to those who liked to use the occurrence of miracles as a theological argument. Perhaps at no time was the difference in outlook so sharply marked as in the second half of the eighteenth century, and it may be helpful to illustrate this by relating a special case in which right and wrong were mixed up in a very queer way.

Old records from many countries speak of solid bodies falling occasionally from the sky. As this was the traditional seat of the gods, these objects were considered as sent by them; the startling light and sound phenomena accompanying the fall certainly strengthened this conviction. The habit of according religious veneration to these "meteorites", as we call them today, was world-wide and persisted through the centuries. One of the best known instances is probably that of the Ephesians, although the unfortunate translation in the authorized English version rather obscures it; the Ephesians were not worshippers of the goddess Diana and of the "image which fell down from Jupiter", but $\tau o\hat{v}$ $\delta\iota\alpha\pi\epsilon\tau o\hat{v}s$ or the "thing that fell from the sky", obviously a meteorite.[12] Similarly, in Delphi besides Apollo a holy stone was the object of adoration.[13] The "iron shield" which fell in Rome in the reign of Numa Pompilius was put in the perpetual custody of the college of the Salian priests. The "Black Stone" of the Kaba, the holiest of holies of the Moham-medans, is no doubt a stone meteorite with its strange black crust. In the ruins of an ancient Mexican temple an iron meteorite was unearthed, carefully wrapped in mummy cloths;[14] another was found upon an altar in prehistoric ruins in Ohio.[15] When in 1402 a stone fell in Alsace, King Maximilian I of Germany took it to be a warning from the heavenly powers and thus an exhortation to a crusade against the Turks; by his order it was hung in the village church, where it can still be seen. In East Africa a stone that came down in 1853 was considered as a god by the natives, anointed with oil, clothed, decorated, and installed in a specially built temple,[16] and a very similar cult is reported from India in the year 1885.[17] Many more examples could be cited.

Now such falls of meteorites are rare; even today, with our improved methods of communication, from all over the earth not more than 4 or 5 are reported in a year; so scientists cannot expect to be just on the spot, and have to rely on reports. But during the so-called period of enlightenment they became very suspicious of anything that savoured of the miraculous, and the distinct favour meteorites found with the churches made the stories of their fall particularly suspect to them. Although in antiquity and in the Dark Ages the sky had belonged to the gods and their whims, since Newton it was a place where the strictest mathematical order reigned; it would be a miracle if flying stones were suddenly appearing there, and it was, therefore, preposterous to ask any self-respecting scientist to believe such a thing. Stories of the uneducated crowd had no weight whatsoever;[18] it was quite easy to detect the age-old superstitions in their incredible narrations.

The highest scientific authority in the eighteenth century was the French Academy in Paris; its members set the fashion in the dispute on meteorites. In the year 1769 a stone was sent to them by an abbé with a detailed description of its fall from the sky which had been observed by several agricultural workers. The Academy asked three of its members to investigate the case; their report[19] makes strange reading. After a few general remarks that "les vrais physiciens" had always been sceptical about such stories and that today one should be still more so, they declare that according to their analysis it was just an ordinary stone and that it had *not* fallen from the sky. Perhaps most astounding in this report is the fact that amongst the chemists who thus failed to recognize the very obvious peculiarities of the stone and who felt entitled flatly to deny the statement of the eye-witnesses we find the glorious name of Lavoisier.*

Scientists in other countries were anxious not to be considered as backward compared with their famous colleagues in Paris. It is a sad reflection that in those days many public museums threw away whatever they possessed of these precious meteorites; it happened in Germany, Denmark, Switzerland, Italy and Austria. When in Vienna the well-known mineralogist von Born was appointed curator of the imperial collections he found a drawer labelled

---

* Lavoisier was then not yet 26 years of age, but to emphasize this as an excuse seems to be too charitable; even much later in life he was inclined to anticipate, and publish, experimental results according to preconceived ideas. See, e.g., D. McKie, *Antoine Lavoisier*, V. Gollancz, Ltd., London, p. 206, 1935.

"Stones fallen from the sky", and, highly amused, ordered them to be discarded, or at least degraded to the rank of ordinary minerals.[20] There was, however, in the collections a meteorite which escaped this fate, and which is now one of the most valuable exhibits in the Vienna museum, the lump of iron which fell at Hraschina, near Zagreb, in Croatia in 1751. Its position was secure—thanks to the protection given to it by the bishop of Zagreb's Consistory. When the first rumours of the strange event reached Zagreb, the bishop's vicar general sent two other canons to investigate. They came back with the iron and the sworn statements of seven eye-witnesses; these were embodied in a Latin document which the vicar general, "in order to perpetuate the memory, and relying on the faithful and unanimous report of his delegates", confirmed by his seal and sent to the Empress Marie Thérèse, accompanied by the iron, to which likewise the official seal was attached. Together, the meteorite and the certificate[21] have weathered the storm of what has been called the "vandalism of enlightenment".[22]

The beneficial influence of this unusual clerical document went even further. It came to the knowledge of the distinguished German physicist Chladni and convinced him that the Paris academicians and their followers had no right to disbelieve this and similar stories. He published a pamphlet[23] in which he applied to the meteorite problem a principle which Hume (admittedly in a different context) had recommended:[24] to believe a miraculous story, if it would be more miraculous still if the documents describing it were false. Chladni was by training a lawyer and not a scientist; he had an open mind as to what might happen in the sky, and complete confidence in the Zagreb document and its sober matter-of-fact descriptions. He recommends it to his colleagues as a model of a truly scientific report which they would be well advised to emulate. In the beginning his book converted only a few; while these men blamed the orthodox physicists for disbelieving any extraordinary event which looked too miraculous for their liking,* the others simply reversed the argument and accused the believers of a kind of "credo quia absurdum".†

---

* Le comte de Bournon, the first mineralogist to analyse a meteorite, complains (*Journal de Physique, de Chimie et d'Histoire Naturelle*, Germinal, **XI**, p. 302) that "le fait de la chûte des pierres de l'atmosphère . . . a toujours été rejetté . . . sous la seule raison qu'il derivoit de l'amours des hommes pour le merveilleux, et ne meritoit pas l'attention de ceux qu'une saine philosophie metoit à l'abri de cette erreur".

† The geologist Patrin (*loc. cit.*, p. 392) concludes his criticism with the words: "Puissent les réflexions que je viens de présenter, contribuer à garantir la science de la nature de son plus dangereux adversaire, l'amour du merveilleux."

However, in 1803 heaven itself took part in the dispute and showered so many stones on the village of l'Aigle, not far from Paris, that the Academy had to give in. Today the study of meteorites is a well-established branch of science, which has most fruitful relations to astronomy, geology, physics and chemistry.

We have devoted some space to this account of the history of meteoritics—as the Americans now call the science of meteorites—because it seems that several important lessons can be learned from it. Firstly, scientists must never deny the reality of a reported phenomenon for no other reason than that it cannot be explained by current theories. Secondly, whether such a report is trustworthy or not must be judged according to principles with which historians, lawyers and clergymen are better acquainted than scientists. Thirdly, an apparent miracle may turn out to be a rare but nevertheless perfectly natural phenomenon.

While physics was defending itself with blind zeal against a purely imaginary danger, the beautiful and imposing structure of its theories began slowly to develop interior menacing cracks. Physicists might have learned much earlier from philosophers that the metaphysical foundations on which they had built were rather questionable; that there was no way of knowing anything certain about a world outside our sensations; that the old and extremely helpful distinction between primary and secondary qualities of matter was quite arbitrary; that even the concept of causality was far from being clear or evident. But if they wanted to they could quite well dismiss all such critical remarks as sophistry, and enjoy the unbroken series of successes which the reliance on the Galileo–Newton metaphysics of nature brought them. Now, however, it became obvious that they could not get over one peculiar difficulty inherent in their own doctrines.

We remarked earlier that atomism was one of the pillars of modern physics; it promised to provide a much deeper understanding of fundamental laws than the conclusions based on energy which in Tyndall's days were considered the surest basis of physics. If one wanted to know why the pressure of a gas was doubled when its volume was reduced to half, the kinetic theory of gases gave a satisfactory answer by showing that after compression twice as many atoms as before were now hitting the walls of the vessel. It was equally easy to explain why two gases, if brought into contact, mixed completely; the movement of the atoms was bound to have this effect. There was, however, one weak point in the argument. All purely mechanical processes are reversible; we can, therefore, easily imagine that at a given moment all the invisible atoms in the mixed gases would move in reversed directions; the observable effect would clearly be that the two gases would separate again. Why had this phenomenon, and analogous ones, never been noticed?

The solution of this paradox is the immortal merit of Ludwig Boltzmann. It is not possible to give an adequate account of it without going rather deeply into theoretical physics; for the present discussion it must suffice to make the underlying idea clear. Before Boltzmann, physicists had tried to prove that these processes which the atomistic theory predicted, but observation failed to confirm, were for some reason or other impossible; Boltzmann came to the conclusion that this is not so: they are possible, but not at all probable. Probability became the deciding factor in the physical world. According to Boltzmann, everywhere in nature less probable states of a system are changing into more probable ones. Disorder is more probable than order because disorder comprises many more possible configurations; to maintain a chosen order demands an effort, but one of the innumerable varieties of disorder establishes itself easily. (Every librarian will certainly agree.) Two separate gases represent a more orderly state than their mixture; that is the reason why we observe only their spontaneous mixing and not their spontaneous separation.

One cannot overrate the importance of Boltzmann's conception. He was able to give a mathematical expression for the connection of one of the fundamental quantities of classical physics, the entropy S, with the atomistic probability W. His tombstone in Vienna has no other inscription to indicate his scientific greatness than his famous formula:

$$S = k \log W$$

The removal of an apparent contradiction in atomistics not only firmly established this theory but had much farther-reaching repercussions. Physicists had to admit that the laws of nature do not state what must happen according to causality, but only what is likely to happen according to probability. The probability of an event may be so low that for all practical purposes we may call it impossible; but it will still have a definite probability which can be expressed mathematically. The probability for instance that at a given moment the molecules of which a chair is composed will instead of their random movement all fly in an upward direction and thus the chair be lifted by itself, is so small that within the limited astronomical duration of our Earth we cannot expect such a miracle to happen; but we cannot deny the theoretical possibility.*

It seems unavoidable to go still a little further into theoretical physics and to sketch briefly the later development of Boltzmann's idea, as the philosophical implications are far reaching.

It is inherent in Boltzmann's theory that regularities can only be found where a great number of atoms is involved. If we have but a few atoms of each of two gases, it will occasionally happen that the two species separate and we may be able to observe this phenomenon; but when their number is so great as is usual in our experiments, then their separation will be so enormously improbable that we shall never live to see it. We may then formulate a law for their behaviour. But can we find laws of nature also for single atoms?

A very important insight into this question was gained by another Vienna physicist, Egon v. Schweidler, whose death occurred early this year.† To him is due the recognition that the theory of radioactive disintegration pronounced by Rutherford and Soddy is purely statistical in character. This well-known theory states that, of a given radioactive substance, in every second always exactly the same fraction disintegrates. Schweidler pointed out that this law can be valid only as long as the number of atoms is sufficiently great; that deviations from the law must occur when their number decreases; and that it is impossible to say anything definite, anything exceeding probability, about the moment at which a single atom will explode; it may happen immediately or it may take hours, days or years. In spite of this uncertainty about the fate of a single atom, we can predict with an ever increasing degree of accuracy the number of atoms which will disintegrate during the next second, if the total number of atoms under observation becomes larger and larger.

This peculiar state of affairs seemed for a while confined to the phenomenon of radioactive disintegration. But a decade later quite an analogous explanation was given by Albert Einstein for the emission of light from an excited atom, and more cases in point followed. But while the physicists had then to admit the statistical character of many laws of nature, most of them were inclined to see in Boltzmann's and Schweidler's introduction of probability, instead of

---

* How revolutionary Boltzmann's view was can be seen from the fact that even a Max Planck found it difficult to follow him; see *Die Einheit des physikalischen Weltbildes*, S. Hirzel, Leipzig, p. 24, 1909. On the other hand, the greatest then living opponent of the atomistic doctrine, Ernst Mach, admitted at least the logical stringency of Boltzmann's conclusions; see *Die Leitgedanken meiner naturwissenschaftlichen Erkenntnislehre und ihre Aufnahme durch die Zeitgenossen* (*Scientia*, **7**, 223 1910), p. 231.

† 1948: see p. 77. [Ed.]

certainty, only a passing phase which would be overcome with the increase of knowledge. They believed that if we could look into the interior mechanism of a radioactive atom we certainly would see differences between them and could then predict that the one will explode earlier than the other.[25] After all, different effects must have different causes; there ought to be laws of nature governing the behaviour of a single atom. That seemed directly to follow from the principle of causality.

Here I have to mention a third physicist of the atomistic school of Vienna who has decisively contributed to the clarification of these ideas. Franz Exner, in publications which were more philosophical than technical and did not exert any immediate influence, expressed the view that it was quite unnecessary to postulate regularities for the behaviour of single atoms; the law of great numbers would see to it that even out of complete irregularity the very laws would emerge which we observe in matter in bulk. He did not dispute the possibility of a lawful behaviour of the single atom; but he denied that such an assumption was necessary.[26] The last three decades have produced much experimental and theoretical material to support Exner's cautious view, and it seems that today one can decide between the two alternatives. Modern theoretical physics is inclined to assume* that the impossibility of predicting the behaviour of a single atom is not due to our ignorance concerning some features of its internal structure or state, but to the fact that there is no causality in elementary processes; the opposite view contradicts some well-established principles essential for their mathematical treatment.[27] Elementary processes are irregular, and laws of nature can only be found in cases where the law of great numbers makes its levelling effect felt.

At the beginning of this lecture we defined a miracle as an event which it is in principle impossible to predict even if the present physical state of the system under observation is completely known to us. In this sense we are entitled to say that every elementary process has the character of a miracle.

Does this imply that physicists today believe that even on the larger scale on which the normally observable events happen, miracles are possible? It would certainly be a mistake to assume that they have less confidence than their fathers and grandfathers in their ability to predict the exact future. It is true that some are

---

* The cautious character of this statement should be noted. The view in question is an *assumption*, regarded by some physicists, including Einstein, as impermissible: see for example, Max Born, *Natural Philosophy of Cause and Chance*, Oxford, p. 122, 1949. [Ed.]

inclined to throw the conception of causality completely overboard; for it seems, as we have already seen, incompatible with elementary processes, and it is not applicable either in any strict sense to matter in bulk, because it has no meaning to speak of "identical causes producing identical effects", or of the "uniformity of Nature", if we have to admit that owing to the irregular distribution and movement of the elementary particles two macroscopic systems are never really identical.* But, even after discarding the old ideas about causality, the aim of theoretical physicists is still the same as in Galileo's days: to derive formulae from which future events can be foretold. And to show how successful they are, it may be helpful to describe just one recent example.

We have heard that the time for the disintegration of a radioactive atom is indefinite. So is the mode of interaction of a single neutron with a uranium atom. However, a wealth of experimental material collected during the war years enabled theoretical physicists to calculate what was bound to happen if specially prepared uranium were made to react with neutrons; it became clear that as long as the quantity of uranium should remain under a critical value nothing extraordinary would occur, but that beyond that size a tremendous effect was to be expected. The first experiment on these lines took place in a lonely region of New Mexico. Early in the morning of July 16, 1945, a vast number of scientists, technicians and military men were assembled there; they were placed several miles away from the uranium and received instructions how to protect their eyes and skin against radiation, how to lie down on the earth to minimize the effect of blast, etc. The automatic trigger was set for 5.30 a.m. Exactly at this moment the biggest explosion ever staged by men took place, a light much brighter than the sun illuminated the landscape and the shock wave reached, but did not endanger, the spectators who had been placed at the right distance. We are not discussing here the very unpleasant military and political associations of this experiment; but we want to point out that as an example of scientific prediction it was of the very highest order, as, by the nature of the experiment, no gradual approach by tests on a smaller scale was possible, and its success depended on a vast number of highly complex mathematical and physical deliberations.

So we see that the explosion of an atom cannot be predicted, but the explosion of an atomic bomb can.

* It is worth mentioning that as long ago as 1872 the mathematician Clifford, in a lecture "On the Aims and Instruments of Scientific Thought", concluded from the statistical character of the gas laws that their "exactness cannot be theoretical or absolute". (W. K. Clifford, *Lectures and Essays*, Macmillan and Co., London, Vol. I, p. 139, 1879.)

This example will, I hope, help to clarify the general position in which science finds itself today. Its foundations have changed, certainty has been replaced by probability. Strict laws for elementary processes do not seem to exist in nature; her background is not order and harmony, but chaos. If we are able to observe laws, it is due only to the levelling influence of great numbers, and exceptions to these laws must be expected. But as in all practical cases enormous numbers are involved, physics is in a position to devise formulae which correctly foretell the future; in spite of the uncertainty of the atomistic events, the result calculated for finite quantities will be as exact a prediction as physics could ever hope to make in the past.

As this conviction of modern physics is now based on the law of great numbers instead of on causality, a few remarks about this law might not be amiss. It has taken the place of causality in the sense too that scientists have again to rely on a fundamental principle without being able to agree on its nature. It is easy to deduce from the number of possible combinations that with two dice it is six times more probable to throw the number 7 than the number 12; but this is only a probability, and nobody can say anything certain about the result of the next throw. However, if we go on throwing the two dice a great number (let us say 10,000) of times, we shall find that we have obtained the number 7 almost exactly 6 times as often as the number 12.

Here lies no longer a mathematical, but a philosophical, problem which has caused almost as much headache as the principle of causality, and for which the same widely varying solutions have been suggested. Some thinkers were satisfied simply to accept as an experimental fact, supported by innumerable observations, that the more probable occurrences are in the long run also the more frequent ones.[28] Others took the opposite line by claiming for the law of great numbers the rank of an aprioristic principle of perception in the Kantian sense,[29] or they saw in it an indication that the Aristotelian logic had to be enlarged.[30] If a mathematical proof of the law of great numbers is offered, we may be sure that the term is used in a different sense; the actual finding in nature of the predicted frequency cannot be deduced from theoretical probability considerations.[31] This frequency problem is usually more thoroughly discussed by philosophers than by mathematicians.[32]

Fortunately, it is not necessary for us fully to understand what lies behind the law of great numbers before we can make use of it. It is as good a guide as was in former days the principle of strict causality, with the important additional advantage that it allows us to formulate also the conditions under which exceptions to the usual laws of physics are to be expected. These exceptions are no miracles, because we can predict their occurrence according to statistical laws; on the contrary, it would be a miracle if an event which depended only on a small number of elementary processes showed absolute regularity and not those fluctuations which we have learned to consider as an integral part of all the micro-processes going on in nature.

What has changed as a consequence of the recent advances is not the attitude of science to the miraculous, but to the mysterious. Much could be said about this point. No longer can even the most naive physicist believe that the world built up by the science of physics is in any sense the "real" world; the development of quantum mechanics in the direction of an abstract mathematical symbolism has certainly had the one wholesome effect of inculcating this elementary philosophical truth.* The world of physics is a mental creation which gives us ever increasing power over what is called nature, but the essence of nature remains obscure; it appears to us under different aspects if the experimental conditions are changed, and we seem to be as far away as ever from solving the old epistemological problems. Mysterious is the uncanny power of mathematical analysis, mysterious the validity of the law of great numbers, mysterious the beginning in time of a world whose development clearly runs in one direction. But inside this world, and during its lifetime, there is no more room for miracles on the macro-scale than in the days of classical physics.

REFERENCES

1. Tyndall, John, *Fragments of Science*, Sixth Edition, Longmans, Green and Co., London, Vol. II, p. 36, 1879.
2. Mozley, J. B., *Eight Lectures on Miracles*, Bampton Lectures for 1865, pp. 24–5, Rivingtons, London, 3rd edition, 1872.
3. *Doctrine in the Church of England:* The Report of the Commission on Christian Doctrine appointed by the Archbishops of Canterbury and York in 1922, Society for Promoting Christian Knowledge, London, p. 51, 1938.
4. Ten incunabula editions; the one consulted was printed in 1483 by A. Koburger in Nuremberg.

* The use of the expression "real" in connection with the modern physical world would amount to nothing more than a new definition of what we understand by "real". cf. R. Blanché, *La Science Physique et la Réalité: Réalisme, Positivisme, Mathématisme*, Presses Universitaires de France, Paris, p. 194, 1948: "Chose en soi, phénomène, objet physique . . . la dissociation de ces trois notions a pour fonction de nuancer l'emploi du mot de réalité, et en marquant les significations diverses".

5. Panofsky, E., and Saxl, F., *Dürer's "Melencolia I"*, B. G. Teubner, Leipzig, p. 4, 1923.

6. Bezold, C., and Boll, F., *Sternglaube und Sterndeutung*, B. G. Teubner, Leipzig, p. 72, 1926.

7. Cassirer, E., *Die Begriffsform im mythischen Denken*, B. G. Teubner, Leipzig, p. 53, 1922.

8. Farrington, B., *Science and Politics in the Ancient World*, Allen and Unwin, London, 1939.

9. Guhrauer, G. E., *Joachim Jungius und sein Zeitalter*, Cotta, Stuttgart, p. 177, 1850.

10. Burtt, E. A., *The Metaphysical Foundations of Modern Physical Science*, Kegan Paul, London, p. 284, 1925.

11. In the sixth chapter of his *Tractatus Theologico-Politicus*; see also his correspondence with Oldenburg of the year 1675.

12. Acts XIX, 35. No image is mentioned in the Greek text, and Zeus stands here for the sky, not for the planet; διπετῆ ἔδατα, rain water, also falls from heaven and not from Jupiter.

13. Gruppe, O., *Griechische Mythologie und Religionsgeschichte II*, München, p. 775, 1906; from Pausanias (Book X, XXIV, 6) we learn that even in his days the stone was still anointed daily.

14. Tassin, W., "The Casas Grandes Meteorite", *Proc. U.S. Nation. Museum*, **25**, 69 (1902).

15. Huntington, O. W., "The Prehistoric and Kiowa County Pallasites", *Proc. Amer. Acad. of Arts and Sciences*, **26**, 1 (1891).

16. Buchner, O., *Die Meteoriten in Sammlungen*, W. Engelmann, Leipzig, p. 85, 1863.

17. Newton, H. A., "The Meteorites, the Meteors and the Shooting Stars", *Proc. Amer. Ass. for the Advancement of Science*, **35** (1886); (Presidential Address).

18. Cf. Patrin, E. M. L., "Considérations sur Les Masses de Pierres et de Matières Métalliques qu'on suppose tombées de l'atmosphère, Journal de Physique, de Chimie et d'Histoire Naturelle", Brumaire, **XI**, p. 379. "Comme parmi tous ces témoins, hommes, femmes et enfans, il ne s'en trouve pas un seul qu'on puisse nommer, il est aisé de voir que ce genre d'evidence n'est pas même une probabilité; car personne n'ignore que des milliers d'absurdités ont été certifiées par des milliers de témoins de cette espèce."

19. Izarn, J., *Des Pierres tombées du Ciel ou Lithologie Atmosphérique*, Delalain Fils, Paris, pp. 61–71, 1803 gives the complete text.

20. See Berwerth, F., "Die Meteoritensammlung des naturhistorischen Hofmuseums als Born der Meteoritenkunde", *Sitzber. Akad. Wiss. Wien*, **127**, 715 (1918), p. 719.

21. A German translation can be found in von Ende, F. A., *Über Massen und Steine, die aus dem Monde auf die Erde gefallen sind*, F. Vieweg, Braunschweig, p. 36, 1804.

22. Chladni, E. F. F., *Über Feuer-Meteore und über die mit denselben herabgefallenen Massen*, J. G. Heubner, Wien, p. 5, 1819.

23. Chladni, E. F. F., *Über den Ursprung der von Pallas gefundenen und anderer ihr ähnlicher Eisenmassen*, J. F. Hartknoch, Riga, 1794.

24. Hume, D., *An Inquiry concerning Human Understanding*, Section X, "Of Miracles", Part I.

25. See, e.g., Smoluchowski, M. v., "Über den Begriff des Zufalls und den

Ursprung der Wahrscheinlichkeitsgesetze in der Physik", *Naturwissenschaften*, **6,** 253 (1918).

26. Exner, F., *Vorlesungen über die physikalischen Grundlagen der Naturwissenschaften*, F. Deuticke, Wien, p. 645 ff., 1919; see also Schrödinger, E., *Naturwissenschaften*, **12,** 720 (1924); **17,** 9 and 732 (1929).

27. Neumann, J. von, *Mathematische Grundlagen der Quantenmechanik*, J. Springer, Berlin, p. 107, 1932; see also Whittaker, E., *Proc. Phys. Soc.*, **55,** 459 (1943).

28. e.g. Exner, F., *Über Gesetze in Naturwissenschaft und Humanistik*, A. Hölder, Wien, p. 19, 1909.

29. e.g., Kries, J. von, *Die Principien der Wahrscheinlichkeitsrechnung*, J. C. B. Mohr, Freiburg i. Br., Capitel VII, 1886; H. Reichenbach, "Philosophische Kritik der Wahrscheinlichkeitsrechnung", *Naturwissenschaften*, **8,** 146 (1920).

30. e.g. Reichenbach, H., *Wahrscheinlichkeitslehre*, A. W. Sijthoff's Uitgivers-maatschappij, Leiden, p. 360, 1935; "Die Wahrscheinlichkeitslogik ist eine stetige Logik." "Die strenge Logik erweist sich als ein Spezialfall der Wahrscheinlichkeitslogik, in dem nur die beiden Extremalpunkte (wahr und falsch) benutzt werden."

31. Mises, R. v., "Über das Gesetz der grossen Zahlen und die Häufigkeits-theorie der Wahrscheinlichkeit", *Naturwissenschaften*, **15,** 497 (1927) has shown that Poisson himself to whom we owe the expression of "law of great numbers" is responsible for this confusion of two different meanings.

32. An exhaustive bibliography comprising also the philosophical writers is given by J. M. Keynes as an appendix to his *Treatise on Probability*, Macmillan and Co., Ltd., London, 1921.

26 | The Salt of the Earth

Matthew 5, 13

Ihr seid das Salz der Erde. Wo nun das Salz dumm wird, womit soll man's salzen? Es ist hinfort zu nichts nütze, denn dass man es hinaus schütte und lasse es die Leute zertreten.

Ye are the salt of the earth: but if the salt have lost his savour, wherewith shall it be salted? It is thenceforth good for nothing, but to be cast out, and to be trodden under foot of men.

Mark 9, 50

Das Salz ist gut; so aber das Salz dumm wird, womit wird man würzen? Habt Salz bei euch und habt Frieden untereinander!

Salt *is* good: but if the salt have lost his saltness, wherewith will ye season it? Have salt in yourselves, and have peace one with another.

Luke 14, 34–35

Das Salz ist ein gutes Ding; wo aber das Salz dumm wird, womit wird man würzen? Es ist weder auf das Land noch in den Mist nütze; sondern man wird es wegwerfen. Wer Ohren hat zu hören, der höre!

(LUTHER)

Salt *is* good: but if the salt have lost his savour, wherewith shall it be seasoned? It is neither fit for the land, nor yet for the dunghill; *but* men cast it out. He that hath ears to hear, let him hear.

(AUTHORISED VERSION)

Few passages in Scripture are better known, or have been quoted more frequently, than Matthew 5, 13. The context explains the metaphorical meaning of the words, but what about their literal meaning? What does it mean to say that salt becomes stupid, as the German text says, and that then we possess nothing wherewith it could be salted? The obscurity of the text is all the more striking when one compares it with the simplicity and clarity of the other images in the New Testament. The Good Shepherd who gives his life for his sheep; the sheep that know his voice; the seed that falls on the road and is trodden under foot; the tares among the wheat: all these are images which must have been familiar to the disciples of Jesus. But when did they notice salt losing its savour?

The difficulties caused by this passage have naturally struck many readers, and diverse ways have been tried to overcome them. In many commentaries we find the explanation that indeed chemically pure salt cannot become stupid, or, as the English translation says, lose its savour, or, according to the version of the new Zürich Bible, lose its "sharpness", but that this might well have been feared when the salt came from the Dead Sea and contained chemical impurities.[1] It must, indeed, be admitted that salt which has been adulterated by magnesium chloride can, because of its hygroscopicity, become humid and perhaps even be washed away, but the brine has still the same salty taste! A somewhat better explanation could be based on Pliny's remark that rain sweetens salt,[2] for if impure salt is left in the open, it may well happen that rain dissolves the NaCl and that only the earthy residue remains which does not have a salty taste; however, this inconsiderable residue need hardly be specially thrown away, seeing that it is out of doors already. A most implausible commentary has been given by A. S. Peake:[3] "Salt was heavily taxed, and therefore often so adulterated as to lose its salinity".

That the remark about salt losing its savour was quite incomprehensible, even in early days, we can gather from a passage in the Talmud which Strack and Billerbeck quote in their "Gospel According to St. Matthew".[4] When Rabbi Jehoshua (about 90 A.D.) was asked: "If salt lose its savour wherewith shall it be salted?", he answered: "With the placenta of a hinny". The subsequent question: "Does the (sterile) hinny have a placenta?" elicited the ironical reply: "Can salt lose its savour?"

In view of the diversity of modern translations of the Bible, it is necessary to go back to the original text. But this leaves us no better off. What is the meaning of μωρανθῇ and ἁλισθήσεται and ἀρτυθήσεται in Matthew and Luke or of ἄναλον γένηται and ἀρτύσετε in Mark? Pallis[5] does not hesitate to replace Matthew's ἁλισθήσεται by ἁγνισθήσεται and simply to assume that Mark misunderstood Matthew, and further that μωρανθῇ is "of course inapplicable" and that μωρανθῆτε is demanded instead. As he quite justifiably takes it to be absurd that anyone in Palestine should have tried to improve the soil with salt, he suggests that γῆν in Luke should be replaced by ταγήν, thus reading "victuals" instead of "soil".

These suggestions have apparently met with a cold reception from the experts. It is even becoming usual nowadays to quote the Lutheran "becomes stupid", and we shall see that it would have been a much wiser course to keep close to the original text and to put up with the obscurity of the passage than, as do modern translators, to insert arbitrarily an apparently plausible but actually completely mistaken interpretation by translating "stupid" by such terms as "insipid" and thus maintaining, in common with the official English version, that the taste of the salt has suffered.

And yet it is a fact that for more than twenty years the way towards a correct translation has lain open, for as early as 1931 Frank Scholten published his photographs from the Holy Land.[6] There we find most interesting photographs of Arab baking ovens lined with salt, on which Scholten comments: "In Arab bakeries, the salt, which is put under the oven, in order to intensify the heat, is removed every fifteen years. The old lumps of salt are then thrown into the street. Cf. 'But if the salt lose its savour wherewith shall it be salted? It is good for nothing any more but to be cast out and to be trodden on by men'."

Thus Scholten deserves the credit not only for having shown us these Arab ovens but also for having pointed out their connection with the famous Bible passage. Ludwig Köhler[7] does not do him justice when he says: "Nobody was able to interpret these pictures published in 1930 and now the chemist comes and tells us what Jesus meant when he spoke of the salt becoming stupid". This last remark by Köhler refers to an essay which E. H. Riesenfeld[8] published in 1935. Riesenfeld does not deserve the credit, which is undoubtedly due to Scholten, for having correctly interpreted the Bible passage for the first time. But his is the by no means lesser merit of having given the scientific explanation of the action of salt in Arab ovens, which in Scholten's expression, "to intensify the heat", still remains a chemical mystery. Anyone who is interested in science should read Riesenfeld's essay on salt as a catalyst and anti-catalyst. Put briefly, he shows that the utilization of salt for the purpose of encouraging a burning process becomes intelligible to the chemist of today when account is taken of the fact that the fuel in the ovens of Palestine was of the inferior quality to be expected of dried camel dung. In such a case a catalyst consisting of salts such as sodium chloride or magnesium chloride can be of great use. Riesenfeld further explains why, after some time, the catalytic effect of the salt ceases, so that, indeed, there is no further use for the slabs of salt polluted by camel dung, and throwing them out into the street would have been the natural thing to do.

What conclusions may we draw from this new knowledge in determining the best translation of the three Bible passages? In applied chemistry, we would say: when the salt loses its catalytic effect, wherewith shall it be restored? But few people would be inclined to insert this modern scientific formulation into the text of the Bible. Luther probably hit upon the best translation when he kept strictly to the meaning of the Greek μῶρος, for Jesus and his disciples too had to be content with a pre-scientific formulation.

The exact translation is, however, a less important point than the fact that, starting from the realization of the actual meaning, we are now able for the first time to interpret correctly some adjacent Bible passages as well. Riesenfeld still remains faithful to the old conception and translation, when he assures us that the salt that has become stupid cannot be used on the dung-heap or in the fields. But the idea of using salt as manure was probably as foreign to the Jews as Pallis assumes. We are glad to be able to report that G. R. Driver,[9] in a review of Köhler's book, gives the undoubtedly correct explanation. He explains that κοπρία here does not mean dung-heap but refers to the dung as fuel, for which the salt had become useless.

We may go even further, for Luke says: οὔτε εἰς γῆν οὔτε εἰς κοπρίαν εὔθετόν ἐστιν. This surely suggests that we ought no longer to take γῆν to mean the field, on which the salt can as little serve a useful purpose as on the dung-heap, but rather the earthen floor of the oven. Let us consider a little more closely the way in which, under primitive living conditions, the catalytic effect of the salt could be utilized in the ovens. It has not yet been possible to find out from experts on the Near East how nomads nowadays utilize salt in the desert for the purpose of accelerating the burning process, but it seems very probable that the lining of the oven with salt slabs as photographed by Scholten was possible only under comparatively stable conditions, and that primitive bakers had often to be satisfied with sprinkling salt on the camel dung or on the floor of the oven. And it can be assumed that both methods did good service. In this context we may remind the reader that even nowadays it is common in England to mix salt with coal dust in order to improve its burning. The following instructive experiment can easily be performed by any reader. Take as an example of a poor fuel not camel dung, which may be difficult to obtain in this country, but rather a lump of sugar, and try to set it alight with a match. This experiment will be a failure and the most that is likely to be achieved will be the melting of the sugar. If, however, pure sodium chloride (not common salt as sold in the shops, to which other substances have frequently been added) is sprinkled on the sugar, one can set it alight, so that the sugar now indeed acts as fuel. In a similar way, the simple sprinkling with salt of the camel dung, or of the floor and the walls of the earthen oven, must have had a beneficial effect on the burning process.

To take yet a further step in our interpretation: on the basis of what has been said so far, one is tempted to establish a concordance between the beginning of the passage in Matthew and the now suggested interpretation of γῆ in Luke. If in Luke we take γῆ to mean the floor of the oven, then we can hardly avoid interpreting Matthew's ὑμεῖς ἐστέ τό ἅλας τῆς γῆς in accordance with this. Thus, "Ye are the salt of the earth" means "Ye are the salt which, when it is put on the earth of the oven, starts the process of burning". The chemist will here feel bound to point out the exact function of salt as a catalyst: a catalyst is a substance which accelerates a process which, without its agency, would proceed only slowly or not at all. Could anything characterize more appropriately the function of the apostles than that they were to accelerate the process of Christianization of the world as far as in them lay? We do not, by any means, want to suggest as a translation of the Bible passage: "Ye are the salt of the floor of the oven", although this would render the meaning correctly. This interpretation must be left for the commentaries.

Perhaps we had better continue to use the vague translation, "salt of the earth", but, on the basis of a logical inference from Scholten's discovery and of the synoptic consideration of the three Bible passages, we should add to it the only rational explanation of a metaphor whose meaning has lain hidden for a long time.

REFERENCES

1. Cf., e.g., Weiss, B., *Die Schriften des neuen Testaments*, **1,** 153 (1906); Thomson, W. M., *The Land and the Book*.
2. Bailey, K. C., *The Elder Pliny's Chapters on Chemical Subjects*, Part I, Arnold, London, pp. 45 and 165, 1929.
3. Peake, A. S., *A Commentary on the Bible*, Nelson and Sons, London, p. 704, 1937.
4. Strack, H. L., and Billerbeck, P., *Das Evangelium nach Matthäus, erläutert aus Talmud und Midrasch*, Beck, München, p. 236, 1922.
5. Pallis, A., *Notes on St. Luke*, Oxford, 1928; *Notes on St. Mark and St. Matthew*, Oxford, 1932.
6. Scholten, Frank, *Palestine Illustrated*, Volume II: *Jaffa the Beautiful*, Longmans, Green & Co., London, 1931.
7. Köhler, Ludwig, *Kleine Lichter; fünfzig Bibelstellen erklärt*, Zwingli Verlag, Zürich, p. 73, 1945.
8. Riesenfeld, E., "Salz als Katalysator und Antikatalysator", *Naturwissenschaften*, **23,** 311 (1935).
9. Driver, G. R., *Journal Theol. Studies*, p. 75, Jan.–Apr. 1946.

27 | How Old is the Universe?

The problem of the age of the universe is a question that was raised in very early times. All the peoples of the earth, whether primitive or highly civilized, have given thought to this question, and long before natural science in our modern sense existed, religions, legends and poetry have given their interpretation. That the age of the world has again acquired topical interest is due to the fact that modern science has established certain facts which can be considered valuable aids in assessing the age of the world.

As recently as about fifty years ago, conscientious scientists had to refuse to make definite numerical statements even about the history of our earth. A well-known English geologist* published in 1905 a book with the promising title *The Age of the Earth*. This book gives the sequence of the geological periods but no indication how long they lasted. In order to give the reader at least some idea of the relative duration of the individual periods, the author compares the thicknesses of the layers of sediment deposited during each period. One can conclude from his survey, for instance, that the Carboniferous formation lasted twice as long as the succeeding Permian formation, but the author does not make any attempt whatever to indicate how long these periods lasted in years, and concludes with the sigh: "How immeasurable would be the advance in our science could we but bring the chief events which it records into some relation with a standard of time!"

Why was the geological calculation of time still so completely unreliable at the turn of the century? Up to the middle of the nineteenth century, many geologists had tried to make do with the 6,000 odd years deduced from the Bible records. If one takes the revised version of the Bible, millions of copies of which have been printed by the University Presses of Oxford and Cambridge and distributed all over the world, one will find in the margin the dates of the events described. Thus we learn that the world was created in the year 4004

* W. J. Sollas. [Ed.]

B.C., that Cain was born as early as 4003, that the flood occurred in 3609, etc.—dates based on the calculations of Archbishop Ussher, a friend of Cromwell's. The first protest was initiated by the English geologist James Hutton who proved in 1781 in his book *Theory of the Earth* that much longer periods of time would have been needed to account for the accumulation of the sediments in the Earth's crust. His work had no noticeable immediate effect—the real struggle began in the 1830s, when another English geologist, Charles Lyell, published his *Principles of Geology* in which he claimed many millions of years for the history of the Earth. Similar spans would clearly be necessary if one wished to explain the origin of species according to Darwin as the result of a process of natural selection. Darwin said himself: "He who can read Sir Charles Lyell's great work, yet does not admit how incomprehensibly vast have been the past periods of time, may at once close this volume". The fact that Darwin's theory, itself the subject of much controversy, was involved, exacerbated the dispute about the age of the Earth. Hutton's pupil, the geologist Playfair, took an even more decisive stand than Lyell and Darwin by declaring that no trace of any process of ageing was to be found on the Earth, that the movement of the planets was unchanging and that the Sun had been shining since time immemorial and would never cease to shine.

William Thomson, later Lord Kelvin, was the first to turn against this revelling in unlimited periods of time. His writings, from the 1860s onwards, represent the earliest attempt on the part of a physicist to come to the aid of the geologists in determining the age of the Earth and the duration of the various periods. Kelvin was convinced that the Sun and the Earth must conform to the same laws of cooling as the terrestrial substances. The Earth must therefore have been so hot 20–40 million years ago that no life could possibly have existed on it; life therefore must have developed within a period of at most 40 million years. With regard to the future he forecast that in view of the sun's constant loss of heat, the inhabitants of the Earth would not enjoy the light and warmth so vital to their existence for many more millions of years. He added cautiously: "unless new sources, now unknown to us, are prepared in the great storehouse of creation". But he evidently considered it more likely that the geologists were wrong, than that such sources existed, for he did not enlarge on the point. For their part the biologists and geologists adopted such a negative attitude towards Kelvin's theory that they were as unwilling to consider this way out of the difficulty as he was himself. But although they were convinced, and rightly so, that the maximum period of time given by Kelvin for the development of life on Earth was far too short, they could not refute his physical calculations.

This obvious contradiction, mooted for many decades, was not resolved until atomic energy, in the form of radium rays, was discovered. That astonishingly high amounts of heat were released was particularly clearly and strikingly demonstrated in 1903 by the famous experiment of the French physicists Curie and Laborde, who observed that the development of heat in a moderately strong radium sample could be demonstrated quite simply by holding a mercury thermometer near it. Shortly afterwards, an Englishman, Strutt, succeeded in demonstrating that radium is distributed throughout terrestrial rocks, and is present in sufficient quantities to contribute considerably to the Earth's temperature. It now became clear that the source of energy mentioned, but not seriously considered, by Kelvin, was actually present in the Earth and was indeed the reason why his calculations concerning the cooling of the Earth were so ill-founded.

We know today that the discovery of atomic energy has completely eliminated the difficulties which Kelvin pointed out, not only with regard to the Earth, but also with regard to the Sun. The disintegration of the radioactive substances in the Earth generates so much heat that it is uncertain whether the Earth is cooling at all. In any case there is no need to assume that it was a molten mass some 40 million years ago. The synthesis of the elements in the Sun enables it to maintain its radiation over thousands of millions of years. While we can only hope to grasp the processes in the Sun from a theoretical point of view, we are not dependent on mere speculation where the Earth is concerned, but can carry out observations which enable us to determine the age of the Earth with an accuracy previously undreamt of. Here again, it was the discovery of the radioactive elements that provided the key.

In principle, all the so-called "primary radioactive elements" can be used for this new method. These elements most probably originated at the same time as the stable elements, but are now found in smaller quantities than were present at the time of their formation, owing to their disintegration. Indeed, it is quite possible that some of the primary radioactive elements are now almost completely extinct and can no longer be traced at all. Others are still present in measurable quantities and are continuously changing into stable elements. The calculation of the age of a sample of rock based on this process is as follows. The amounts of the radioactive element and of its stable disintegration product are determined in one and the same sample. As the rate of disintegration of the radioactive element tells us the amount produced each year, it is easy to calculate from the amount of the disintegration product present in the rock, how many millions of years were required for its formation. Although this is simple enough in principle, the practical side of the matter is beset by such a variety of difficulties that only a relatively small selection of the age determinations made by the radioactive method can be regarded as really reliable.

Age determinations by the so-called "lead method" and "helium method" have the longest standing. Both of these are based on the same principle, namely, that the radioactive elements, uranium and thorium, are converted into stable lead atoms after emitting a certain number of α-particles, which collect in the form of helium gas. It should therefore be possible along these lines to determine, from the amount of helium or lead present, the period of time required for the formation of these two products from the uranium and thorium of the rock. In using the lead method, the main difficulty lies in the fact that all minerals contain lead as a primary stable element, but that only the quantities of lead derived from the radioactive elements, uranium and thorium, may be taken into consideration in determining the age of the rock sample in question. It is not always possible to distinguish between the two.

The helium method has quite a different drawback. On comparing the results obtained by this method in the case of a large number of rocks with those obtained by the lead method, it was noticed that the helium method almost regularly gave values that were too low. The most obvious explanation was that helium, being a rare gas, had not been completely retained by the minerals. In the light of our present knowledge it is therefore assumed that the helium method would only in exceptional cases give reliable results for determining the age of the minerals. However, there is a type of important natural substance from which the helium is unable to escape, namely, the native metals. Their crystal lattices enclose the helium so completely and securely that it cannot escape, even when the metals are heated to a high temperature. We may therefore expect good results if we use the helium method to determine the age of the most interesting group of metals that occur in nature, namely, the iron meteorites. Our expectation that the helium method would yield reliable results in such cases has been confirmed; the fact that it is nevertheless very difficult to determine the age of such samples by the helium method will be discussed at a later stage. In addition to the disintegration of uranium and thorium into lead and helium, the transformation of potassium into argon, of rubidium into strontium and of rhenium into osmium have also been used for age determination, but we shall not go further into these methods and their difficulties.

Wherever possible, several methods are used when determining the age of rock samples. This has already been done in many cases and, thanks to the combined efforts of chemists, physicists and geologists in a large number of laboratories, it has been possible to draft a chronological outline of the major periods in the Earth's history. The wish expressed by the English geologist half a century ago has been completely fulfilled, and we have now brought the chief events in the history of our Earth "into relation with a standard of time".

We know, for example, that the Carboniferous period lasted 60 million years, that the Permian formation lasted 30 million years, and that the latter ended 190 million years ago. The oldest samples of rock tested with the methods described above were about 4,500 million or $4\frac{1}{2}$ milliard years old. The earliest traces of living creatures were found in rocks which are $1\frac{1}{2}$ milliard years old. Thus life did not first arise 40 million years ago, as Kelvin believed, nor does it date back to "infinite" or "incomprehensible" time, as Kelvin's biologist opponents maintained.

After the success achieved with the radioactive methods in determining the age of the Earth, the temptation to apply the same methods to the much smaller amounts of cosmic matter available, namely to meteorites, was very great. Several of the methods discussed have already been used on stone meteorites with great success. The most important result obtained from these examinations is the realization that the age of these meteorites, i.e. the time that has passed since their solidification, is the same as that of the oldest rock formation of the Earth. The reliability of the results obtained is confirmed by the fact that the age of many of the stone meteorites was determined by more than one method, and the results tallied very well.

At first glance it would appear that the helium method offers the best chance of success in determining the age of iron meteorites; but although it was possible to measure the helium content of the iron meteorites, which are, as we have already mentioned, gastight, with satisfactory accuracy, two quite unexpected difficulties prevent the use of these results in determining the age of the meteorites. First of all, the uranium and thorium content of the iron meteorites proved to be so small that it was not possible to measure it by the usual methods. Further, in full agreement with this fact, came the realization that most of the helium found in iron meteorites was not a product of the disintegration of uranium and thorium, but was due to the breaking-up of the iron atoms by cosmic radiation to which the meteorites are exposed to a very high degree while circling round the Sun. That the helium originated from this process can be seen from the fact that the helium found in meteorites consists in roughly equal parts of atoms of weight 3 and atoms of weight 4, whereas the helium obtained from terrestrial sources consists almost entirely of atoms of weight 4. From this it is clear that, while measuring the amount of helium in iron meteorites affords an interesting insight into the disintegration of atoms exposed to cosmic radiation, it cannot be used for age determinations in the simple way we had hoped. The lead method is also impracticable, owing to the exceedingly small amounts of lead and uranium present. The only methods that could be used to determine the age of iron meteorites were based on the measurement of the content of potassium and argon, and gave the same results as those obtained with stone meteorites, i.e. $4\frac{1}{2}$ milliard years.

The most important result obtained from these age determinations, namely, that the oldest terrestrial rocks and the meteorites solidified simultaneously about 4,500 million years ago, is quite consistent with the view generally held today that meteorites are the fragments of a celestial body which belonged to the solar system, probably of a small planet or even of several of them. The fact that there is agreement between the composition of the meteoritic and that of the terrestrial chemical elements clearly shows that—apart from the changes caused at a later stage by the primary radioactive elements—the formation of the chemical elements was already completed at the time the Earth and the small planets came into existence, and that the different types of atoms were already completely mixed. Is it also possible to make a statement about the time at which the elements were formed?

This actually seems possible, and requires only a relatively simple calculation, which was first suggested by the late Göttingen physicist, Wefelmeyer, and later worked out in detail by various other scientists without any fundamental change in the result. Clearly marked regularities have been established in the proportions of the isotopes found in the stable chemical elements, and these give rise to the belief that it is most probable that the two primary uranium isotopes, 238 and 235, were originally formed in equal amounts. The element uranium consists today of 99 per cent uranium 238 and 1 per cent uranium 235. As uranium 235 disintegrates more quickly than uranium 238, the proportions must have been more favourable to uranium 235 in former times. It is easy to calculate, by means of the disintegration constants known to us, when both isotopes were present in the world in equal amounts. The result obtained showed that the time when the primary radioactive elements apparently came into existence and began to disintegrate according to the laws known to us was about 6 milliard years ago.

This conclusion, based on considerations founded on nuclear physics, becomes even more interesting if we remember that astronomers assume for various reasons that the distribution of the stars that we know today did not take place much earlier than this. Double stars and globular star clusters, for example, which we now observe, could not have resisted the dispersive effect of the gravitational forces from the sum total of the celestial bodies for more than 10 milliard years at the most. They must, therefore, have been created during this period of time, perhaps 6 milliard years ago. The well-known theory of the expanding universe leads us to similar views. This theory is based on the red-shift of the spectral lines of the distant galaxies. This expansion of the universe, too, can obviously have operated in the manner observed now only for a limited time, and from this, too, attempts have been made to calculate the age of the world. As these considerations are much more uncertain, however, than those based on radioactive measurements, we shall not go into them any further.

Thus numerous independent scientific considerations clearly point to the conclusion that the present state of the universe is at least $4\frac{1}{2}$ milliard years old, and not more than 10 milliard at the outside. Are we justified in referring to this period of time as the "age" of the world, as is often done nowadays? It appears to be established that the world familiar to us did not exist before that time, and we are tempted to connect this result with the idea of a creation of the world as handed down from time immemorial. Various attempts have been made in this direction. For example, at a ceremonial session of his Academy in Rome in November, 1951, the late Pope made a speech entitled "The Proof of God's Existence in the Light of Modern Science". The Pope explained that science was now in a position to determine the time of the creation of the world in a number of different ways. The scientific results discussed by us are mentioned—the astronomical calculations as well as those based on radioactive measurements carried out on rocks and meteorites—and lead to the conclusion: "Creation, then, in Time: therefore a Creator, and thus a God. This is the message which we demanded from science, although not explicitly and conclusively, and which mankind expects from it today." At another point, however, he emphasizes that "the proof as such lies outside the scope of natural science".

Every scientist will gladly agree with this last statement, for in the scientific proofs for an upper age limit of the elements or of the time that has passed since the stars were distributed throughout the universe, nothing is said about a state of things prior to that time. They lead us to the conclusion that the world known to us cannot have been in existence for more than a certain length of time according to the laws known to us, but do not say more than that in any respect. If we want to talk about a "creation of the world" we must first be quite clear about what we consider as a "world" which did not exist before. We shall certainly not consider the existence of atoms as the prime condition for the existence of a material world, as was usual during the last century. Even if there had been a time when no atoms existed, but merely the conditions essential for their synthesis, such as neutrons, neutrinos, photons, etc.—in short, energy in one form or another—no one would term the evolution of the world as we know it, from such a state, a creation from nothing.

Adapting a famous saying of Laplace, we can still say today that "such a hypothesis is not necessary" and that we are only obliged to assume a different state of the world before that time and perhaps different natural laws as well. We should do well to remember in this connection that the invariability of natural laws seems to hold good for our limited sphere of knowledge but that some of the greatest scientists have occasionally pointed out that we have no proof that they are of necessity valid for all time. None of the facts so far established gives us any indication whatsoever concerning the duration of a previous state, in which other natural laws might have been valid and from which the present course of the world might have developed.

There are indeed theoretical speculations about the world which preceded the one we know, e.g. about a "pulsating universe", which is expanding now, but which was contracting previously. But even if one believes that the universe has always been expanding and never contracting, one need not assume a limited duration, as did most of the earlier supporters of the theory of the expanding universe. The hypothesis of a "continuous creation" supported by a group of young English astronomers offers another possibility: according to them the galaxies travelling away from us disappear from our universe as soon as they attain the velocity of light, and the loss of matter is compensated for by the continual formation of fresh matter in all parts of the universe. Experimental proof of such a theory is, however, quite impossible, as it would only require the formation of a single hydrogen atom in a milliard years for each litre of space to compensate for the loss of matter caused by the disappearance of the galaxies.

Even if one accepts these new ideas, one does not necessarily have to agree with the further inference, which the said astronomers consider to be an integral part of their theory, namely that this process of creation of matter is "continuous". It is possible that it, too, is only characteristic of the present state of our world. The question of "infinite duration" or "limitation in time" of the world process presumably belongs to the field of philosophy and not to that of the natural sciences, and it would appear that Kant was right when he said in the first of his antinomies that the question is not decidable in principle. "One may assume", he said, "that the world, judging by the time that has passed, is boundless, or one may assume that it is finite; in either case one gets involved in unavoidable contradictions with oneself." Kant sees the very impossibility of ever deciding the question as a welcome proof of the fundamental tenet of his theory of knowledge, namely that time is not something objective, but just an aspect of our perception. In any case, the modern scientist will agree with him to this extent, that empty time, in which the world does not yet exist, is not an assumption that can be used in physics, and that a beginning of the world in such a time—as Leibniz emphasized even before Kant—contradicts the law of sufficient reason. The concept of time, which has a clear physical meaning when used in connection with the course of events in the world, loses all meaning when applied to the history of the cosmos, to the universe at large, as there is no longer a reference system— which is probably the reason why Augustine said: "The world was created not in time, but together with time".

If we wish to summarize what has already been said, we must admit that we are unable to give, by scientific methods, an answer to the question concerning the age of the cosmos, the universe in the fullest sense. The coming into existence of the stars and of the chemical elements are the earliest events which we can establish in the history of the universe. These took place about 6,000 million years ago, and this figure we may term the age of the world that is known to us.

Appendix I—Bibliography

I. *Radioactivity and the Transformation of Elements*

1. 1912. "Radiochemie" in *Real-Enzyklopädie der gesamten Pharmazie*, 2nd Ed., Vol. 10, Wien, Berlin, Verlag Urban und Schwarzenberg.
2. 1912. (With St. Meyer.) "Über die Intensität der α-Strahlung von Uran", *Sitzber. Akad. Wiss. Wien, Abt. IIa*, **121**, 1403.
3. 1912. "Über eine neue Methode zur Konzentrierung von Polonium", *Sitzber. Akad. Wiss. Wien, Abt. IIa*, **121**, 2193; *Mh. Chem.*, **34**, 40.
4. 1913. (With G. v. Hevesy.) "Über die elektrochemische Vertretbarkeit von Radio-elementen", *Sitzber. Akad. Wiss. Wien, Abt. IIa*, **122**, 1037; *Mh. Chem.*, **34**, 1593.
5. 1913. (With G. v. Hevesy.) "Über die Gewinnung von Polonium", *Sitzber. Akad. Wiss. Wien, Abt. IIa*, **122**, 104.
6. 1913. "Über kolloide Lösungen radioaktiver Substanzen", *Sitzber. Akad. Wiss. Wien, Abt. IIa*, **122**, 1079; *Kolloid-Z.*, **13**, 1.
7. 1913. "Über kolloide Lösungen radioaktiver Substanzen, II", *Sitzber. Akad. Wiss. Wien., Abt. IIa*, **122**, 1637; *Kolloid-Z.*, **13**, 297.
8. 1914. (With G. v. Hevesy.) "Zur Elektrochemie des Poloniums", *Sitzber. Akad. Wiss. Wien, Abt. IIa*, **123**, 1619; *Mh. Chem.*, **36**, 45.
9. 1914. (With St. Meyer and V. F. Hess.) "Neue Reichweitenbestimmungen an Polonium, Ionium, und Actiniumpräparaten", *Sitzber. Akad. Wiss. Wien, Abt. IIa*, **123**, 1459.
10. 1914. (With K. Fajans.) "Über den Zusammenhang des Aktiniums mit der Uranreihe", *Sitzber. Akad. Wiss. Wien, Abt. IIa*, **123**, 1627.
11. 1915. "Über die Arbeiten des Instituts für Radiumforschung", *Naturwissenschaften*, **3**, 437.
12. 1915. "Über galvanische Ketten aus Blei-Isotopen", *Sitzber. Akad. Wiss. Wien, Abt. IIa*, **124**, 381; *Mh. Chem.*, **36**, 795.
13. 1915. "Über die chemischen Reaktionen der Radioelemente", *Jb. Radioaktivität u. Elektronik*, **11**, 451.
14. 1916. (With St. Meyer.) "Notiz über die Zerfallskonstante des Radiothor", *Sitzber. Akad. Wiss. Wien, Abt. IIa*, **125**, 1253.
15. 1918. (With St. Meyer.) "Über die Actinium-Zerfallsprodukte", *Sitzber. Akad. Wiss. Wien, Abt. IIa*, **127**, 147.
16. 1923. (With G. v. Hevesy.) *Lehrbuch der Radioaktivität*, Barth, Leipzig. (1924–25, translated into Russian and Hungarian.)
17. 1925. "Über Polonium und Wismut als Zwitterelemente", *Z. Elektrochem.*, **31**, 572.
18. 1925. (With W. Bothe.) "Messungen auf dem Gebiete der Radioaktivität", in Ostwald-Luther, *Handbuch physiko-chemischer Messungen*, Akad. Verlagsges., Leipzig, 643.
19. 1926. (With K. Peters.) "Über die Verwandlung von Wasserstoff in Helium", *Naturwissenschaften*, **14**, 956; *Ber. deut. chem. Ges.*, **59**, 2039.
20. 1926. (With C. Ulrich.) "Radium I. Allgemeine Chemie des Elementes Radium", *Handbuch der Mineralchemie von C. Doelter*, Verlag Steinkopff, Dresden, **3**, 306.

21. 1926. (With G. v. Hevesy; translated by R W. Lawson.) *A Manual of Radioactivity*, O.U.P.
22. 1927. "The transmutation of hydrogen into helium", *Nature*, **119**, 706.
23. 1927. (With K. Peters and P. Günther.) "Über die Verwandlung von Wasserstoff in Helium". *Ber. deut. chem. Ges.*, **60**, 808.
24. 1927. "Neuere Versuche über die Verwandlung von Wasserstoff in Helium", *Naturwissenschaften*, **15**, Heft 16.
25. 1930. (With W. Bothe.) "Messungen auf dem Gebiete der Radioaktivität" in Ostwald-Luther-Drucker, *Handbuch physiko-chemischer Messungen*, Akad. Verlagsges. Leipzig, 5th Ed., Chap. 22, 787.
26. 1931. (With G. v. Hevesy.) *Lehrbuch der Radioaktivität*, Verlag J. A. Barth, Leipzig, 2nd Ed.
27. 1933. "Die Zertrümmerung der Atome", *Berg- und Hüttenmännische Zeitschr. Glückauf*, **69**, 57–63.
28. 1933. (With P. L. Günther.) "Der chemische Nachweis künstlicher Elementverwandlungen", *Naturwissenschaften*, **21**, 367; "Chemical detection of artificial transmutation of elements", *Nature*, **131**, 652.
29. 1935. (With J. W. J. Fay.) "Concentration of artificially produced radioelements by an electric field", *Nature*, **135**, 820.
30. 1935. (With H. Loleit.) "Chemical detection of artificial transmutation of elements", *Nature*, **136**, 950.
31. 1935. "Role of chemistry in the study of atomic transmutation", *Nature*, **137**, 560.
32. 1936. (With J. W. J. Fay.) "The concentration of artificially produced radioelements by means of an electric field", *J. Chem. Soc.*, 384.
33. 1937. "Study of transmutation in the chemical laboratory", *J. Chem. Soc.*, 642.
34. 1937. (With E. Glückauf.) "Chemical detection of helium formed in beryllium by gamma rays", *Nature*, **139**, 712.
35. 1937. (With C. Rosenblum.) "Thermal precipitation of radio-active substances", *Nature*, **139**, 796.
36. 1938. (With E. Glückauf.) "Identification and measurement of helium formed in beryllium by γ-rays", *Proc. Roy. Soc. A*, **165**, 229.
37. 1938. (With G. v. Hevesy; translated by R. W. Lawson.) *A Manual of Radioactivity*, O.U.P., 2nd Ed., 1939. The same, New York.
38. 1947. "The making of the missing chemical elements", *Nature*, **159**, 8.
39. 1947. "International standards and units of radioactivity", *Nature*, **160**, 778.
40. 1950. "Radioactive standards and units", *Nature* **166**, 931.
41. 1950. "The making of the elements 97 and 98", *Nature*, **165**, 748.
42. 1951. "Radioactive standards and units", *Nucleonics*, **8**, 38.
43. 1953. "L'importance de la Radiochimie pour la Chimie Générale", *Ind. chim. belge.*, **18**, 1037.
44. 1955. "La Radioactivité Artificielle et la Chimie", *J. phys. radium*, **16**, 753.

II. *Radioactive Indicators and Adsorption*

1. 1913. (With G. v. Hevesy.) "Über Versuche zur Trennung des Radium D von Blei", *Sitzber. Akad. Wiss. Wien, Abt. IIa*, **122**, 993; *Mh. Chem.*, **34**, 1393.
2. 1913. (With G. v. Hevesy.) "Über Radioelemente als Indikatoren in der analytischen Chemie", *Sitzber. Akad. Wiss. Wien, Abt. IIa*, **122**, 1001.

3. 1913. (With G. v. Hevesy.) "Die Löslichkeit des Bleisulfids und Bleichromats", *Z. anorg. Chem.*, **82**, 323.

4. 1914–1915. (With K. Horovitz.) "Über Adsorptionsversuche mit Radioelementen", *Sitzber. Akad. Wiss. Wien, Abt. IIa*, **123**, 1819; *Z. phys. Chem.*, **89**, 513.

5. 1914. "Über Adsorbierung und Fällung der Radioelemente", *Sitzber. Akad. Wiss. Wien., Abt. IIa*, **122**, 2349; *Mh. Chem.*, **36**, 303; *Phys. Z.*, **15**, 924.

6. 1914. (With G. v. Hevesy.) "Über die Darstellung von RaD in sichtbaren Mengen und seine chemische Identität mit Blei", *Ber. deut. chem. Ges.*, **47**, 2784.

7. 1922. (With W. Vorwerk.) "Über eine Methode zur Bestimmung der Oberfläche adsorbierender Pulver", *Z. phys. Chem.*, **101**, 445.

8. 1922. (With W. Vorwerk.) "Über die Dicke der adsorbierten Schicht bei der Adsorption von Farbstoffen an Kristallen", *Z. phys. Chem.*, **101**, 480.

9. 1922. "Über eine Methode zur Bestimmung der Oberfläche adsorbierender Pulver", *Z. Elektrochem.*, **28**, 113.

10. 1922. "Über Radioelemente als Indikatoren bei chemischen Untersuchungen", *Z. angew. Chem.*, **35**, 549.

11. 1924. (With W. Thimann.) "Über die Adsorption von Farbstoffen an Kristallen", *Ber. deut. chem. Ges.*, **57**, 1215.

12. 1924. (With A. Radu.) "Über die Adsorption von Farbstoffen an Diamant, Kohle und Kunstseide", *Ber. deut. chem. Ges.*, **57**, 1221.

13. 1925. (With W. Bothe.) "Radioelemente als Indikatoren", in *Handbuch der Arbeitsmethoden der anorganischen Chemie*, de Gruyter-Verlag, Berlin, Vol. 2, 1027.

14. 1927. "The use of radio-elements as indicators", *Nature*, **120**, 884.

15. 1928. *Radio-Elements as Indicators and other Selected Topics in Inorganic Chemistry*, McGraw-Hill, New York.

16. 1929. "Physikalische Methoden im chemischen Laboratorium: IX, Verwendung von Radioelementen als Indikatoren", *Z. angew. Chem.*, **42**, 189.

17. 1929. "Über einige radioaktive und spektroskopische Methoden in der Mikrochemie", *Mikrochemie*, **7**, 417.

18. 1937. (With G. v. Hevesy.) "Radio-elements as indicators in chemical and biological research", *Sci. Progr.*, **32**, 38.

19. 1948. "The preparation of radioactive tracers", *Quart. Revs. Chem. Soc. (London)*, **2**, 93.

20. 1948. "Échange des ions entre les surfaces des cristaux et les solutions", *J. chim. phys.*, **45**, 205.

21. 1948. "Preparation of radioactive tracers", *Inst. intern. Chim. Solvay, Conseil chim.*, p. 220.

22. 1948. "Radioelements as a tool in scientific research", *Nature*, **161**, 456.

23. 1949. "Use of radioactive tracers in biological research", *Nature*, **163**, 388.

24. 1949. "Los radioindicadores", *Revista IBYS (Madrid)*.

III. *Gaseous Hydrides*

1. 1918. "Über Wismutwasserstoff: Über Poloniumwasserstoff", *Akad. Anz.*, 3.

2. 1918. "Über Wismutwasserstoff und Poloniumwasserstoff", *Sitzber. Akad. Wiss. Wien., Abt. IIa*, **127**, 1729; *Ber. deut. chem. Ges.*, **51**, 1704.

3. 1918. "Zur Frage des Wismutwasserstoffs", *Z. Elektrochem.*, **24**, 298.

4. 1918. (With E. Winternitz.) "Über Wismutwasserstoff, II", *Ber. deut. chem. Ges.*, **51**, 1728.

5. 1919. (With K. Fürth.) "Über Zinnwasserstoff", *Ber. deut. chem. Ges.*, **52**, 2020.

6. 1919. "Über Wismutwasserstoff und Zinnwasserstoff", *Naturwissenschaften*, **7**, 482.

7. 1920. "Über die gasförmigen Hydride von Polonium, Wismut, Zinn und Blei", *Z. Elektrochem.*, **26**, 452.

8. 1920. (With O. Nörring.) "Über Bleiwasserstoff", *Ber. deut. chem. Ges.*, **53**, 1693.

9. 1920. "Welche Elemente bilden gasförmige Hydride?", *Ber. deut. chem. Ges.*, **53**, 1710.

10. 1922. (With A. Johannsen and M. Matthies.) "Über die Darstellung gasförmiger Metallhydride aus Legierungen und Lösungen", *Ber. deut. chem. Ges.*, **55**, 769.

11. 1922. (With M. Matthies and E. Schmidt-Hebbel.) "Über die Darstellung gasförmiger Metallhydride durch Glimmentladung", *Ber. deut. chem. Ges.*, **55**, 775.

12. 1922. (With E. Schmidt-Hebbel.) "Über Germaniumwasserstoff", *Ber. deut. chem. Ges.*, **55**, 2615.

13. 1922. (With A. Johannsen.) "Über Poloniumwasserstoff II", *Ber. deut. chem. Ges.*, **55**, 2622.

14. 1922. "Über eine eigenartige katalytische Wirkung bei chemischen Synthesen durch Glimmentladung", *Z. phys. Chemie*, **100**, 367.

15. 1923. "Über die elektrochemische Darstellung von Zinnwasserstoff", *Z. Elektrochem.*, **29**, 97.

16. 1924. (With E. Rabinowitsch.) "Über die Gewinnung des Zinnwasserstoffs durch kathodische Reduktion", *Ber. deut. chem. Ges.*, **57**, 1877.

17. 1924. (With W. Haken and E. Rabinowitsch.) "Über die Reindarstellung und Eigenschaften des Zinnwasserstoffs", *Ber. deut. chem. Ges.*, **57**, 1891.

18. 1924. (With G. Joachimoglu.) "Über die pharmakologischen Eigenschaften des Zinnwasserstoffs und Germaniumwasserstoffs", *Ber. deut. chem. Ges.*, **57**, 1925.

19. 1924. (With G. Joachimoglu.) "Über vermeintliche ökonomische und gewerbliche Vergiftungen mit Zinnwasserstoff", *Münch. med. Wschr.*, **71**, 1647.

20. 1925. (With E. Rabinowitsch.) "Über die Gruppe der flüchtigen Hydride", *Ber. deut. chem. Ges.*, **58**, 1138.

21. 1925. (With E. Rabinowitsch.) "Über die Gruppe der flüchtigen Hydride (Nachtrag)", *Ber. deut. chem. Ges.*, **58**, 2446.

22. 1925. (With G. Joachimoglu.) "Über angebliche Vergiftungen mit Zinnwasserstoff", *Münch. med. Wschr.*, **72**, 390.

23. 1930. "Bemerkungen zu der Arbeit der Herren G. Schultze und E. Müller über Bleiwasserstoff", *Z. phys. Chemie, Abt. B.*, **7**, 155.

24. 1950. "Aus der Frühzeit des Wiener Radiuminstituts: Die Darstellung des Wismutwasserstoffs. Festschrift des Instituts für Radiumforschung anlässlich seines 40 jährigen Bestandes", *Sitzber. öst. Akad. Wiss.*, IIa, **159**, 1-2.

IV. *Free Radicals*

1. 1929. (With W. Hofeditz.) "Über die Darstellung von freiem Methyl", *Ber. deut. chem. Ges.*, **62**, 1335; *Forsch. u. Fortschr.*, **5**, 357.

2. 1930. (With W. Lautsch.) "Über die Darstellung von freiem Äthyl", *Naturwissenschaften*, **18**, 307.

3. 1930. (With W. Lautsch.) "Isolation of the radical ethyl", *Nature*, **125**, 564.

4. 1931. (With W. Lautsch.) "Über freie organische Radikale im Gaszustand; II, Über die Darstellung von freiem Äthyl", *Ber. deut. chem. Ges.*, **64**, 2702.

5. 1931. (With W. Lautsch.) "Über freie organische Radikale im Gaszustand: III, Über den Mechanismus des Reagierens der freien Radikale", *Ber. deut. chem. Ges.*, **64**, 2708.

6. 1931. (With K. Herzfeld.) "Über freies Methyl und freies Äthyl", *Z. Elektrochem.*, **37**, 577.

7. 1934. "The use of free methyl and ethyl in chemical synthesis", *Trans. Faraday Soc.*, **30**, 179.

8. 1935. (With H. Loleit.) "Free organic radicals in the gaseous state, IV", *J. Chem. Soc.*, 366.

9. 1935. (With W. Hofeditz and A. Wunsch.) "Free organic radicals in the gaseous state, V", *J. Chem. Soc.*, 372.

10. 1935. (With W. Lautsch.) "Free organic radicals in the gaseous state, VI", *J. Chem. Soc.*, 380.

11. 1948. "Reactivity and structure of molecules", *Nature*, **161**, 901.

12. 1952. (With A. Hollis.) "Radiochemical studies on free radicals", *Nature*, **169**, 618.

V. *Helium Investigations*

1. 1926. (With K. Peters.) "Abscheidung von Helium aus Gasgemischen", *DRP*, 431.507, ausgegeben am 8. Juli.

2. 1928. (With K. Peters.) "Heliumuntersuchungen: I, Über eine Methode zum Nachweis kleinster Heliummengen", *Z. phys. Chemie, Abt. A*, **134**, 353.

3. 1928. (With K. Peters.) "Heliumuntersuchungen: II, Anwendung des empfindlichen Heliumnachweises auf Fragen der Elementumwandlung", *Z. phys. Chemie, Abt. B*, **1**, 170.

4. 1928. (With K. Peters.) "Heliumuntersuchungen: III, Über das Verhalten von Helium zu Glas und Palladium und über die Frage der Heliumverbindungen", *Z. phys. Chemie, Abt. B*, **1**, 253.

5. 1928. (With H. Gehlen and K. Peters.) "Heliumuntersuchungen: IV, Über den Heliumgehalt von Erdgasen", *Z. anorg. Chem.*, **175**, 383.

6. 1929. (With K. W. Petersen and J. Chloupek.) "Heliumuntersuchungen: VI, Über den Heliumgehalt von 'Moldaviten' und künstlichen Gläsern", *Ber. deut. chem. Ges.*, **62**, 801.

7. 1930. (With W. D. Urry.) "Heliumuntersuchungen: VII, Über eine Methode zur Mikro-Analyse von Helium-Neon-Mischungen", *Mikrochem. Emich-Festschrift*, 233.

8. 1931. (With W. D. Urry.) "Heliumuntersuchungen: VIII, Über eine Methode zur quantitativen Bestimmung kleinster Heliummengen", *Z. phys. Chemie, Abt. A*, **152**, 110.

9. 1931. (With W. Koeck.) "Heliumuntersuchungen: X, Über eine Methode zur Messung kleinster Radiummengen", *Z. phys. Chemie.*, (*Bodenstein Festbd.*), 145.

10. 1935. (With P. L. Günther.) "Heliumuntersuchungen: XI, Über den spektralanalytischen Nachweis kleinster Wasserstoff- und Neonmengen in Helium", *Z. phys. Chemie, Abt. A*, **173**, 401.

11. 1935. (With G. P. Thompson.) "Attempts to produce helium 3 in quantity", *Nature*, **136**, 334.
12. 1936. (With A. Holmes.) "Helium ratios of rocks and minerals from the diamond pipes of South Africa", *Proc. Roy. Soc. A*, **154**, 385.
13. 1936. (With E. Glückauf and H. Loleit.) "Spectroscopic identification and manometric measurement of artificially produced helium", *Proc. Roy. Soc. A*, **157**, 412.
14. 1937. *Helium: The science of petroleum.* O.U.P., 1511.
15. 1938. (With J. W. J. Fay and E. Glückauf.) "On the occurrence of helium in beryls", *Proc. Roy. Soc. A*, **165**, 238.
16. 1951. "Production d'hélium par les particules alpha du radium en solution", *J. chim. phys.*, **48**, 163.
17. 1953. "Microanalysis of inert gases", *Endeavour*, **12**, 5.

VI. *Atmosphere and Stratosphere*

1. 1935. (With E. Glückauf.) "Helium content of the stratosphere", *Nature*, **136**, 717.
2. 1936. "Helium content of the atmosphere", *Current Sci.*, **4**, 804.
3. 1936. "The composition of the troposphere and stratosphere", *Sci. J. Roy. Coll. Sci.*, **6**, 120.
4. 1936. "Über den Heliumgehalt der Troposphäre und Stratosphäre" (in Russian), *W. J. Wernadski Festschrift*, **1**, 317.
5. 1937. "The chemical exploration of the stratosphere", *Proc. Roy. Inst. Gt. Brit.*, **29**, 350.
6. 1937. "The chemical composition of the atmosphere", *Quart. J. Roy. Meteorol. Soc.*, **63**, 433.
7. 1937. "Chemical exploration of the stratosphere", *Nature*, **139**, 180, 220.
8. 1938. (With J. L. Edgar.) "Concentration and measurement of atmospheric ozone", *Nature*, **142**, 112, 571.
9. 1939. "Die chemische Erforschung der Stratosphäre", *Neue Wege exakt. Naturerkenntnis*, 1.
10. 1939. "The atmosphere", *Encyclopaedia Britannica, Book of the Year*, 80.
11. 1939. "The upper atmosphere: direct chemical investigation", *Quart. J. Roy. Meteorol. Soc.*, **65**, 281.
12. 1939. "Composition and temperature of the upper atmosphere", *Nature*, **143**, 1074.
13. 1941. (With J. L. Edgar.) "The separation of ozone from other gases", *J. Chem. Soc.*, 511.
14. 1941. (With J. L. Edgar.) "The determination of ozone and nitrogen dioxide in the atmosphere", *J. Chem. Soc.*, 519.
15. 1941. (With E. Glückauf.) "Measurement of atmospheric ozone by a quick electrochemical method", *Nature*, **147**, 614.
16. 1944. (With E. Glückauf, H. G. Heal and G. R. Martin.) "A method for the continuous measurement of the local concentration of atmospheric ozone", *J. Chem. Soc.*, 1.
17. 1945. (With E. Glückauf.) "The helium content of atmospheric air", *Proc. Roy. Soc. A*, **185**, 89.
18. 1949. (With K. F. Chackett and E. J. Wilson.) "Chemical composition of the stratosphere at 70 km. height", *Nature*, **164**, 128.
19. 1950. (With K. F. Chackett and E. J. Wilson.) "Helium researches: XVII,

Chemical analysis of stratosphere samples from 50 and 70 km. height",
J. Atmospheric Terrest. Phys., **1**, 49.

20. 1951. (With K. F. Chackett, P. Reasbeck and B. S. Wiborg.) "Variations in the chemical composition of stratospheric air", *Nature*, **168**, 358.

21. 1952. "The chemical exploration of the stratosphere", *J. Chem. Soc.*, 3651.

22. 1953. "L'Exploration chimique de la Stratosphère", *Bull. Soc. chim. France*, **20**, 1.

23. 1954. "The chemical exploration of the stratosphere", *Proc. Roy. Inst. Gt. Brit.*, **35**, 740.

24. 1954. "The chemical analysis of atmospheric air", in *Rocket Exploration of the Upper Atmosphere*, Pergamon Press, London, 157. With sections on "Chemical Analysis of Upper Atmosphere Air Samples from 50 km. to 93 km. height" (by P. Reasbeck and B. S. Wiborg), and "The Composition of the Atmosphere above 60 km" (by G. R. Martin).

VII. *Meteorites*

1. 1928. (With H. Gehlen and P. L. Günther.) "Heliumuntersuchungen: V, Über den Heliumgehalt und das Alter von Meteoriten", *Z. Elektrochem.*, **34**, 645.

2. 1928. "Über Herkunft und Alter von Meteoriten", *Forsch. u. Fortschr.*, **4**, 356.

3. 1930. (With W. D. Urry and W. Koeck.) "The age of iron meteorites", *Nature*, **125**, 490.

4. 1930. (With W. D. Urry and W. Koeck.) "Zur Frage des Ursprungs der Meteorite", *Z. Elektrochem.*, **36**, 727.

5. 1931. "Über die Zuverlässigkeit der Heliummethode und das Alter von Eisenmeteoriten", *Naturwissenschaften*, **19**, 164.

6. 1931. (With W. D. Urry.) "Heliumuntersuchungen: IX, Über den Heliumgehalt im Eisen und in den akzessorischen Bestandteilen von Eisenmeteoriten sowie in irdischen Metallen", *Z. phys. Chemie, Abt. A*, **152**, 127.

7. 1937. "Meteorites: the number of Pultusk stones, and the spelling of 'Widmanstätten Figures' ", *Nature*, **140**, 504, 809.

8. 1939. "The age of meteorites", *Roy. Astron. Soc., Occasional Notes*, **5**, 57, *Sci. Abstr. A*, **42**, 501, 856.

9. 1940. *The origin of meteorites: Being the Halley Lecture* (delivered on 16 May 1940), Clarendon Press, Oxford.

10. 1942. (With W. J. Arrol and R. B. Jacobi.) "Meteorites and the age of the solar system", *Nature*, **149**, 235.

11. 1946. "Meteorites and the age of the solar system", *Astron. Newsletter*, No. 36 (February).

12. 1948. "Meteorites", *Encyclopaedia Britannica*, Vol. 15, 340.

13. 1949. "The frequency of meteorite falls", *Proc. Roy. Inst. Gt. Brit.*, **34**, 375.

14. 1950. (With K. F. Chackett, J. Golden, E. R. Mercer and P. Reasbeck.) "The Beddgelert meteorite", *Geochim. et Cosmochim. Acta*, **1**, 3.

15. 1950. "The Akaba meteorite", *Geochim. et Cosmochim. Acta*, **1**, 70.

16. 1950. "Geological age of meteorites", *Nature*, **165**, 454.

17. 1951. "A 17th century report on copper meteorites", *Geochim. et Cosmochim Acta*, **1**, 117.

18. 1952. (With P. Reasbeck and K. I. Mayne.) "^{3}He content and age of meteorites", *Geochim. et Cosmochim. Acta*, **2**, 300.

19. 1953. (With P. Reasbeck and K. I. Mayne.) "Production by cosmic rays of ^{3}He in meteorites", *Nature*, **172**, 200.
20. 1953. (With J. C. Dalton, P. Reasbeck, S. J. Thomson and K. I. Mayne.) "Cosmic-ray production of helium in meteorites and their ages", *Nature*, **172**, 1168.
21. 1953. "Recent studies on iron meteorites", *Geochim. et Cosmochim. Acta*, **3**, 257.
22. 1954. "Die Heliummethode zur geologischen Altersbestimmung und das Alter der Eisenmeteorite", *Z. Elektrochem.*, **58**, 567.
23. 1954. "Das Alter von Eisenmeteoriten", *Naturwissenschaften*, **41**, 99.
24. 1955. (With G. R. Martin and S. J. Thomson.) "Origin and age of meteorites", *Nature*, **175**, 1003.
25. 1956. "Geological records of radioactive events", *Nature*, **178**, 56.
26. 1956. "The frequency of Meteorite Falls throughout the Ages", in *Vistas in Astronomy*, (A. Beer, Editor), Pergamon Press, Vol. 2, 1681.
27. 1956. "Über Alter und Herkunft der Meteorite", *Österr. Chemiker-Ztg.*, **57**, 1.
28. 1958. "Wie alt ist die Welt?", *Universitas*, **8**, 855; in English, **3**, 189 (1959–60).
29. 1958. "Hat Chladni das Pallas-Eisen in Petersburg gesehen?", *Österr. Chemiker-Ztg.*, **59**, 289.
30. 1959. "Der Meteorit von Breitscheid", *Geochim. et Cosmochim. Acta*, **17**, 315.
31. 1960. "The discovery and earliest reproductions of the Widmanstätten figures", *Geochim. et Cosmochim. Acta*, **18**, 176.

VIII. *Periodic System and Isotopes*

1. 1914. (With G. v. Hevesy.) "Zur Frage der isotopen Elemente", *Sitzber. Akad. Wiss. Wien., Abt. IIa*, **123**, 1909; *Phys.-Z.*, **15**, 797.
2. 1915. (With G. v. Hevesy.) "Zur Frage der isotopen Elemente: Erwiderung auf die gleichnamige Abhandlung von K. Fajans", *Phys. Z.* **16**, 45.
3. 1916. (With G. v. Hevesy.) "Zur Frage der isotopen Elemente, III", *Mh. Chem.*, **36**, 75; *Phys. Z.*, **17**, 4.
4. 1916. "Über den Element- und Atombegriff in Chemie und Radiologie", *Z. phys. Chem.*, **91**, 171.
5. 1917. "Elementtabelle und Atomtabelle", *Z. phys. Chem.*, **92**, 677.
6. 1918. "Zur Begriffsbestimmung des chemischen Elements", *Naturwissenschaften*, **6**, 646.
7. 1918. "Über den Begriff des chemischen Elements", *Z. phys. Chem.*, **93**, 86.
8. 1920. "Die neueste Entwicklung der Lehre von den chemischen Elementen", *Naturwissenschaften*, **8**, 839.
9. 1922. "Das periodische System der chemischen Elemente", *Ergebn. exakt. Naturwissenschaften*, **1**, 362.
10. 1923. "Über das Element 72 (Hafnium)", *Ergebn. exakt. Naturwissenschaften*, **2**, 163.
11. 1923. "Über die heutige Schreibweise des periodischen Systems der Elemente", *Z. angew. Chem.*, **36**, 407.
12. 1924. "Über die heutige Schreibweise des periodischen Systems der Elemente (Nachtrag)", *Z. angew. Chem.*, **37**, 421.
13. 1926. "Das natürliche System der chemischen Elemente", in *Handbuch der Physik* by Geiger und Scheel, Springer-Verlag, Berlin, Vol. 22, 520.
14. 1930. "Die Entwicklung und der heutige Stand unserer Kentnisse über das natürliche System der Elemente (Lothar Meyers Geburtstag)", *Naturwissenschaften*, **18**, 964.

15. 1931. "Über die erkenntnistheoretische Stellung des chemischen Elementbegriffs", *Schriften Königsberg. gelehrt. Ges.*, Naturw. *Kl*, **8**, 101.
16. 1932. "Isotopie", *Z. Elektrochem.*, **38**, 496.
17. 1933. "Das natürliche System der chemischen Elemente", in *Handbuch der Physik* by Geiger and Scheel, Springer-Verlag, Berlin, 2nd Ed., vol. 22, 424.
18. 1935. "Éléments Chimiques et Unité de la Matière", *Scientia*, **58**, Supplement: 93 and 128.
19. 1936. "Chemische Elemente, und Urmaterie", *Akad. Nauk U.S.S.R., Trav. Congr. jubilaire Mendeléev.*, **1**, 113 (German); 129 (Russian); *Scientia*, **58**, 219.
20. 1942. "Radioactivity and the completion of the periodic system", *Nature*, **149**, 565.
21. 1947. "The name of element 23", *Nature*, **160**, 164.
22. 1956. "Isotopenforschung in Geochemie und Kosmochemie", *Jahrestagung Verband deut. phys. Ges.*, 40.
23. 1957. "Beiträge der Isotopenforschung zur Chronologie der Welt", *Svensk. Kem. Tidskr.* **69**, 257.
24. 1957. "Die Bedeutung der Isotopenforschung für geochemische und kosmochemische Probleme", *Arbeitsgem. Forschung, Nordrhein-Westfalen*, Heft 67.

IX. *Historical Studies*

1. 1918. "St. Joachimstal und die Geschichte der chemischen Elemente", *Lotos*, **66**, 1.
2. 1925. "Die geochemischen Arbeiten von V. M. Goldschmidt", *Naturwissenschaften*, **13**, 805.
3. 1926. "Ancient and modern alchemy", *Science*, **64**, 409.
4. 1928. "The teaching of chemistry in German universities", *J. Chem. Educ.*, **5**, 705.
5. 1928. "Zum siebzigsten Geburtstag Auer von Welsbachs", *Naturwissenschaften*, **16**, 1037.
6. 1929. "Über eine alchemistische Handschrift des 14. Jahrhunderts und ihr Verhältnis zu Albertus Magnus' Buch 'De Mineralibus' ", *Arch. Ges. Math. Naturwissenschaften u. Tech.*, **12**, 33.
7. 1930. "Zur 100. Wiederkehr von Lothar Meyers Geburstag", *Forsch. u. Fortschr.*, **6**, 329.
8. 1930. "Über die Schrift Alberts des Grossen: 'De Alchimia' ", *Arch. Ges. Math. Naturwissenschaften u. Tech.*, **12**, 408.
9. 1931. "Herman Matthes (Nachruf)", *Ber. deut. chem. Ges.*, **64**, 107.
10. 1931. "The German Bunsen Society in Vienna", *Nature*, **128**, 94.
11. 1932. "Albertus Magnus as chemist", *Nature*, **129**, 612.
12. 1933. "Chinese Alchemy", *Laboratory*, **6**, 34.
13. 1933. "Faradays Tagebuch", *Naturwissenschaften*, **21**, 749.
14. 1933. Die Naturwissenschaften im Bildungsleben der Vereinigten Staaten, *Auslandsstudien*, Verlag Gräfe & Unzer, Königsberg, Vol. 8, 113.
15. 1934. "Etymologie des Namens Wolfram: Besprechung des Teiles 54 des Gmelinschen Handbuches", *Naturwissenschaften*, **36**, 608.
16. 1934. "The Mendeleeff Centenary and Scientific Progress in the U.S.S.R.", *Nature*, **134**, 799.
17. 1935. "Die Herstellung von Schreibfedern: Ein Vortrag Faradays vor 100 Jahren" (Translation), *Naturwissenschaften*, **23**, 352.
18. 1938. "Faradays Tagebuch", *Naturwissenschaften*, **24**, 456.

19. 1936. "Johan Gadolin, Finnlands grosser bahnbrechender Chemiker", *Suomen Kemistilehti*, **9**, 64.

20. 1938. "The role of chemistry in the study of atomic transmutation", *Oxford Science*, **1**, 25.

21. 1941. "Thomas Wright of Durham and Immanuel Kant", *The Durham University Journal (New Series)*, **2**, 111; *Observatory*, **64**, 71.

22. 1942. "Paracelsus and Basil Valentine", *Nature*, **150**, 380.

23. 1948. "John Newlands and the periodic system", *Discovery*, **9**, 286.

24. 1948. "Scientific research in the British Zone of Germany", *Nature*, **161**, 191.

25. 1949. "Science and miracle", *The Durham University Journal (New Series)*, **10**, 45.

26. 1949. "Professor Egon von Schweidler", *Nature*, **163**, 240.

27. 1950. "Thomas Wright", *Endeavour*, **9**, 117.

28. 1950. "Cinquantenaire de la découverte du Radium", Allocution au nom des délégués étrangers, Paris, July 1950.

29. 1950. "Professor Stefan Meyer", *Nature*, **165**, 548.

30. 1950. "Thomas Wright's 'Original Theory' of the Milky Way", *Nature*, **166**, 49.

31. 1950. "Classical radio-activity and its sequence", *Nature*, **166**, 799.

32. 1951. "Thomas Wright and Immanuel Kant, Pioneers in Stellar Astronomy", *Proc. Roy. Inst. Gt. Brit.*, **35**, 114.

33. 1951. "Naturwissenschaft und Wunder" (Translation of 25), *Jb. d. Albertus-Universität zu Königsberg i. Pr.*, **1**, 123.

34. 1951. "The trend of inorganic and physical chemistry since 1850" (Summary), *Nature*, **168**, 371; full text: *Advanc. Sci.*, **8**, 397 (1952).

35. 1953. (With Sigrid Bender.) "Das 'Salz der Erde' ", *Deut. Pfarrerblatt*, No. 2, 31.

36. 1954. "Goethe's scientific background", *Nature*, **173**, 846.

37. 1955. "Über die echte Schrift Alberts des Grossen 'De Alchimia' ", *Jahrbuch 1955 der Max-Planck-Gesellschaft zur Förderung der Wissenschaften*.

38. 1955. "Marie Sklodowska-Curie", in *Forscher und Wissenschaftler im heutigen Europa—Weltall und Erde*, Stalling-Verlag, Oldenburg, 139.

39. 1955. "Die Erkenntnis des Weltbaus durch Thomas Wright und Immanuel Kant", *Kant-Studien*, **47**, 337.

40. 1956. "Extension of microchemistry", *Nature*, **177**, 953.

41. 1956. (With J. Mattauch.) "Über die Tätigkeit des Max-Planck-Institutes für Chemie seit 1951", Zur Feier der Einweihung seiner Neubauten in Mainz am 9. Juli, *Mitt. Max.-Planck-Gesell.*, **3**, 131.

42. 1957. "Avogadro's number and Loschmidt's number", *Nature*, **179**, 145.

43. 1957. "Diskussionsbemerkung zu dem Vortrag von W. Walcher", *Naturwissenschaften*, **44**, 145.

44. 1957. (With J. Mattauch.) "Das Max-Planck-Institut für Chemie in Mainz", *Achema-Jahrbuch*.

45. 1957. "A tribute to Frederick Soddy", *Nature*, **180**, 1085.

X. *Various*

1. 1911. "Über die Umlagerung des Chinidins und Chinchonidins durch Schwefelsäure", *Sitzber. Akad. Wiss. Wien.*, Abt. IIb, 117; *Mh. Chem.*, **32**, 257.

2. 1924. (With K. Peters.) "Über Kondensation und Wiederverdampfung von aktivertem Wasserstoff", *Z. Elektrochem.*, **30**, 504.

3. 1925. (With E. Thilo.) "Über neue Verbindungen von Nickel und Kupfer mit Diacetyldioxim", *Z. anorg. Chem.*, **147,** 196.
4. 1927. (With E. Klever and K. Peters.) "Zur Frage der Existenz eines dreiatomigen Wasserstoffs", *Z. Elektrochem.*, **33,** 102.
5. 1928. "Über physikalische Methoden im chemischen Laboratorium: I, Zur Einführung", *Z. angew. Chem.*, **41,** 507.

[Based on the bibliography, compiled by Professor K. Peters, in the *Österreichische Chemiker-Zeitung*, **59,** 289 (1958).]

Appendix II—The F. A. Paneth Meteorite Trust

It was Paneth's intention to leave his collection of meteorites "accessible to scientific research", and an "F. A. Paneth Meteorite Trust" has been set up on the following lines.

1.

The Trust is to be called "The F. A. Paneth Meteorite Collection".

2.

The Collection shall be administered by Trustees, who shall be:

not less than three, nor more than five, scientists, including always a representative appointed by the Royal Astronomical Society (Great Britain).

3.

The object of the Trust is to encourage and further research concerned with meteorites. Although the Collection may be exhibited, the meteorites are to be available to qualified scientists for research, including investigations in which samples are used up.

4.

With the consent of the Max-Planck Gesellschaft, the Collection shall continue, for the time being, to be housed in the Max-Planck-Institut für Chemie, Mainz. If, in the opinion of the Trustees, the purposes of the Trust would be better served by so doing, they may authorize its transfer, in whole or in part, to some other Institution.

5.

The Trustees shall endeavour, as far as is possible, to augment the Collection by the addition of new samples, especially those representing newly fallen meteorites. For this purpose they may accept any support compatible with the objects of the Trust. The Trustees may impose such conditions as they see fit (being consistent with the stated objects of the Trust) upon the use of the Collection or upon the supply of samples from it.

6.

The official language of the Trust shall be English.

7.

The Secretary of the Trust is Dr. H. Wänke, Max-Planck-Institut für Chemie, Mainz, Germany.